donnelly

About the Inside Covers of LIVING THINGS

The color painting on the inside covers shows a diver exploring a coral reef. Such reefs are found in many warm, shallow seas. The corals are small animals and many of them live together in colonies. Their hard skeletons remain long after the animals have died.

Bright colors are the rule in such underwater spots. The corals themselves are often colored. So are some of the simple plants which live on and among the corals. The fish of these tropical seas often have bright colors and striking patterns. Many of these tropical fish are shown in the painting. For them the coral reef is a home and a refuge.

HENRY HOLT

AND COMPANY

NEW YORK

LIVING THINGS

Frederick L. Fitzpatrick

Thomas D. Bain

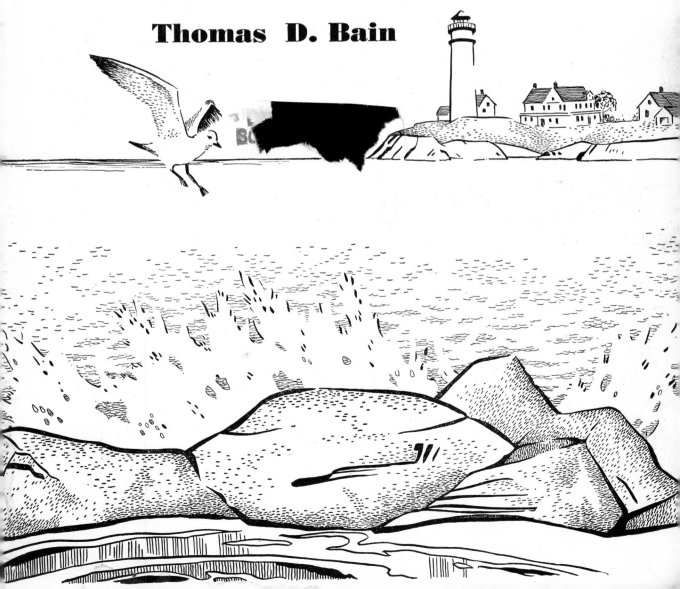

About the Authors of LIVING THINGS . . .

FREDERICK L. FITZPATRICK is Head of the Department of Teaching of Natural Sciences at Teachers College, Columbia University, New York, N.Y.

THOMAS D. BAIN is a teacher of Biology in the Harding High School, Mari̶̶̶̶̶̶

12845–0113

3–57

Copyright, 1953 by
HENRY HOLT AND COMPANY, INC.
Printed in the United States of America

Library of Congress Catalog Card Number 52–12250

Preface . . .

Changes in the common school population during the past fifty years have been profound. The day of the small and highly selected group and the single objective of preparation for college is no more. The modern secondary school draws its students from all socio-economic groups, and these students of necessity vary greatly in out-of-school experiences, ability, interests, and needs. The challenge presented by this new kind of student population has brought about a re-examination of our science courses, of the methods used in teaching these courses, and of various aids to instruction, including textbooks.

Meanwhile, an emphasis on general education has been developing. We have available a vast and growing store of knowledge. We also have a knowledge of methods that can be used to solve problems, including scientific methods. Although leaders in general education may disagree about many things, most of them concur in the idea that our resources of knowledge and methods should be made available to young people in some meaningful and coherent pattern, and that the main goal of this education is more intelligent behavior. The things that students learn, then, should be functional in the sense that they foster development of desirable attitudes, and make for improved ability to deal with individual and group problems.

LIVING THINGS has been planned and written with a very definite emphasis on the functional materials of biology. The criterion for selection has been the question: Is this material meaningful — is it related to the needs and interests of students as they meet their everyday problems? The authors believe that the result is a book that supports the general education aim, and presents the phases of biology that the average student needs to know.

Another main concern of the authors has been to deal with the subject in simple language — in fact, in the language of the average student. The result does not, of course, handicap the gifted student, and it does make learning possible for those of lesser ability.

The typical nonacademic student who shows a great resistance to traditional, formal science instruction, but who is keenly interested in the world outside of his school will find in LIVING THINGS a textbook geared to his needs.

The book is organized in the form of eight units, and units are divided into topics, which in turn are made up of chapters. The order in which materials are taken up can be altered by the teacher at will, since the units, topics, and chapters are complete in themselves.

At the end of each chapter is a group of short-answer items, which can be used by the reader to check his memory. Scientific words used for the first time are defined at the beginning of each topic. At the end of each topic is a summary, a list of scientific terms, a series of questions which emphasize applications to human problems and concerns, and a series of suggestions for demonstrations, field excursions, and a variety of other learning experiences. At the end of each unit is a unit summary and a list of reference books which deal with the materials of the unit. Simplified reference tables of important plant and animal groups will be found in the back of the book, on pages 387, 389, and 390.

The authors wish to express their grateful appreciation and indebtedness to Mrs. Edith Kraeft Gardner of the Manual Arts High School, Los Angeles, California, and to Mr. Joseph B. Fish of Boys High School, Brooklyn, New York, who have read the book in manuscript and offered many helpful and useful suggestions for its improvement.

Acknowledgment is also due to the following artists for their valuable contributions: Jack Donnelly, Jr. for the overall design of the book, the outside and inside covers, and the panels which introduce each unit; Hugh Spencer for many of the line drawings; Felix Cooper for other line drawings; Vincent Mielcarek for the topic introduction drawings; and Roger Crumling for the small drawings which appear at the top of each unit introduction page.

Appreciation is also given to Dorothy Garbose for her painstaking work in securing the photographs which appear in this book.

F. L. F.
T. D. B.

November, 1952

Contents . . .

Preface v
Suggestions to Students xi
Acknowledgments for Illustrations xiii

Unit 1   Biology Concerns Your Everyday Life   3

TOPIC 1   WHAT BIOLOGY CAN DO FOR YOU   4
Chapter 1   Biology Helps You Find a Place in the World   5
Chapter 2   Biology Can Be Fun   8
Chapter 3   How to Be a Scientist   11

Unit 2   This World in Which You Live   21

TOPIC 1   THE LIVING THINGS OF YOUR WORLD   22
Chapter 4   What Are Living Things?   23
Chapter 5   What Can Living Things Do?   26
Chapter 6   How Are Animals and Plants Alike?   30
Chapter 7   How We Name Living Things   33
Chapter 8   How Plants and Animals Live Together   37

TOPIC 2   WHAT ARE THE THINGS AND FORCES AROUND YOU?   45
Chapter 9   The Soil Is Full of Life   46
Chapter 10   Why Do Living Things Need Water?   49
Chapter 11   Why Do Green Plants Need Sunlight?   53
Chapter 12   There Are Barriers to Life   56

Unit 3   Life in the Plant World   65

TOPIC 1   SOME SIMPLE FORMS OF PLANT LIFE   66
Chapter 13   Algae Are Simple Green Plants   67
Chapter 14   Bacteria Are Tiny Non-Green Plants   69
Chapter 15   Some Bacteria Are Useful   72
Chapter 16   Yeasts and Molds Are Fungi   75
Chapter 17   Some Fungi Cause Trouble   77
Chapter 18   Mosses and Ferns Are Green Plants   81

TOPIC 2   THE SEED PLANTS   87
Chapter 19   Roots and Stems Are Parts of Seed Plants   88
Chapter 20   Flowers Form Fruits and Seeds   91
Chapter 21   Crop Plants Provide Food   94
Chapter 22   Vegetables and Fruits Are Foods   98
Chapter 23   How We Use Lumber and Plant Fibers   102
Chapter 24   How We Use Plant Saps and Oils   105
Chapter 25   How We Use Other Plant Products   107
Chapter 26   Some Drugs Come from Plants   111

Unit 4   Life in the Animal World   119

TOPIC 1   ANIMALS WITHOUT BACKBONES   120
Chapter 27   One-Celled Animals Are Everywhere   121
Chapter 28   Sponges and Corals Are Interesting Animals   124
Chapter 29   Some Worms Can Be Dangerous   127
Chapter 30   Why Are Earthworms Important?   131
Chapter 31   Oysters and Clams Make Pearls   133
Chapter 32   You See Joint-Legged Animals Every Day   137
Chapter 33   Most Insects Are Small   141
Chapter 34   There Are Many Kinds of Insects   144

TOPIC 2   GETTING ACQUAINTED WITH THE LARGER ANIMALS   151
Chapter 35   All Fish Have Backbones   152
Chapter 36   Why Are Frogs and Some Snakes Useful?   155
Chapter 37   Birds Are Adapted for Flying   159
Chapter 38   What Are Mammals?   163
Chapter 39   Many Mammals Have Been Tamed   167
Chapter 40   Some Animals Are Sources of Leather   171
Chapter 41   Some Animals Are Sources of Fur   174

Unit 5   Your Body and How It Works   183

TOPIC 1   HOW YOUR BODY IS PUT TOGETHER   184
Chapter 42   What Are the Regions of Your Body?   185
Chapter 43   Your Body Has Over 200 Bones   189
Chapter 44   How Do Your Muscles Work?   194

TOPIC 2   HOW YOUR BODY USES FOODS   200
Chapter 45   What Is Digestion?   201
Chapter 46   How Do You Use Food?   206
Chapter 47   How Does Food Supply Energy?   209
Chapter 48   What Are Vitamins?   214
Chapter 49   What Are Allergies?   218
Chapter 50   Why Are Alcohol, Tobacco, and Some Drugs Harmful?   221

TOPIC 3   HOW YOUR BODY USES ENERGY   227
Chapter 51   How Does Your Blood Flow?   228
Chapter 52   Why Your Body Needs Oxygen   232
Chapter 53   How Your Body Gets Rid of Wastes   236
Chapter 54   Do You Always Look Your Best?   239

TOPIC 4   WHY DO YOU ACT THE WAY YOU DO?   245
Chapter 55   How Your Special Senses Serve You   246
Chapter 56   Your Nerves Control Many Body Actions   250
Chapter 57   How Smart Are You?   253
Chapter 58   Chemical Messengers Affect Your Behavior   256

Unit 6   Most Diseases Can Be Controlled   265

TOPIC 1   GERMS CAUSE MANY DISEASES   266
Chapter 59   What Are Disease Germs?   267
Chapter 60   How You Can Get Diseases   270
Chapter 61   Your Body Can Fight Disease Germs   273

TOPIC 2   YOUR DOCTOR CAN PROTECT YOU FROM MANY DISEASES   280
Chapter 62   What Is Immunity?   281
Chapter 63   Public Health Concerns Everyone   285

Chapter 64   Why We Have Pure Food and Drug Laws   289
Chapter 65   Drugs Are Used in Fighting Diseases   292
Chapter 66   Not All Diseases Are Caused by Germs   295

Unit 7   All Living Things Reproduce   305

TOPIC 1   REPRODUCTION DEPENDS ON CELL DIVISION   306
Chapter 67   What Is Reproduction?   307
Chapter 68   How Cells Divide   310
Chapter 69   Living Things Start as One Cell   313

TOPIC 2   HOW PLANTS AND ANIMALS BEGIN LIFE   319
Chapter 70   How Are Seeds Formed?   320
Chapter 71   How Do Seeds Sprout?   323
Chapter 72   How Do Animals Reproduce?   326

TOPIC 3   WHY LIVING THINGS VARY   332
Chapter 73   How Do Living Things Vary?   333
Chapter 74   How Living Things Struggle to Exist   336
Chapter 75   How You Inherit Your Traits   340
Chapter 76   How We Get Better Plants and Animals   344

Unit 8   Conserving Our Resources   353

TOPIC 1   WHAT ARE NATURAL RESOURCES?   354
Chapter 77   What Causes Erosion?   355
Chapter 78   How We Can Keep Our Soil Fertile   359
Chapter 79   Forests Are Valuable   363
Chapter 80   How We Can Save Our Water Supplies   367

TOPIC 2   HOW WE KEEP A BALANCE AMONG LIVING THINGS   374
Chapter 81   Our Wildlife Must Be Protected   375
Chapter 82   You Should Practice Conservation Every Day   379

Important Plant Groups   387
Important Animal Groups   389
Glossary of Words   393
Index   405

Suggestions to Students . . .

When you get a new book, the first thing to know is how to use it. Some books are story books; others are textbooks. But all books have something in them that you enjoy reading. They also have something that you'll want to learn and remember.

Units and chapters. First of all, let's turn to the *Contents* on pages vii, viii, and ix in the front of the book. You'll see that there are eight units. Each unit deals with some part of biology. Note, too, that each unit is usually divided into two or more topics. Each topic, in turn, consists of several chapters. These chapters are numbered 1, 2, 3, 4, and so on up to 82 which is the last one.

Studying the assignment. Now, turn ahead to page 5 and look at Chapter 1. Your teacher may assign all of this or just a certain amount for one day's reading. You'll want to read all the printed matter carefully. Take a good look at the pictures and drawings. They tell an important part of the story. Note especially the words which are printed in **heavy black type, like these.** They're important new words or terms. If you know what they mean, you'll find that your biology course will be much more interesting.

Looking up words. You'll probably want to look up the meanings of cer-

tain words. If so, turn to *Among the New Words for This Topic* at the top of page 5. This list includes only the more important words in each topic. If your word doesn't appear there, look at the back of the book on pages 393 to 401. This *Glossary of Words* contains all the biological words and terms used in the book. Try to remember the meanings of the words you look up because you'll meet them time and again.

Check on what you know. Ever wish that tests didn't bother you? Here are some helps. At the end of each chapter you'll find six questions called *Check Your Facts*. They're really self-tests, that's all. Don't feel that you have to answer all six every day. The idea is to see how many you can do that refer to the assignment.

You'll find different kinds of questions in these self-tests. They'll help you from day to day. Get a pencil and a sheet of paper. Write the answers to each question you can answer. But *please don't write in the book!* If you find you can't answer a question, check back over what you've read. See where you've missed important points. Then, go back and write the correct answer to the question. If you answer the questions as well as you can, you'll find that tests aren't really hard, after all. They're rather fun!

Tying it together. At the end of each topic there's a short summary called *In a Nutshell*. If you've read each chapter carefully, the summary will sound familiar. Read all of it to refresh your memory. The summary brings together the most important facts and conclusions in each topic.

Checking your vocabulary. Following the summary, you'll find a list of words called *What Do These Words Mean?* You'll want to use this as a further check on what you've learned in reading the chapter. Try to give the meaning of each of the words listed. If you have any doubt about the meaning of a word, look it up in *Among the New Words for This Topic* or in the *Glossary of Words* on pages 393 to 401 at the back of the book. Then try using it in a sentence and pronouncing it correctly.

Using the questions. You'll find a group of questions at the end of each topic. They're called *Ask Yourself*. Many deal with common problems you meet in everyday life. They give you another chance to find out if you're learning the important things in your book.

Getting the facts. You like certain things better than you like others. You'll probably like certain parts of your biology course better than others. If you like one particular thing, you want to learn more about it.

At the end of each topic, there are some outside activities and projects called *Getting the Facts*. Some of these require simple apparatus which you can make. Others require none. Your teacher will gladly help you in doing as many of them as you wish.

Reading up on biology. You'll be interested in special topics on which you'll want to read further. Look through some of the books given in *Books You May Like* at the end of each unit. Your teacher and your school librarian will suggest others which aren't listed in this book. Read as much as you want about any topic in any of the books.

If you know how to use your textbook properly you'll get a lot out of your biology course. Now, turn to page 3 and start reading. See for yourself that biology is fun.

Acknowledgments for Illustrations . . .

The authors gratefully acknowledge the courtesy and co-operation of the following individuals and organizations who have been kind enough to supply the photographs.

In the listing below, the letter *a* refers to the photograph at the left or the top of the page, the letter *b* to the photograph at the right or in the center, and the letter *c* to the last photograph in the series.

AMERICAN FOREST PRODUCTS: Figs. 11-3, 23-3, 79-1, 79-2

AMERICAN MUSEUM OF NATURAL HISTORY: Figs. 5-1 *c*, 8-1, 8-3, 12-3 *a* and *b*, 18-4, 27-4, 28-5, 31-5 *b*, 36-1, 36-2 *a*, 36-4, 36-5, 36-6 *a*, 37-2 *a* and *c*, 37-3, 40-4, 72-3, 74-2, 74-3

AMERICAN RED CROSS: Fig. 52-2

AUSTRALIAN NEWS AND INFORMATION BU–REAU: Fig. 40-1

BAKER'S WEEKLY: Fig. 16-3

BAUSCH AND LOMB OPTICAL CO.: Fig. 27-2

BLACK STAR: Figs. 1-1, 1-3, 14-3, 41-3, 49-3, 74-4, 82-3

BOARD OF EDUCATION, CLEVELAND, OHIO: Fig. 2-2

BRITISH INFORMATION SERVICES: Fig. 24-1

CALIFORNIA REDWOOD ASSOCIATION: Fig. 6-4

CASE INSTITUTE OF TECHNOLOGY: Fig. 1-2

CATERPILLAR TRACTOR CO.: Figs. 21-3, 21-4, 25-4

DEVANEY, A., INC.: Fig. 32-2 *b*

DU PONT DE NEMOURS, E. I. AND CO.: Fig. 21-2

FIELD AND STREAM MAGAZINE: Figs. 2-3, 35-3 *a* and *b*, 73-2, 73-3

GALLOWAY, EWING: Figs. 3-2, 9-1 *a*, 12-2, 22-3, 32-2 *a*, 41-2, 48-2, 51-4, 58-1, 61-1, 63-2, 80-4

GENDREAU, PHILIP D.: Figs. 10-1, 22-1, 26-2, 31-4, 47-2, 54-2, 58-4, 61-3, 73-2, 81-2

GENERAL BIOLOGICAL SUPPLY HOUSE: Figs. 4-1, 6-1, 14-2, 44-2, 61-2, 69-3

GENERAL FOODS CORP.: Figs. 31-2, 35-2

HARPER & BROTHERS (from *Devils, Drugs and Doctors* by Howard W. Haggard, 1944): Fig. 59-1

INTERNATIONAL HARVESTER CO.: Fig. 21-1

IOWA AGRICULTURAL EXPERIMENT STATION: Fig. 22-2

JENNISON, DR. MARSHALL: Fig. 60-3

LEWIS FREDERICK: Figs. 22-4, 26-1, 32-3 *a*, 39-2, 57-3

MARINE STUDIOS: Fig. 31-6

MASSACHUSETTS GENERAL HOSPITAL: Figs. 60-1, 62-3

METROPOLITAN LIFE INSURANCE COMPANY: Fig. 66-1

MIAMI CHAMBER OF COMMERCE: Fig. 20-1

MONKMEYER PRESS PHOTO SERVICE: Figs. 10-2, 18-3, 48-3, 74-1

NATIONAL AUDUBON SOCIETY: Figs. 2-1, 37-1, 37-5, 73-4

NATIONAL RESOURCES BOARD: Fig. 62-1

NATIONAL SAFETY COUNCIL: Fig. 50-2

NEW YORK BOTANICAL GARDEN: Fig. 13-3

NEW YORK DEPT. OF SANITATION: Fig. 63-3

NEW YORK ZOOLOGICAL SOCIETY: Figs. 5-1 *b*, 31-3 *a*, 37-2 *b*, 39-3, 40-2, 40-3, 41-1

PROPHYLACTIC BRUSH CO.: Fig. 54-1

ROBERTS, ARMSTRONG: Figs. 47-1, 54-3

ROCKEFELLER INSTITUTE FOR MEDICAL RE–SEARCH: Fig. 66-3

RESSETAR, S. J.: Fig. 5-1 *a*

SPENCER, HUGH: Figs. 8-5, 17-1 *a* and *b*, 17-2, 28-2, 30-1, 30-3, 31-5 *a*, 32-1, 32-3 *c*, 32-4, 32-5, 35-3 *b*, 36-2 *b*, 38-3, 49-1, 49-2, 72-4, 73-1, 81-5 *a* and *b*

SPRINGFIELD WATER DEPT.: Fig. 64-2

SQUIBB, E. R. AND SONS: Figs. 48-1 *a* and *b*, 63-1, 65-2

TENNESSEE EASTMAN CO.: Fig. 25-2

U.S. DEPT. OF AGRICULTURE: Figs. 9-1 *b*, 15-2, 24-3, 39-1 *a, b,* and *c,* 60-4, 64-3, 76-1, 76-2, 76-3, 76-4, 76-5, 77-3, 78-4

Bureau of Entomology and Plant Quarantine: Figs. 32-6, 60-5

Bureau of Reclamation: Fig. 80-5

Forest Service: Figs. 11-4, 17-3, 23-1, 79-3, 79-4

Soil Conservation Service: Figs. 23-4, 77-1, 77-2, 77-4, 77-5, 77-6, 78-1, 78-2, 78-3, 80-5

U.S. FISH AND WILDLIFE SERVICE: Figs. 28-4, 31-3 *b,* 35-1, 35-3 *c, d,* and *e,* 36-6 *b,* 81-1, 81-3, 81-4, 82-2

U.S. GEOLOGICAL SURVEY: Fig. 9-2

U.S. NAVY: Fig. 12-1

U.S. PUBLIC HEALTH SERVICE: Figs. 34-3, 63-4

UNITED STATES RUBBER CO.: Fig. 25-3

WEST COAST LUMBERMEN'S ASSOCIATION: Fig. 23-2

LIVING THINGS

Unit 1

Biology

Concerns Your

Everyday Life

Ed and Jim were twins. Their sister Ann was a year older and had already studied biology. The boys came home from the opening day of school in September as Ann was leaving to visit some friends.

" We're taking biology," Ed announced, " and it sounds good to me. I'll be glad to learn about insects."

" You'll learn a lot more than just about insects," Ann told him. " You'll learn about plants and animals, and your own body. Biology is about all living things."

" Flowers too? You mean I've got to study flowers? " Jim asked.

" Relax," Ann reassured him. " Flowers are only part of it. You'll find how all plants grow — trees and shrubs, too. They're just as much alive as you and Ed and I — and Skipper your dog, too."

" I'll like that part about my body and how it works," Ed said. " Sounds like something everyone ought to know about."

" You both will," Ann said as she started for the door. " If I hadn't taken it last year I'd never have decided to take nurse's training when I finish school. I'd probably be wondering what to do with myself."

Topic 1

WHAT BIOLOGY CAN DO FOR YOU

What's biology anyway? It's a *science*, or branch of learning dealing with many facts. You use these facts to solve problems. And who doesn't have problems?

Biology is the science of all living things. You'll study *botany* (*bot*-uh-nee) or plant life, *zoology* (zoh-*ol*-uh-jee) or animal life, and *human biology*, or how your own body works.

Biology will help you to get fun out of life when you're in school. But even more important is the fact that biology can help you after you finish school.

Biology will help you to solve many personal problems.

AMONG THE NEW WORDS FOR THIS TOPIC

- **BACTERIA** (bak-*tih*-ree-uh).   A large group of tiny, one-celled living things, seen only with a microscope.
- **BIOLOGY** (by-*ol*-uh-jee).   The science of living things — plants, animals, and man.
- **BOTANY** (*bot*-uh-nee).   The study of plant life.
- **HUMAN BIOLOGY.**   The part of biology which deals with man.
- **HYPOTHESIS** (hy-*poth*-uh-siss).   A "best guess" about a question or problem in the light of known facts.
- **SCIENCE.**   That branch of learning dealing with many facts, from which you draw conclusions.
- **SCIENTIFIC METHODS.**   The methods used by scientists in solving problems.
- **ZOOLOGY** (zoh-*ol*-uh-jee).   The study of animal life.

CHAPTER 1

Biology Helps You Find a Place in the World

Some of you know what you'll do when you finish school.   But quite a few of you don't.   And whenever you study a new subject, you always ask: "What good will this do me?"   Or, "What's this all about?"

The answers to these questions are simple.   Biology deals with all living things.   You're sure to learn things which will help you in planning your life work.   It will give you a chance to explore new fields.   You'll discover certain abilities you didn't dream you had.   There's a big need today for people who've had some biology in school.

Biology trains you for outdoor work.   Some people like outdoor work better than indoor activity.

There are plenty of good jobs that take you outdoors.   As a *nurseryman*, you'll help to raise trees, shrubs, and vines.   And you'll learn how to produce new types of these plants.   If it's flowers you like best, you can go places as a *florist*.   Here, you'll learn how to buy and sell flowers at wholesale or retail.   But there's more to it than merely buying or selling!   Flowers have to have care, not only in the garden but in a greenhouse as well.

Or, you may prefer working with all kinds of fruit trees as an *orchardist*.   Oranges, grapefruit, lemons, apples, pears, peaches, plums, and nut trees are orchard crops.   They need specially trained men and women to keep them producing at their best.   You'll learn something about the different varieties of trees and the soils in which they grow.

Still another type of work is *landscape gardening*.   This has to do with

Fig. 1-1. Work in an orchard includes a lot of things — even picking the fruit. To be an orchardist you must have a special kind of training. What are some of things you must know? How does biology help you?

planting trees, shrubs, and flowers in parks and public places, as well as around homes. You must know about trees and shrubs and which ones go best together. You should also know how to plant them and when and where.

Then, there's the big field of *forestry*. Here you need to know about timber trees and lumber. Forestry is like farming, because a forester raises trees much as a farmer raises crops.

The federal and state governments own many of our larger forests. You can start as a park or forest ranger and work up from there. Or, if you're especially interested in trees, you might like *tree surgery*. This is fascinating

work requiring certain skill. Tree surgeons prune trees, treat diseased ones, and spray them to control insects and other pests.

Of course, we mustn't forget *farming*. A farmer today is one of our most respected citizens. There are many different kinds of farmers, each raising certain kinds of plants and animals. To be a good farmer, you really must know your biology.

Biology prepares you for indoor jobs. You'll find that biology will help you in almost any kind of work, but some kinds require more biology than others.

The *food industry* needs people who've had biology. Canners, preservers, vegetable and fruit graders and packers, dairymen, bakers, and restaurant workers all find their work easier if they've had some biology in high school.

Large manufacturing plants which make *drugs* and *medicines* need help from biologists. If you're interested in this type of work, you'll find good opportunities in the making of medicines, serums, vitamins, and other things. There are many jobs in these companies which don't call for a college education.

Doctors, dentists, and *opticians* (op-*tih*-shans) can use assistants who've had some high-school biology. If you apply for work with any of them, a pleasing personality and knowing how to meet people will help you. Then, there are the various kinds of medical laboratories which employ high-school graduates.

The laboratory will probably train you for the particular job you are to do.

The *nursing profession* is one of the most honored of all. To be a nurse, it's necessary to have high-school biology, and other science courses, too. You may want to become a Registered Nurse and be able to sign " R.N." after your name. Or, you may prefer to be a Practical Nurse. She has less training than a Registered Nurse. Whichever type of nurse you wish to be, you should know the requirements of the hospital where you'll take your training. You'll save a great deal of time when you start your training by being prepared beforehand.

Lastly, certain *government agencies* hire high-school graduates for special work in various fields of biology. Your school librarian will lend you pamphlets describing many other types of work for biology students.

There are so many possibilities in biology it's hard to list them all. You'll be glad to know, right at the start, that biology is such a practical subject. The job you'll take when you finish school may depend on whether or not you've had biology.

There may be some type of work you have in mind and don't find listed here. Ask your teacher or your guidance counselor for help. If you prepare yourself, you'll find it worth your while. You'll certainly do better in any job you select. And that job will be one for which you're qualified.

Fig. 1-2. **Farming today is big business. Machines do much of the work. This farmer is using a tractor to pull a harrow over his land. This makes the topsoil fine-grained and ready for him to plant his crops.**

CHECK YOUR FACTS . . .

Number 1 to 6 on a sheet of paper. Write the answers to each of the following items.

1. An " R.N." written after a person's name stands for a: (nurseryman, forester, nurse) ...?...

2. A man who makes a specialty of working with fruit trees is a: (forester, orchardist, landscape gardener) ...?...

3. Biology is the study of (plants, animals, all living things) ...?...

4. An orchardist is an expert in choosing and arranging flowers, trees, and shrubs on home yards. *True or False?*

5. A knowledge of biology is useful to a: (fruit grader, food preserver, canner, dairyman, all of these) ...?...

6. Forest trees are now raised in a good many places just as we raise ordinary crops. *True or False?*

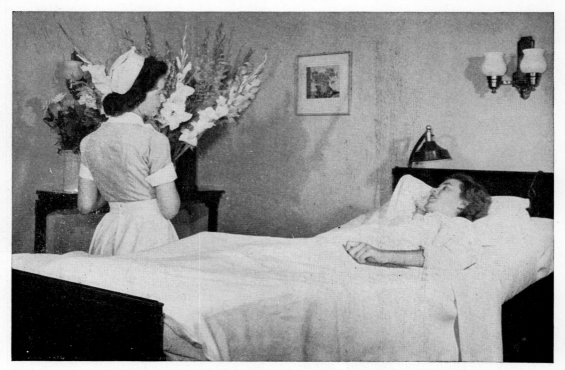

Fig. 1-3. A nurse must know a good deal about biology.

CHAPTER 2

Biology Can Be Fun

Everybody must have some time to play to get the most out of life. A hobby, sport, or pastime will take your mind off worries. Play helps to keep you in good health and gives you relaxation. The person who has a hobby is a better person than one who doesn't. Winston Churchill and President Eisenhower paint pictures. The late President F. D. Roosevelt collected stamps. Biology offers a great variety of pleasant, interesting, and healthful hobbies.

Making biological collections. There's something about collecting that holds your interest through life. Many people have fun collecting, preserving, and labeling plant and animal parts. Such things as leaves, flowers, fruits, seeds, wood, insects, and shells are good items. A collector learns the names and something about each thing he collects. He's proud of his collection because he knows the history of every item in it.

Of course you know that you shouldn't destroy some things. There are laws that protect many birds and their eggs, as well as some other animals and some plants. The first thing a collector learns is what things he should protect. He knows they're too valuable or rare for him to destroy.

Fig. 2-1. Many people find fun and profit when they study living things out-of-doors.

You may become a member of a hobby club and exchange with friends. Good collectors love to exchange with others who collect the same kinds of thing. You'll want to bring your material to school and show it to the class. Some of it may be so good that you'll be asked to exhibit it.

Wildlife study. Wildlife study means taking hikes or trips to special outdoor places off the beaten track. This is another way biology can help you enjoy life. People who like the outdoors get much pleasure out of such trips. They observe trees, flowers, mosses, ferns, and other plants. They also watch for birds, insects, snakes, and other animals.

Many wildlife fans organize special clubs such as bird clubs or nature study clubs. The fine thing about these clubs is that the members learn to take notes on what they see. But they never pick any flowers or kill any animals.

A vegetable garden is a good hobby. Some of you may think it's work to dig in the garden. Others like it because it's fun.

Everyone likes to see things grow. If you have space for a garden, you can learn which vegetables grow best. You may be able to keep the family supplied with fresh vegetables several months of the year. As you get more interested, you can try new kinds. In time you may be raising

Fig. 2-2. A lot of young people find that gardening is an interesting hobby. It requires a lot of work. But the results will give you a great deal of pleasure and satisfaction.

plants that you don't even know to-day.

Gardening with flowers is fun. And while we're on the subject of gardens, don't overlook flowers. This hobby can last all year long. During the spring, summer, and fall you can have continual bloom if you plan your garden right. And in the winter, you can raise flowers on a sunny window shelf. It's a fine thing to learn about the different kinds of flowers, how to plant them, and how to grow them. The packet of seeds you buy includes full directions. You'll have to protect many kinds of flowers

in winter. For these, you'll learn special methods.

Sports are for everyone. Who doesn't like to hunt or fish? A fisherman learns the different kinds of fish in his region. He learns what bait to use and how to use it. He also learns the rules of a good sportsman, and he respects them.

Some fishermen never hunt and some hunters never fish. But many people enjoy both sports. Hunting laws differ in various states, but they all limit the time during which you can hunt certain animals. A true sportsman knows these laws and obeys them.

Pets as a hobby. Most of you like to have at least one pet around the house. Pets range from dogs and cats to tropical fish or even white mice. Many animals make fine pets, if you know about them and how to keep them. In your biology course you'll learn a lot about making a better home for your pets.

Biology is the study of all living things. It's fun to study plants and animals. And you also learn many practical things. After all, our world is full of plants and animals. The thing is to find out where they live, how they live, and how they're useful.

CHECK YOUR FACTS . . .

Number 1 to 6 on a sheet of paper. Mark each of the following items True *or* False.

1. The only advantage in having a hobby is the pleasure it gives you.

Fig. 2-3. You don't need fancy equipment to enjoy fishing in a nearby stream.

2. It's against the law to collect some plants and some animals.

3. There are many different kinds of plants and animals in our world.

4. The purpose of a wildlife study group is usually to collect birds and other animals.

5. A collector learns something about each thing he collects.

6. Biology is the study of all living things.

CHAPTER 3

How to Be a Scientist

Biology is just one of a number of sciences. A biologist uses certain methods to get more facts about liv-

ing things. He performs experiments to help solve his problems.

How to perform an experiment. You'll be interested in learning the general methods scientists use. How do they discover facts? What are their ways of thinking?

Let's begin with a problem of your own. Suppose you have an English walnut kernel like the one in Fig. 3-1. If you rub the kernel on a piece of brown paper, an oily smudge will remain. Many nuts contain oil. Oil will burn, as you know from watching an oil burner furnace, or a kerosene lamp. The two questions are: (*1*) will the English walnut kernel burn; and (*2*) will it give off heat?

You may decide in advance that the kernel will probably burn. You may even think that it will burn enough to heat some water. Suppose you guess that the heat might boil a test tube two-thirds full of water. But these are just your own *opinions*. To get the *facts*, you must perform an ex-

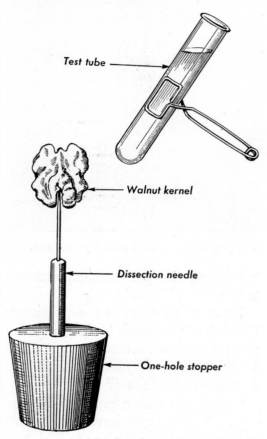

Test tube

Walnut kernel

Dissection needle

One-hole stopper

Fig. 3-1. Will the kernel burn? Will it boil the water in the test tube?

periment. Scientists get most of their facts by performing experiments.

Here goes! First, put the kernel on a dissecting needle as you see in Fig. 3-1. You should hold the needle upright by thrusting its base into a one-hole stopper. Now, use a match to set fire to the kernel. Does it burn

easily? Now, hold a test tube with two-thirds water in the flame. After a few minutes you'll see that the water is boiling. Now you have the answers to your two questions. You know the kernel burns, and you know it gives off enough heat to boil the water.

You've done an experiment. You began with a problem about the English walnut kernel. You knew certain facts about nuts and about oils. From these facts you formed a "best guess" about the problem. This "best guess" is called a **hypothesis** (hy-*poth*-uh-siss). You made your guess from certain facts you already knew. But you weren't sure. To test your hypothesis, you had to plan an experiment. And you had to carry it out.

Your results showed that the kernel would burn. You also found that it burned enough to boil some water. But you did this experiment *only once!* How do you know that the results will always be the same? You don't know, and you won't know until you've done the experiment several other times. Use different English walnut kernels each time. If your results are always the same, you can form a **conclusion.** Your conclusion will be: English walnut kernels will burn. Each will burn enough to heat half a small test tube of water.

You've not only done an experiment. You've also followed the steps in the **scientific method.** You can see that the success of your experiment depended on several factors. *First,* you had to think carefully, and make a "best guess" as to what might be true. *Second,* you had to plan and carry out an experiment. This experiment tested your hypothesis. *Third,* you had to repeat your experiment and check your results. At all times you had to observe these results carefully.

Scientists use various methods. Different problems need different kinds of experiments and observations. The steps you've followed, however, are the ones most scientists use. Look at each step in the following chart. They're the ones scientists use most in solving problems. They're the ones you just followed in your experiment.

What are controls? You've probably read about the great French scientist, Louis Pasteur (pas-*ture*). One of his problems had to do with a disease of sheep called *anthrax.* Pasteur found that this disease was caused by certain bacteria (bak-*tih*-ree-uh). *Bacteria* are a group of tiny one-celled living things.

Pasteur found that he could raise anthrax bacteria in his laboratory. Then he discovered a way to weaken the bacteria so they were no longer dangerous. When he injected these weakened bacteria into healthy sheep, the sheep didn't get anthrax. Instead, they became immune to the disease. *Immune* means that they would not get the disease.

Some people questioned Pasteur's discovery. So he carried out an experiment to prove to these doubters that he was right. This is what he did.

STEPS IN THE SCIENTIFIC METHOD

What You Do	*How Or Why You Do It*
1. Recognize a problem	1. To answer some question
2. Consider all the facts	2. To use what you already know
3. Make a hypothesis	3. To include all the facts
4. Plan an experiment	4. To test your hypothesis
5. Perform the experiment and record data	5. To test your hypothesis
6. Repeat experiment many times, recording data each time	6. To be sure the results are the same
7. Form a conclusion from the experiment	7. To decide if your hypothesis is right or wrong
8. Apply results to a new problem	8. In case new facts arise

Fig. 3-2. Here you see Louis Pasteur working in his laboratory. He found out many things about diseases by using the scientific method. One of the things he discovered was that germs in the air cause diseases and decay. He also found a way to treat and prevent rabies.

He treated two groups of sheep as follows:

1. An *experimental group* of 25 sheep. He gave weakened anthrax bacteria to each of these sheep to make them immune.

2. A *control group* of 25 sheep. He gave these sheep no bacteria.

After a few days he gave all 50 sheep active anthrax bacteria. A few more days passed. Each sheep in the control group died of anthrax. They weren't immune. Each sheep in the experimental group was alive and well. These sheep were immune to anthrax.

Do you see why Pasteur needed the control group in his experiment? If he'd used only the sheep in the experimental group, no sheep would have died. A question would have remained. Without this check, or control group, how would he have known that the active anthrax bacteria caused the disease? The control groups differed in only one way from the experimental group. The control group had not been made immune.

The good scientist takes pains with his work. In the story of Louis Pasteur which you've just read, you noticed that he observed carefully. He wrote everything down so he wouldn't forget the facts. He always took great pains with his work. He tested his hypothesis. He didn't jump at conclusions. He proved to people that he was right.

Pasteur was a good scientist. He had the real scientific attitude. Today, scientists are just as careful as Pasteur was. They're always willing to consider a new idea, and to test it and prove or disprove it.

CHECK YOUR FACTS . . .

Number 1 to 6 on a sheet of paper. Answer each of the following items.

1. In Pasteur's experiment, the control group of sheep (were, were not) given weakened anthrax bacteria.

2. The good scientist clings to his hypothesis when the results of his experiments prove it false. *True* or *False?*

3. The good scientist can depend on a conclusion only when he knows all the related facts. *True* or *False?*

These next three items refer to the experiment you performed on pages 11 and 12. Answer each one True or False.

4. The experiment proved that English walnut kernels won't burn.

5. From previous knowledge I assumed that oil would burn.

6. Before the experiment I thought that the English walnut kernel would burn. This belief was my hypothesis.

Science deals with many proved facts. From these you draw conclusions. Biology is the study of plants, animals, and man. Botany deals with plants; zoology deals with animals, and human biology concerns the human body. Biology prepares you for both indoor and outdoor work for your future activity. Biology also helps you choose a hobby.

Scientists use the scientific method which includes: (*a*) recognizing the problem; (*b*) gathering all the facts about the problem; (*c*) forming one or more hypotheses; (*d*) experimenting to test the truth of the hypotheses; (*e*) forming conclusions from facts; and (*f*) proving these conclusions by further tests. The good scientist observes carefully. He keeps accurate records. He's always willing to change his ideas when new facts show they aren't true.

WHAT DO THESE WORDS MEAN?

Bacteria	Forestry	Orchardist
Biology	Human biology	Scientific method
Botany	Hypothesis	Tree surgery
Florist	Nurseryman	Zoology

ASK YOURSELF . . .

1. Why is biology a science?
2. What three other sciences does biology include?
3. What do you think your course in biology will do for you as a person?
4. (a) Name some different types of farming. (b) How many of these do the farmers in your area use?
5. What should you do to be a good nurseryman?
6. What types of work does a landscape gardener do?
7. How is a knowledge of biology important to a tree surgeon?

8. What are some advantages of having a hobby?
9. (*a*) Do you have a hobby now?   (*b*) If not, which one mentioned in Chapter 2 especially appeals to you and why?
10. How does a scientist test his hypotheses?
11. (*a*) Do you form hypotheses about any of your everyday problems? (*b*) Give some examples.   (*c*) Do you ever test these by experiment and observation?
12. (*a*) Can you use the scientific method to find the answers to any of your ordinary problems?   (*b*) Give an example.
13. How can you be sure your conclusions about an experiment are right?
14. Why was Louis Pasteur a good scientist?

GETTING THE FACTS . . .

1. Fill a large glass jar half-full of water. Look at Fig. 3-3 to see how to do it. Float an empty culture bowl on the surface of the water. Now mark the

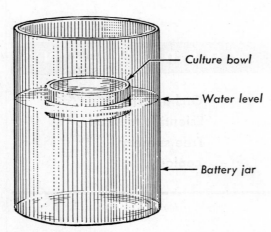

Culture bowl

Water level

Battery jar

Fig. 3-3. If the bowl sinks, what happens? Does the water level rise, go down, or stay the same?

level at which the water stands in the jar. The questions are these: (*a*) What will happen if the bowl sinks to the bottom of the jar? (*b*) Will the level of the water rise? (*c*) Will the level of the water be lowered? (*d*) Will it stay the same?

Form your hypotheses and test them *by experiment*.

2. Bring in about 10 leaves of any one tree, but don't take them from a tree on the school grounds. Paste them on a large sheet of cardboard and display them in the classroom. Make a short report which tells of any differences you see in the leaves. What do you think may be the possible causes for these differences?

3. Have each member of the class examine the fingers of his or her right hand. Place the hand, palm down, on a flat surface. Count the thumb as the first finger. Each student should decide whether: (*a*) the second and fourth fingers are about the same length; (*b*) the second is longer than the fourth; (*c*) the fourth is longer than the second. Record the results on the blackboard. Now, have each student look at his or her left hand. Record the results on the blackboard. Do the results agree with those which you found for the right hand? What do you think these figures show?

4. Suppose someone asks you this question: "Will bean seeds sprout in the dark?" Form one or more hypotheses based on what you already know. Test these by experiment. Use controls to be sure the seeds will sprout under normal conditions.

5. Collect about 30 earthworms. Put them in a tray. Examine them with a hand lens. Are they all exactly alike? What does this tell you about living things around you?

6. Arrange a visit to a nursery if one is nearby. Find out what ornamental plants are raised. Find out what sort of things you have to do to be a nurseryman. You may also wish to know how many ornamental plants are used around homes and public buildings.

7. Discuss some real problem of the group or a member of the class. Refer to the "Steps in the Scientific Method" on page 13. See what facts you know about the problem. Form one or more hypotheses in the light of these facts. Now consider what other facts you need to test the hypotheses. See if you can get these facts and arrive at a sound conclusion.

8. After checking the "Books You May Like" on this page, prepare and give a report on outdoor hobbies. Show how many hobbies are related to what you learn about biology. Do the same thing with the topic "What Are Some Strange and Interesting Facts About Animal Habits?"

Books You May Like . . .

Axelrod, Herbert R. *TROPICAL FISH AS A HOBBY.* McGraw-Hill Book Co., New York. 1952. An interesting account of how to raise various types of tropical fish. It includes discussions of the home aquarium, and how to keep fish healthy.

Devoe, Alan. *THIS FASCINATING ANIMAL WORLD.* McGraw-Hill Book Co., New York. 1952. This easy reading book answers a lot of questions about interesting animals and their habits.

Eastman Kodak Company. *HOW TO MAKE GOOD PICTURES.* Eastman Kodak Co., Rochester, New York. 1951. If you are interested in taking pictures of plants and animals, you will want to know about cameras and how to use them. This book will give you a good start.

Hegner, Robert W. and Jane Z. *PARADE OF THE ANIMAL KINGDOM.* The Macmillan Co., New York. 1935. A popular and interesting account of various animals and how they're adapted for life in this world.

Mathiews, Franklin K. (Editor). *THE BOY SCOUT BOOK OF OUTDOOR HOBBIES.* D. Appleton-Century Co., New York. 1938. A collection of chapters by experts on such topics as hiking, living things in the wild, canoeing, athletics, marksmanship, nature photography, and outdoor cooking.

Perry, Josephine and Slauson, Celeste. *FORESTRY AND LUMBERING.* Longmans, Green and Co., New York. 1939. A book for young people which deals with forests, the U.S. Forest Service, state forestry, forest fires, and lumbering practices.

Selsam, Millicent E. *PLAY WITH PLANTS.* William Morrow and Co., New York. 1949. A book for young people full of practical suggestions for experiments with plants.

Fig. 3-4. Raising fish in an aquarium is a hobby that appeals to many people.

HIGH LIGHTS OF UNIT 1

knowledge dealing with facts from which
gical conclusions. Biology is the science
facts about plants, animals, and man.
sions about how living things grow,
hem best in his daily life.
or solving his problems. First,
ms one or more hypotheses
he plans and performs ex-
s the experiments again
can. Finally he con-
of certain facts be-
's problem. This

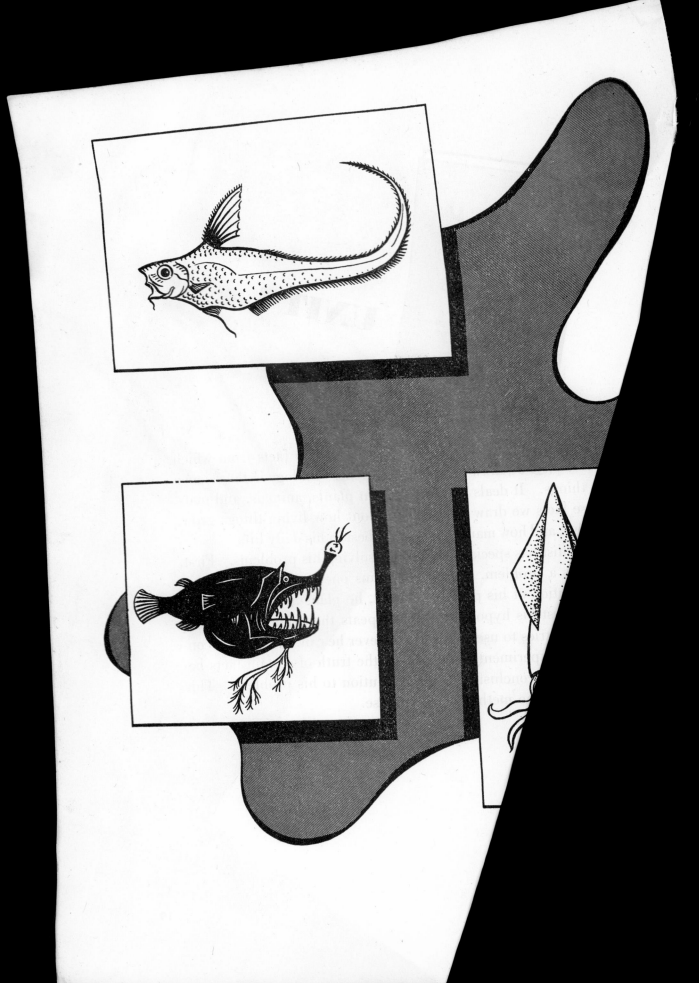

Unit 2

This World

in Which

You Live

The man from the natural history museum was showing lantern slides about life in the ocean to the biology class.

" If you went down ten thousand feet," the speaker said as a picture flashed on the screen, " you might see something like this. But we have to guess what it looks like. No man has ever been down that far. It's nearly freezing and there's terrific pressure on everything. Only animals that can stand such pressure live there. Bit by bit, scientists have built up this picture of deep-sea environment."

" What's environment? " Jim asked the speaker.

" It's the things and forces around you," he replied. " The deep sea is one kind of environment. Special animals live there."

" How does sunlight get down there? " Ed asked.

" It doesn't. The only light comes from the glowing structures on the bodies of these animals. Notice the mouth and teeth of these fish. They capture and eat smaller animals. That one at the top left is an angel fish. The one at the bottom left is an angler fish. And that queer looking animal on the right is a deep sea squid."

Topic 1

THE LIVING THINGS OF YOUR WORLD

Ever see a really tall building? Ever try to push your way along a crowded city street? Quite an experience for someone who has always lived in the country.

Or, maybe you were born and raised in a city. The wide-open spaces with their many plants and animals seem strange the first time you see them. You feel lost until you learn about environment.

City and country are two types of environment. Like the deep sea, environment includes the things and forces around you — plants, animals, rocks, soil, sunlight, clouds, winds, rain, and snow.

AMONG THE NEW WORDS FOR THIS TOPIC

- **CELLS.** Tiny parts or units of which living things are made.
- **COMMUNITY.** A region of the environment set off from other regions by natural barriers.
- **ENVIRONMENT.** The things and forces around you.
- **FOOD CHAIN.** A series of plants and animals which are dependent, one on another, for food.
- **NUCLEUS** (*noo-klee-us*). A special structure of living substance inside a cell.
- **ORGAN.** A group of tissues doing a special activity.
- **PARASITE** (*par-uh-syte*). A plant or animal which lives at the expense of another living thing.
- **PROTOPLASM** (*proh-toh-plazm*). The living substance in a cell.
- **SPECIES** (*spee-sheez*). One particular kind of living thing.
- **SYSTEM.** A group of related organs doing a general activity.
- **TISSUE.** A group of similar cells doing some special activity.

CHAPTER 4

What Are Living Things?

Let's begin your study of environment by learning about living things. What are living things? Why, they're plants, animals, and man.

No doubt you can name quite a few plants and animals. You see them every day. But there are some interesting things that you may not know. Take a look at Fig. 4-1. Ever see a thin slice from the stem of a plant? Well, here's one.

You say that the stem seems to be made up of little cells? That's just what they're called. These *cells* make up the bodies of every living thing. Your own body is made up of billions of cells.

What are cells? Not all cells are alike. But most of them are so small you need a *microscope* (*mike*-roh-skope) to see them. You can see a diagram of a simple plant cell in Fig. 4-2.

Notice that this plant cell has a *cell wall* on the outside. The cell wall is a nonliving covering. Inside the wall is a substance called *protoplasm* (*proh*-toh-plazm). Protoplasm makes plants, animals, and man act as they do. It's the living substance. It's what makes them alive.

Protoplasm is nearly colorless. Often it contains a lot of tiny granules. If you watch the same living cell under a microscope, you can see that protoplasm moves and changes its appearance. But it usually looks like a thick, heavy liquid.

Now look again at Fig. 4-2. No-

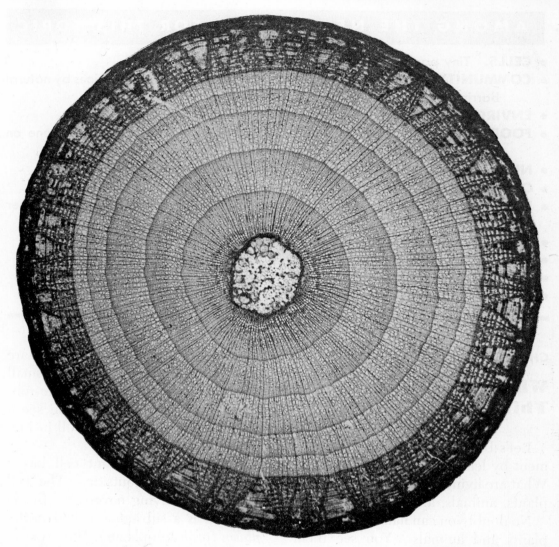

Fig. 4-1. A section through a plant stem. The stem is made up of many tiny cells.

tice that this cell has a *nucleus* (noo-klee-us). It's a special part of the protoplasm. Scientists think the nucleus controls the activities of the cell. Even today there are still many things scientists need to learn about cells and the living protoplasm in them.

Protoplasm in your body. "Does my body contain protoplasm?" you

ask. The answer is: yes, it does. It fills your body cells.

There are billions of cells in your body. And there are many kinds of cells, too. You'll see some human body cells in Fig. 4-3.

Protoplasm is made up of common chemicals that are about us everywhere in the world. You might not

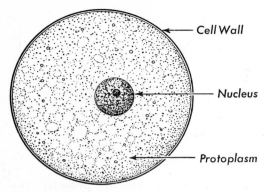

Fig. 4-2. Diagram of a plant cell. The protoplasm of the cell is the living substance.

think so, but it's true. This chart lists some of them.

COMMON CHEMICALS IN PROTOPLASM			
Oxygen	65%	Nitrogen	3%
Carbon	18%	Calcium	2%
Hydrogen	10%	Phosphorus	1%

These substances are combined in protoplasm to form various things. One of them is water. Suppose you weigh 100 pounds. If all the water were removed from your body, you'd weigh only about 30 pounds. So, you see about two-thirds of your body weight is water.

Protoplasm and foods. Other things found in protoplasm are *carbohydrates* (kar-boh-*hy*-drates), *fats,* and *proteins* (*proh*-tee-ins).

" But I thought carbohydrates, fats, and proteins are foods," you say.

Right you are. Ever stop to think that your foods come from plants and animals? Actually, you eat the cells of these plants and animals.

Groups of cells. In plants, animals, and man groups of similar cells form tissues. A number of similar cells used for the same purpose make up a *tissue.* When you throw a ball you use several muscles. These muscles are made up of muscle tissue, for the most part.

Often, two or more tissues act together to do a special job. When this happens, these tissues form an **organ.** For instance, your stomach contains gland tissue, muscle tissue, and nerve tissue. Your stomach is, therefore, an organ.

Even groups of organs may act together to carry out a general function. Such a group of organs is called a **system.** Your digestive system includes your stomach and your intestines. (There are some other organs too, about which you'll learn later.)

CHECK YOUR FACTS . . .

Number 1 to 6 on a sheet of paper. Answer each of the following questions.

1. What part of a cell do scientists think controls its activities?

2. What are three kinds of tissue found in the human stomach?

3. What is the name of the outer, non-living covering of some cells?

4. Are there millions or billions of cells in your body?

5. What food materials are present in protoplasm?

6. How much of your body is made up of water?

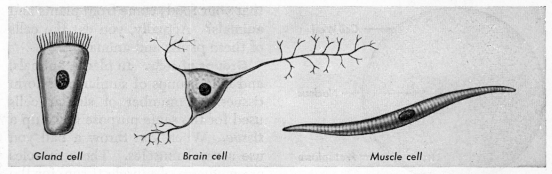

Gland cell   Brain cell   Muscle cell

Fig. 4-3. Cells from the human body. Many other kinds of cells are present also.

CHAPTER 5

What Can Living Things Do?

Did you know that the air overhead contains living things? Well, it's a fact. When airplanes tow collecting nets, the nets pick up all sorts of living things.

Most of the plants and animals that get into this upper air are tiny. They often float on air currents. Pollen grains from plants have been found far out over the Atlantic Ocean. Little spiders, riding on their webs, have been picked up thousands of feet above ground.

You see, there's another environment high up in the air. In it certain plants and animals can live quite well. But we've raised some questions. How do plants and animals live? Why do they behave as they do? What can they do?

One of the best ways to answer these questions is to study a simple form of life. Let's use a tiny animal called Amoeba (am-*ee*-bah). This

little animal consists of only one cell. That's all there is! You can sometimes find it in ponds, perhaps on the undersides of lily pads. It's really not much more than a drop of protoplasm. But to see what it's like, you need a microscope.

Amoeba moves. Look at the drawing of an Amoeba in Fig. 5-2. See any cell wall? No, because there isn't one. Instead a *cell membrane* surrounds this drop of protoplasm. It's much thinner than a cell wall and is different in other ways, too. Amoeba has a nucleus, as you can see. The living substance outside the nucleus is a special kind of protoplasm called *cytoplasm* (*sy*-toh-plazm).

When you watch an Amoeba, you'll note that it changes shape. It also moves from place to place. But this motion is a sort of gliding over the surface. Here then is one of the things that protoplasm, the living substance, can do. It can change shape and it can move.

Amoeba gets food. Yes sir, a large Amoeba will capture and eat a smaller Amoeba. But an Amoeba will also

Fig. 5-1. These pictures show three different types of animals that take to the air. On the left-hand side are two birds. In the center is a bat. On the right-hand side is a grasshopper. Many other animals also fly. What others can you think of that have this ability?

feed on other tiny plants and animals that live in ponds.

Fig. 5-4 shows how the Amoeba takes in food. A pocket forms in the Amoeba's surface. The animal then surrounds the food particle and captures it.

Amoeba digests food. To get any benefit, the Amoeba must digest the food particle. Then the Amoeba must make the digested material a part of its protoplasm. Otherwise, this material wouldn't be of any use to it.

Any part of an Amoeba's cytoplasm can form digestive fluids. These fluids fill a space which surrounds a food particle inside the cytoplasm. The food particle is then digested, and useful parts are taken into the protoplasm. So you see, another thing protoplasm can do is to digest food.

Amoeba uses energy and grows. An Amoeba uses some of the food it takes in to provide energy. Energy is used in movement, and in carrying out all other life functions. Probably an Amoeba uses some food to repair parts of the cell, too. What is left over provides for the growth of this tiny, one-celled animal.

So an Amoeba becomes larger. But this growth doesn't go on forever.

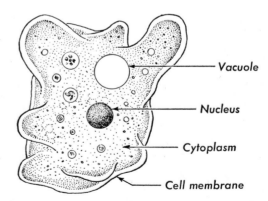

Fig. 5-2. An Amoeba. This one-celled animal is one of the simple forms of life.

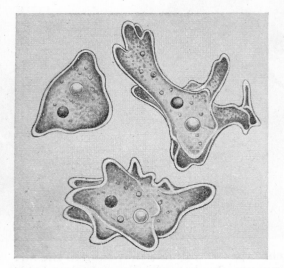

Fig. 5-3. Different shapes in which an Amoeba may appear. Change of shape is due to contraction of the living substance.

Sooner or later an Amoeba reaches full size. Then it divides to form two cells.

Amoeba uses oxygen. Oxygen is one of the gases of the air, as you probably know. Various amounts of this gas are found in the water of ponds and streams.

All living things need oxygen. Oxygen burns food and sets free the en-ergy in that food. You need energy to do work, such as moving from place to place. An Amoeba gets the oxygen it needs from the air in the water around it. The oxygen just comes in through the cell membrane.

Amoeba gets rid of wastes. When food is burned in the protoplasm, waste products are formed. One of these wastes is a gas called *carbon dioxide* (dy-*ox*-syde). Other wastes are in liquid form.

How does an Amoeba get rid of such wastes? Well, probably some of the carbon dioxide passes out through the cell membrane. The liquid waste (and maybe some gas, too) collects in spaces called **vacuoles** (vack-*yoo*-oles). Such a vacuole is shown in Fig. 5-2. From time to time, the contents of a vacuole break out through the cell membrane.

Amoeba must also get rid of solid wastes. These are foreign materials that can't be digested. They too break out through the cell membrane from time to time.

Amoeba is sensitive. Any protoplasm is sensitive, and Amoeba is no

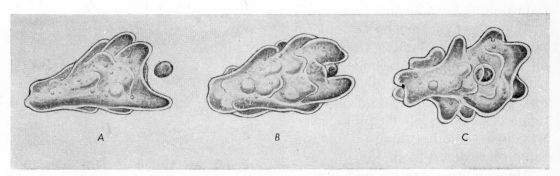

A   B   C

Fig. 5-4. Diagram to show how an Amoeba captures a food particle.

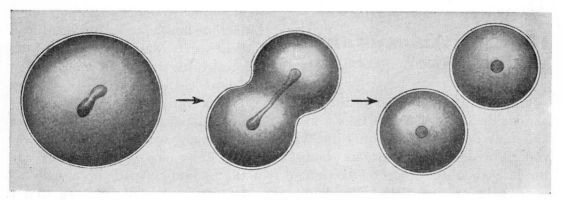

Fig. 5-5. Diagram to show how an Amoeba divides. The result is two new cells.

exception. When an Amoeba meets a solid object in its path, the Amoeba moves away. If an Amoeba touches a food particle, it captures it.

An Amoeba will avoid poisonous chemicals in the water. It will also move away from bright light.

Amoeba reproduces. You'll be interested to know that a full-sized Amoeba divides to form two cells. How it does this is shown in Fig. 5-5. First, the nucleus begins to divide. Soon the cytoplasm also begins to divide.

The process ends when the two halves of the old cell pull apart. The result is two new cells. Each new cell is just like the parent cell except that it's smaller. Each new cell goes its own way, takes in food, and grows.

Maybe you've noticed a rather startling fact. Most of the plants and animals around you grow old and die sooner or later. But not Amoeba. It can be killed but it can't die of old age.

A student of biology once said, "Wouldn't it be wonderful to be an Amoeba and live forever?"

His teacher replied, "Maybe so, but remember that you'd have no more sense than an Amoeba. Probably you wouldn't even know that you were alive!"

CHECK YOUR FACTS . . .

Number 1 to 6 on a sheet of paper. Select the description in the right-hand column which is best for each item in the left-hand column.

1. Vacuole (Amoe-   *a.* Acts to digest
ba)   foods

2. Oxygen   *b.* Surrounds the cytoplasm

3. Digestive fluid   *c.* A waste formed when energy is set free

4. Carbon dioxide   *d.* Space in which liquid wastes collect

5. Cell membrane (Amoeba)   *e.* Used by cells to set free energy

6. Protoplasm   *f.* Manufactures food

   g. The living substance

CHAPTER 6

How Are Animals and Plants Alike?

What is it that you see on the left-hand side of Fig. 6-1? Looks just like some dead leaves, doesn't it? As you know, leaves are parts of plants. But how about the object on the right-hand side of Fig. 6-1? No doubt about it. It's a butterfly, and therefore an animal.

As a matter of fact, both pictures show the same thing. It's a dead-leaf butterfly from the East Indies. This butterfly has wings that are brightly colored on their upper surfaces. Their lower surfaces look like dead leaves. So, when the butterfly is flying, it looks like a lot of other butter-flies. But when it's resting on a branch, it looks like an old dead leaf.

Fool you? Maybe not, but it fools a lot of birds and other animals that eat dead-leaf butterflies.

Plants versus animals. This reminds us that plants and animals are alike in many ways. Both contain the living substance — protoplasm. In both, the body is made up of cells.

Of course, you'd soon see that a dead-leaf butterfly was an animal rather than a plant. But many of the small, simple living things might puzzle you. They even puzzle trained biologists. Some of them seem to be part plant and part animal.

Living things and their environments. Biologists have learned that there are many kinds of living things. We find them in all sorts of environ-

Fig. 6-1. A dead-leaf butterfly at rest on leaves, and with its wings spread.

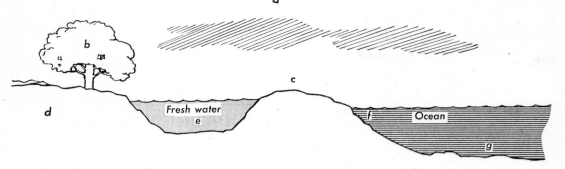

a

b

c

d

Fresh water
e

f   Ocean

g

Fig. 6-2. Different kinds of places where living things live: (*a*) **in the air;** (*b*) **in the trees;** (*c*) **on land;** (*d*) **in the soil;** (*e*) **in fresh water;** (*f*) **in the shallow sea;** (*g*) **in the deep sea.**

ments. Some live on land. Some live in the soil. Some are found in trees or in the air. Others occur in ponds, lakes, streams, and the ocean.

You can see the different kinds of environments where plants and animals live in Fig. 6-2. You might be in any one of these, except the deep sea.

Many living things are small. In any environment there's an unseen world of tiny living things. They greatly outnumber the larger plants and animals. Most of these tiny forms of life are simple in structure like Amoeba. Most of them are one-

celled. Some can make their own food, but others feed on smaller plants and animals.

The green plant cells you see in Fig. 6-3 contain granules of a green-colored material called *chlorophyll* (*kloh*-roh-fill). Such plant cells can make their own food.

This green material isn't found in all plant cells. Plants like mushrooms don't have it at all. And it's never found in animal cells. Cells which don't have this green material can't make food.

Maybe you've heard of the *viruses*

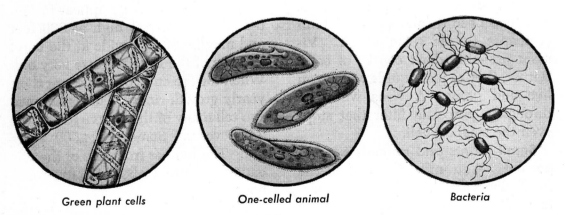

Green plant cells   One-celled animal   Bacteria

Fig. 6-3. Three kinds of simple living things.

Fig. 6-4. The Big Trees of a West Coast forest are enormous. Automobile roads have been cut through some of these trees. The lumber is popular for the inside finishes of houses, for shingles, railway ties, and fence posts.

(*vy*-rus-sez). They cause 'flu and other diseases. They're also among the simplest forms of living things. Scientists need the most powerful microscopes to see them at all. Viruses probably don't consist of cells. Rather, they're just liquids which can live and grow. A virus will pass through a porcelain filter that stops even the smallest cell.

Small plants and animals are important. You may think that the small plants and animals aren't important. If you do, you're wrong. Many of these small forms of life serve as food for the animals that you use. Others live in the soil and help to make it fertile.

On the other hand, a great many small plants and animals are **germs.** Germs, as you know, cause diseases. These diseases attack our own bodies, as well as the bodies of the plants and animals we raise.

Other small pests include certain worm parasites, and some of the insects. *Parasites* (*par*-ah-sytes) are types which live in or on other living things and get food from them. Parasites give nothing in return. Nowadays man doesn't need to worry so much about the larger plants and animals. He can see them easily enough. And he can usually control them. But the small pests are another story. Unseen for the most part, they're very numerous. Their small size and their large numbers make them hard to control.

Large plants and animals. There are large plants and animals in most environments. Did you ever see pictures of one of the Big Trees in California? Some of these appear in Fig. 6-4. They grow as high as 330 feet and may be 30 feet wide at the base.

Some of the Big Trees are very old. When they're cut, you can count their yearly growth rings. This is how we can tell many of them have lived over 2,000 years. Some are 4,000 years old. The lumber from one of them is enough to build about 20 five-room houses.

The largest living animal is the blue whale. But don't try to find one unless you sail on the ocean! A blue whale is about 95 feet long when full grown. It may weigh as much as 120 tons. You probably think that some of the extinct *dinosaurs* (*dy*-nuh-sawrs) were large. And so they were. However, no dinosaur ever weighed more than 50 tons.

So you see, plants and animals of the environment include the large and the small. Some are simple in structure and some are complex. Some are pests, and some are useful.

CHECK YOUR FACTS . . .

Number 1 to 6 on a sheet of paper. For each of the following items, select the best answer.

1. A living material which will pass through a porcelain filter unchanged is a(n): (*a*) Amoeba; (*b*) virus; (*c*) plant; (*d*) animal.

2. The largest animal in the following list is a(n): (*a*) elephant; (*b*) blue whale; (*c*) dinosaur; (*d*) hippopotamus.

3. Some of the Big Trees are thought to live as long as: (*a*) 100 years; (*b*) 200 years; (*c*) 500 years; (*d*) 4,000 years.

4. The green-colored material of some cells is: (*a*) found only in viruses; (*b*) associated with food-making; (*c*) related to diseases; (*d*) found mostly in animals.

5. Some of the smallest plants are useful because they: (*a*) cause disease; (*b*) serve as food for animals we use; (*c*) are eaten by other plants; (*d*) use the oxygen of the air.

6. Plants and animals are alike because they both: (*a*) make their own food; (*b*) move around from place to place; (*c*) contain the living substance protoplasm; (*d*) can live in the deep sea.

CHAPTER 7

How We Name Living Things

Plants and animals were important to early man. From them he got food, material for clothing, fuel, building materials, and even medicines.

Early man had names for the plants and animals he knew. But in old times there was often confusion about these names. A plant or animal had one name in one country. It had an entirely different name in another country.

A standard system of names. Biologists now have a standard system of names for all plants and animals. It's used all over the world.

In this system, the name of a plant or animal, or man himself, has two parts. Thus, man is *Homo sapiens*.

"Sounds like Latin," you say.

Yes, the names are Latin, or they're words with Latin endings. *Homo* is the name of the genus (*jee*-nus) to which man belongs. The **genus** is a group of related plants or related animals. *Sapiens* is the name of the species (*spee*-sheez) to which man belongs.

A **species** is one kind of living thing. To study the living things in any environment, you need names for them. So each kind of plant or animal is called a species. Dogs make up one species, but cats make up another species.

"But there are different kinds of dogs," you'll say. Surely, and we sometimes call these different kinds of dogs, **breeds.** They aren't different enough to be put in different species.

Even members of the same breed aren't exactly alike. Two dogs may look similar until you examine them carefully. Then you begin to see some differences.

Or, take identical twins. They look strikingly alike — often you can't tell one from another. But among other things, their fingerprints are different.

Now, you see that the members of a species aren't exactly alike. But they're similar in many of their features.

The two great kingdoms. The two great groups of living things in our world are the **plant kingdom** and the **animal kingdom.** Most of the living things you know belong to one or the other. Let's look at some of the members in Figs. 7-1 and 7-2.

There are, however, quite a few questions. What, for instance, would you do with the viruses? In some ways they're different from both plants and animals.

Some smaller groups. The two kingdoms are divided into smaller groups as you can see in the following chart.

Let's consider an example. All plants belong to the plant kingdom, which is a very large group. This kingdom is first divided into a number of *phyla*. Members of a **phylum** (*fy*-lum) are more nearly alike than members of a kingdom. A phylum may contain several classes. Again, members of a **class** are more nearly alike than members of a phylum.

When you get down to the level of a species, all members are fairly similar. But remember, there are still differences. No two members of a species are exactly alike any more than two men are alike.

What things are similar? Deciding whether parts of plants and animals are similar isn't always easy. Scientists ask the question: "Do these two parts have the same origins?"

For instance, look at Fig. 7-3. It shows the wing of a grasshopper and the wing of a bat. Surely, grasshoppers and bats both have wings. Both can fly. Does this mean that they're closely related?

Now look at the facts. A grasshopper's wing develops from a part of the body covering. The grasshopper's legs have nothing to do with the growth of its wings.

THE GROUPS OF PLANTS AND ANIMALS

1. Kingdom [kingdoms]	5. Family [families]
2. Phylum (fy-lum) [phyla]	6. Genus [genera]
3. Class [classes]	7. Species [species]
4. Order [orders]	8. Breed [breeds]

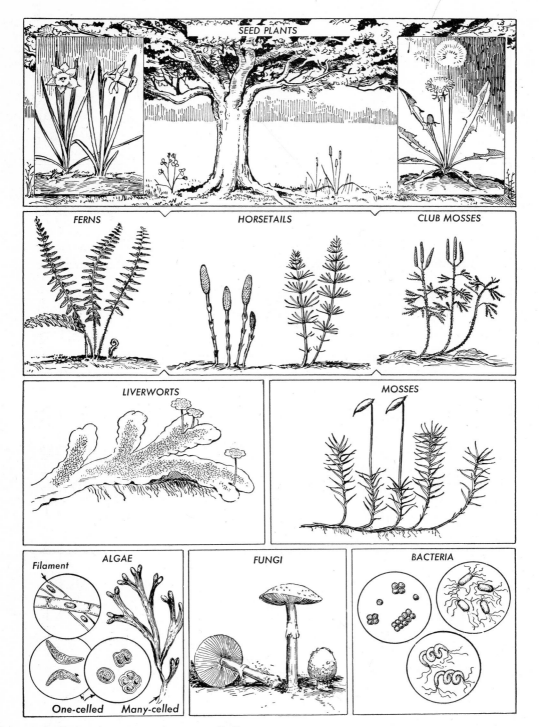

Fig. 7-1. Some important types of plants.

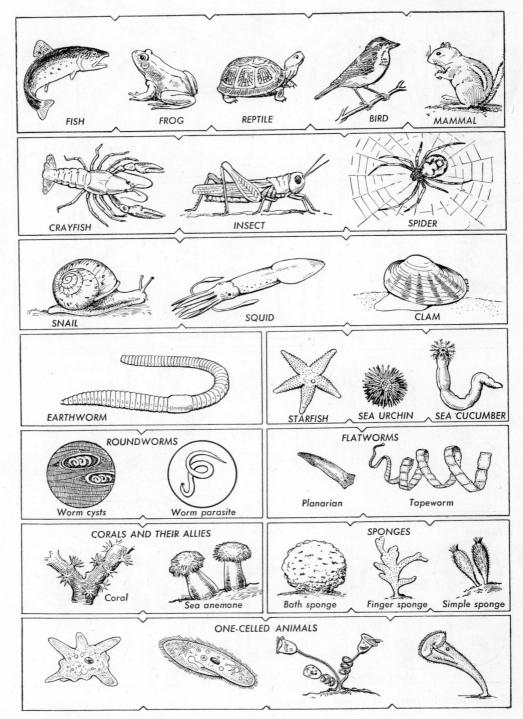

Fig. 7-2. Some important types of animals.

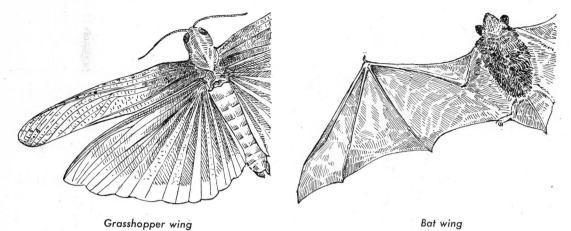

Grasshopper wing   Bat wing

Fig. 7-3. Two types of animal wings. The origins of these wings are quite different.

The bat's wing is a thin, fleshy part covered with skin. It's mainly supported by the bat's front limbs.

So the two types of wings are really very different. They have different origins. The evidence of the wings doesn't show that bats and grasshoppers are closely related.

On the other hand, consider the front leg of a horse and the front leg of a dog. They don't look much alike, do they? The horse's leg has only one toe, on which is a hoof.

Yet the two legs are both front limbs. Both have the same origins. Both have similar bony structures. As a matter of fact, horses and dogs belong to the same class of animals.

CHECK YOUR FACTS . . .

Number 1 to 6 on a sheet of paper. Mark each of the following items True *or* False.

1. The wings of grasshoppers and bats show that they're closely related.

2. In the name *Homo sapiens, Homo* is the name of the genus.

3. Parts used for the same purposes always have the same origins.

4. Some simple living things are hard to classify as either plants or animals.

5. All members of a species are exactly alike.

6. In the name for the house sparrow, *Passer domesticus,* the second word, *domesticus,* is the name of the species.

CHAPTER 8

How Plants and Animals Live Together

There are many strange animals in the world and among the strangest are the anteaters. You won't find them in your environment because they live in Central America and South America. Fig. 8-1 shows you what these animals look like.

Fig. 8-1. An anteater. The long, slender, sticky tongue of this animal is well suited for picking up ants.

When it's hungry, what does an anteater do? It looks for an ant hill. Then it breaks open the ant's burrows with sharp claws on its front feet. Out goes the long tongue and down into the burrows. The ants stick to the tongue which the animal then quickly draws back into its mouth. The ants are swallowed and make a nice meal for the anteater. It has no teeth, so it can't chew.

You can see how well an anteater is prepared to capture and eat ants. But it's not so well prepared to capture and eat other things. Its welfare depends on a good ant supply. It's a case of no ants, no anteater!

What is a community? An anteater must live in the right kind of community or he'll starve. So must many other animals and plants. A *community* is a region of the environment that is set off from other regions by natural boundaries.

You've already learned that some plant and animal communities are located in the sea. Others are in lakes and streams. Still others exist on land.

Boundaries of land communities are such things as rivers, deserts, swamps, mountains, lakes, and oceans. You live in many of these communities. This is why they're important in your lives.

There are food groups in each community. In any community, the plants and animals make up several *food groups.* Look at Fig. 8-2 for some of these. Here's a list of the different food groups:

1. *The food-makers.* These are the green plants. They're the only living things that can make their own food. All other living things, including man, depend on green plants for food, either directly or indirectly.

2. *The plant eaters.* These are the animals that feed largely on plant materials. Among them are some animals we raise for food, such as cattle and sheep.

3. *The flesh eaters.* Those animals that feed chiefly on other animals belong here. Some, like the foxes, provide us with useful furs.

4. *The parasites.* These animals and plants live at the expense of other animals and plants. They include the germs and other disease producers. But some of them attack pests, rather than ourselves or the plants and animals we raise.

5. *The eaters of dead matter or saprophytes* (*sap*-roh-fytes). Most of these are small forms of life. They speed up the decay of dead plants and

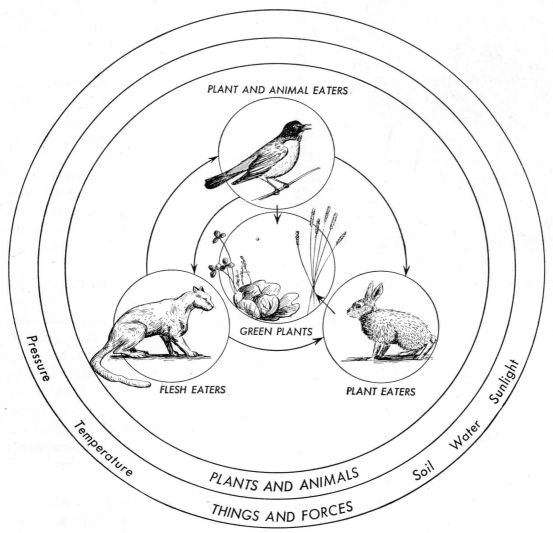

Fig. 8-2. The foods all animals eat come originally from the green plants.

animals. Thus, useful materials of decay are returned to the soil. Molds are good examples.

6. *Animals that eat a variety of things.* This is a smaller group. It includes man, too. And it also includes rats, mice, and pigs.

" Not very good company," you say.

Well, perhaps not, but there's one advantage in belonging to this group.

You can eat different kinds of foods and live in many communities.

Plants and animals depend on each other for food. You've heard people say: " The big ones eat the little ones." To some extent it's true.

What goes on in pond water like that in Fig. 8-3? Simple types of green plants live here. These little green plants make their own food.

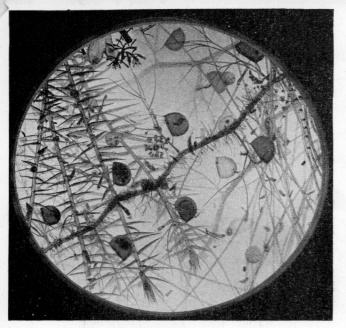

Fig. 8-3. Simple forms of plant and animal life in the water magnified many times. In what way do these plants and animals form food chains? List various ways in which these animals are indirectly important in your everyday life.

The plants are eaten by simple animals. Small, fresh-water shrimp eat both the plant and animal cells. The shrimp, in turn, are eaten by small fish. Larger fish eat the small fish. And, if you're a fisherman, you catch and eat the large fish!

What you have here is a food chain. A *food chain* consists of a series of plants, animals, and man, all of whom depend on one another for food. In the case in Fig. 8-3 it begins with the simple plants. It ends with the fish you eat. You don't have to eat the simple plants or the fresh-water shrimp directly. But they're important to you just the same. Without them, there wouldn't be any large fish.

Other food chains exist in lakes, in the sea, and on land. In them are many small plants and animals that

have no direct importance to you. But they're important indirectly. They're parts of other food chains from which you profit.

The community food supply. Any community can support just so many living things and no more. How large this number can be depends on the food supply.

Green plants make all basic food. *Basic food* is the simple sugar which the green cells make. If conditions favor plant growth, there'll be plenty of basic food. Otherwise, basic food will be scarce.

Right away you can see there's a lot less basic food in winter. Production also varies from year to year. In a hot summer, drought kills many plants. Even plants have to have water.

The amount of green plant food in the community determines how many plant-eating animals can live there. The plant-eating animals provide food for the flesh eaters. Other animals feed on both plant eaters and flesh eaters.

When there is plenty of basic plant food, animals grow in numbers. More animals survive. Other animals move in from nearby communities.

But when plant food is scarce, many animals die. Others become inactive, especially during winter. And some animals move away.

CHECK YOUR FACTS . . .

Number 1 to 6 on a sheet of paper. Select the description in Column B *which is best for each item in* Column A, *and write its letter on your paper.*

Column A

1. Men
2. Cattle
3. Green plants

Column B

a. Make their own foods
b. Feed largely on green plants
c. Feed on dead materials only
d. Eat a variety of foods

Column A

4. Basic food
5. Parasite
6. Food chain

Column B

a. Food relationships within a community
b. Made by green plants
c. Relates to animals alone
d. Live at expense of living plants and animals

Plants and animals are the living things in your environment. Their bodies, like your own, are made up of cells. The living substance in these cells is protoplasm. In the larger plants and animals, groups of cells form tissues, organs, and systems.

There are many kinds of living things in, on, or near the earth's surface. They live in many kinds of environments. Scientists call each kind of living thing a species. Some species of living things are one-celled. Others are large in size.

Scientists use a special system of names for plants and animals. They say that living things which have similar parts that are of similar origin are related.

Plants and animals live together in natural communities. Food groups and food chains exist in these communities. Your problem is to take part in community life for your own good.

WHAT DO THESE WORDS MEAN?

Carbohydrate
Cell
Cell wall
Chlorophyll
Community
Cytoplasm
Environment

Fat
Food Chain
Genus
Germ
Nucleus
Organ
Parasite

Phylum
Protein
Protoplasm
Species
System
Tissue
Virus

ASK YOURSELF . . .

1. What kinds of factors are present in any environment?

2. (a) How do city and country environments differ?   (b) In what ways are they the same?

3. (a) What units make up a plant stem?   (b) Are animals composed of similar units?

4. (a) What substance is found in cells?   (b) Of what is it made?

5. What are some of the things that living cells do?

6. What evidence can you find that individual differences occur among people?

7. Why are the viruses important in our lives?

8. What is the advantage in having scientific names for plants and animals?

9. (a) To which food group does man belong?   (b) What is the advantage of this?

10. (a) Name one animal parasite.   (b) Name one plant parasite.

11. What types of plants and animals make up a typical food chain?

12. What are the two great groups of living things?

13. What happens when there's a lot of food in a community?

14. What happens when food is scarce in a community?

15. How are you dependent on green plants for survival?

16. In what ways are food chains related to your welfare?

GETTING THE FACTS . . .

1. Learn to use a microscope. The names of its parts are shown in Fig. 8-4. Look through the eyepiece and adjust the mirror to get a good light. Learn to open and close the *diaphragm* (dy-uh-fram). What effect does this have on the light?

Now put a glass slide on the microscope stage. Turn the low power objective into position. Use the coarse adjustment to lower the objective until it's just above the slide. Then turn the coarse adjustment up until the image comes in view. Use the fine adjustment to get a sharp focus.

Note that if you focus up you won't jam the objective against the slide. Don't pick up the microscope. Always leave it on the table unless your teacher tells you to put it away. Then carry it by the arm.

2. Peel off an outer layer of an onion. Between the inner layers you'll find a very thin membrane. Put this on a glass slide. Add a drop of water and a cover glass. Look at your specimen under the microscope. What do the cells look like?

3. If a suitable place is near your school, your teacher may want to take the class on a field trip. A meadow or a place with a stream or pond and bordered by woods is fine. Such a trip will give you a better idea of a community.

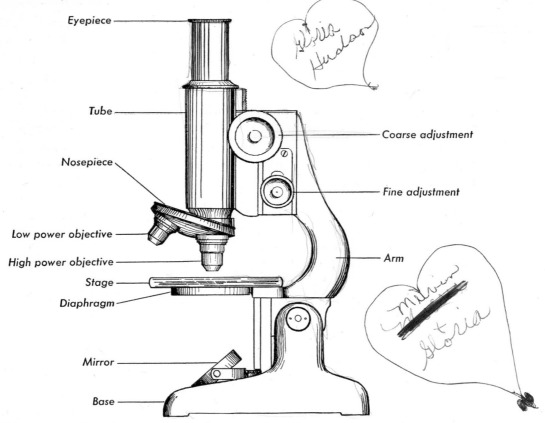

Eyepiece

Tube

Nosepiece

Low power objective

High power objective

Stage

Diaphragm

Mirror

Base

Coarse adjustment

Fine adjustment

Arm

Fig. 8-4. A diagram of a microscope showing its different parts.

Try to find out: (a) what plants and animals live in the meadow, the stream, and the woods; and (b) how each type gets its food.

4. Here's how you can make a pond culture. Get a quart jar and go to the edge of a pond or stream if one is nearby. Fill the jar about half-full of water. Now add some of the decayed matter you find on the bottom in shallow water. Add a few growing plants such as the " pond scums " you'll find on the surface. Examine drops of your culture under the microscope. Describe what you see.

5. Your teacher will help you make an

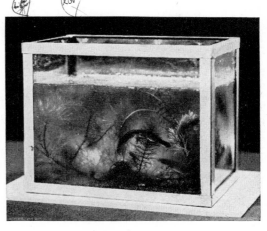

Fig. 8-5. A school aquarium. You can even use a gallon battery jar to set up a small aquarium. Cover it with a glass plate. The cover will serve to prevent rapid loss of water.

aquarium. First, get an aquarium jar or a large gallon jar and a glass plate. Cover the bottom of your container with clean sand about three inches deep. Add some stones or pebbles to the sand. Now fill the container with clean pond water. Or, you can use city water if it doesn't have much chlorine in it.

Add a few water plants to your aquarium as you see in Fig. 8-5. Add also a small fish and perhaps a pond clam and a crayfish. Then put in four or five pond snails. You can buy all these plants and animals or you can collect them along the edges of a pond. Cover your aquarium with the glass plate and put it on or near a sunny window sill. Remember, your aquarium must have some sunlight if the green plants are to grow. And you must also add water as needed.

Topic 2

WHAT ARE THE THINGS AND FORCES AROUND YOU?

Here's a lungfish. It has both gills and lungs. When the pond or lake where it lives is full of water, it swims around like any other fish.

What happens when the pond dries up? The lungfish goes down into the mud. There it coils up in a mud-lined nest. It leaves a hole to let in the air, and the lungs take in oxygen. When it rains again, the pond fills up with water. The lungfish comes out of its nest and is active once more.

Plants and animals have many *adaptations*. They must be able to meet changing conditions of life. Otherwise they can't survive.

AMONG THE NEW WORDS FOR THIS TOPIC

- **BASIC FOOD.**   The simple sugar made by green plant cells.
- **CYST** (*sist*).   A protective covering formed around certain living things.
- **GROUND WATER.**   Water from rain or melted snow that has seeped down into the soil.
- **SOIL.**   A mixture of rock particles and decayed remains of plants and animals.
- **SUBSOIL.**   The lower level of soil, usually lacking in decayed remains of plants and animals.
- **TOPSOIL.**   The upper level of soil, usually rich in decayed remains of plants and animals, and full of tiny, living organisms.
- **WATER TABLE.**   The upper level at which ground water stands in the soil.

CHAPTER 9

The Soil Is Full of Life

How much of the earth's surface is covered by seas?   More than half. But after all, you live on the land so you're probably more interested in this part of the earth.

Not all land areas are equally good places for plants and animals.   In some spots there's good climate and a fertile soil.   In such places you'd find a great many plants and animals.

On the other hand, consider a desert.   The soil of some deserts is fertile enough, but there's little water. Only a few types of plants and animals can survive in such a place.   When some desert lands are *irrigated* (that is, water is brought to them) fine crops will grow there.

The value of soil.   Maybe you've heard people say: "Our food comes from the soil."   And so it does, at least

most of it.   Our crop plants grow on or in the soil.

You also know that some soil is good and other soil is poor.   What's the difference between the good and the poor soil?   To get the answers you must first learn how soil is formed.

Rocks are broken up and form soil. If you dig deeply enough into the soil, you'll find layers of rocks.   These are the rocks which form the *earth's crust.* Sometimes rock layers appear at the surface.   In other cases, the soil covers them.   When soil begins to form, this means that the rocks are being broken up.

"What can break up such rocks?" you ask.

Chemicals in the air or water in the soil will do the trick.   Sometimes it's a slow job, but remember that the earth is very old.   Rocks have been breaking up for a long time.

Other forces act on rocks, also. Water gets into tiny cracks.   It freezes

Fig. 9-1. A tropical jungle (left) and some dry land (right).   In which place is life more abundant?

and expands.   Then pieces of rock split apart.

Water currents in streams roll the smaller rocks along the bottom.   They grind against each other and against other rocks.   This action breaks them up and they form pieces of gravel and sand.   All this takes time and goes on slowly.

Rocks also wear away due to the action of the wind.   In many places, the wind carries sand particles.   These sand particles are swept against rock surfaces.   Slowly but surely, the rocks are worn away.

Plant and animal remains are added to the soil. The wearing away of rocks   makes   sand   and   gravel.

These two materials make up a large part of soil.   But there are other things present in soil, too.

Most important are the products of decay which come from plants and animals.   What a world this would be if dead plants and animals didn't decay.   Fortunately, they do, and the products of this decay are added to the soil.

Fallen leaves in a forest become, in time, a part of the surface soil.   This surface soil, enriched by decay products, is the *topsoil*.   Under it is the *subsoil* which is usually much less rich.   Topsoil and subsoil are shown in Fig. 9-3.   You'll find this drawing on page 49.

Fig. 9-2. When rains come, the rushing waters roll rocks along the bottom of the stream. Slowly but surely the rocks are ground or broken up.

What makes a soil fertile? Ever hear anyone say that a certain place is a "garden spot"? They mean, of course, that the soil will grow fine crops. Why should some soils be that way while other soils are just about worthless? What do you think makes a soil fertile?

To begin with, a *fertile soil* must contain certain chemicals. Some of these chemicals come from broken-up rocks. Others come from the decay of plants and animals. But you soon find that chemicals aren't the whole story. In addition, soil particles mustn't be too coarse or too fine. Coarse soil doesn't hold water well. It dries out much too quickly after a heavy rain.

On the other hand, a very fine-grained soil tends to keep out air and water. Plants need both air and water to grow.

Finally, certain small living things tend to make soil more fertile. Among them are a group of bacteria. These bacteria live in the soil. They pro-duce certain chemicals that crop plants need.

Soil is full of life. Don't ever get the idea that soil is just a mass of "dirt." Not only does it contain certain bacteria, but also molds, earthworms, and many other small living things. When you scoop up a handful of soil, you've got a tiny environment in the palm of your hand.

There are several common soil types. Look around your home area. You'll find several types of soil right there. Probably *gravel* will be among them. Gravel particles are larger than those of sand. Usually gravel is too coarse to be fertile. It dries out quickly, and doesn't hold the decay products of plants and animals.

Sand is like gravel except that the rock particles are smaller. Like gravel, sand doesn't hold water or decay products very well.

Clay is different. You've used clay in modeling. If so, you know that it's very fine-grained. Clay comes from the break-down of a special kind of rock. It holds water well. However, pure clay is so fine-grained that it tends to keep out air.

Loam is a mixture of all other kinds of soil. It's porous but not too porous (that is, like a sponge). Under favorable conditions, its topsoil may be very fertile. This is just what you need to grow the best crops.

Silt is formed from soil particles that have been carried by water. It may, for example, collect on the bottom of a lake. Silt usually is fine-grained, but not as fine-grained as pure clay.

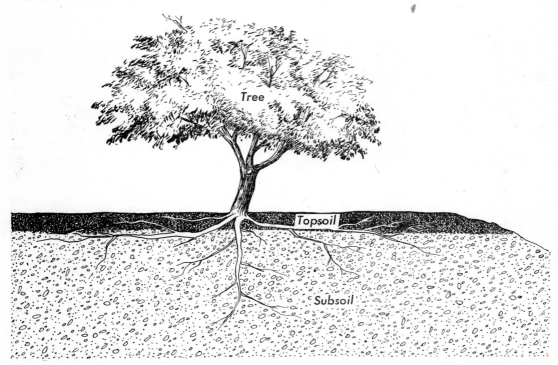

Tree

Topsoil

Subsoil

Fig. 9-3. In many places, the topsoil is filled with products that come from the decay of plants and animals.

CHECK YOUR FACTS . . .

Number 1 to 6 on a sheet of paper. Select the best answer for each item.

1. The layer of soil at the surface of the ground is: (*a*) subsoil; (*b*) clay; (*c*) topsoil; (*d*) sand.

2. What causes the wearing away of rocks: (*a*) chemicals; (*b*) running water; (*c*) wind; (*d*) all of these?

3. The soil that is likely to produce the best crops is: (*a*) loam; (*b*) gravel; (*c*) clay; (*d*) sand.

4. Which of the following soils can hold water least well: (*a*) clay; (*b*) sand; (*c*) loam; (*d*) silt?

5. Which of the following soils always consist of particles that have been carried by water: (*a*) silt; (*b*) gravel; (*c*) clay; (*d*) loam?

6. Which of the following soils is most likely to keep out air: (*a*) loam; (*b*) gravel; (*c*) sand; (*d*) clay?

CHAPTER 10

Why Do Living Things Need Water?

Ever visit Palm Springs, California? Or any other place where men " have made the desert bloom"? It's quite an experience to see what you can do in the right place with a little water.

The fact is, a good many desert soils are fertile enough. But without

Fig. 10-1. Good crops are produced in many dry land areas provided that water can be brought to the soil.

water, few things will grow in them. This is because water is an important part of living protoplasm. You know how much your own body needs water.

What are desert plants like? You may say: " But some plants *do* live in deserts, or at least in very dry places." Of course they do!

However, dry land plants are special types. Look at the giant cactus plants in Fig. 10-2. They have no broad leaves. Plants that have broad leaves lose a lot of water to the air. But giant cactus plants lose very little water in this way.

When it rains, or when snow melts in the mountains and runs down to the valleys, the cactus roots take in water. This water is stored in their roots and stems. And it's useful when the plant needs it.

What happens when a pond dries up? Even in a rainy area, a good many ponds dry up in midsummer. What happens to the plants and animals that live in these ponds? Do they just die?

As the pond begins to dry up, some of the animals in it may leave. Turtles and frogs, for instance, can travel on land. They can get to other ponds and streams. But fish, other small animals, and many water plants aren't so lucky. When the pond dries up, their lives are usually ended.

An interesting exception is in the case of some of the very small living things. Take, for example, the tiny animal you see in Fig. 10-3. When the pond dries up, this tiny animal forms a *cyst* (*sist*). The cyst is a protective outer covering.

Inside the cyst the animal cell is inactive. It can resist the effects of drying for a long time. The wind may even sweep it up and carry it to another pond. If this happens, the animal comes out of its cyst and is active again.

Water is necessary to active life. The cactus in the desert has to have water. The tiny animal inside its cyst is inactive during the time of drought. Even seeds won't sprout and produce new plants unless they have water. It is necessary for active life.

Your own body is about two-thirds water. And some living things contain even more. A potato is about three-fourths water. The lettuce you eat in salads is about 94% water. Some of the jellyfish that live in the sea are about 98% water.

Of course, plants and animals that live in the water have plenty at hand. But on the land, things are different. Land animals may drink from streams and pools. Some of them get enough water from the foods they eat.

Land plants get water from the soil through little hairs on their roots. Among them are our crop and garden plants. This is why soil water is so necessary for farming and gardening.

Fig. 10-2. Giant cactus plants of dry land areas in the Southwest. Green stems are the food-making parts of these plants.

What is the water table? When it rains, the surface of the soil gets wet. Then there's plenty of water for the roots of plants. But of course it doesn't rain every day. Sometimes the topsoil dries out. Does this mean that plants die? Not necessarily. There often is ground water in the soil. This *ground water* is water that has soaked deep down into the soil from rains and melted snow. It collects in the soil or in rock layers.

If you dig down far enough at any

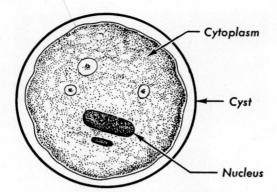

Fig. 10-3. Diagram of a one-celled animal within a cyst. The cyst is a protective outer covering.

point, you come to soil or rock that contains ground water. The upper level of this water-bearing area is called the *water table.* In certain places, the water table is close to the surface. In other places, it lies at a greater depth.

When you think about the water table, you may think of wells. Wells must be drilled down into the water table.

The water table is important in another way. If it's close enough to the surface, it supplies water for the roots of plants. If it's too far under the surface, it doesn't help the plants, unless they have long, deep roots. Some trees have these, but most plants don't.

CHECK YOUR FACTS . . .

Number 1 to 6 on a sheet of paper. Mark each of the following items True or False.

1. Water makes up a large part of all living things.

2. Winds carry some one-celled animals from one place to another.

3. The water table is at the same depth in all places on the earth's surface.

4. Many plants lose water to the air through their leaves.

5. Dry land plants, such as cactus plants, don't need water to continue active life.

6. Nine-tenths of the human body is composed of water.

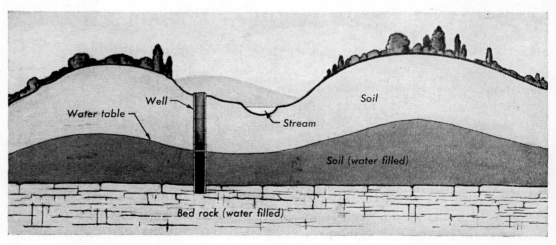

Fig. 10-4. The depth at which the water table lies varies in different places. If it is too far below the surface, the roots of crop plants get no water from it.

CHAPTER 11

Why Do Green Plants Need Sunlight?

"Say," Jim said to Ed, "did you know that if there wasn't any sun there wouldn't be anything to eat?"

"Quit kidding," Ed replied. "There'd be plenty to eat, but it would be dark and cold outdoors."

Who was right?

Ed's ideas about a dark and frozen world were good enough. But Jim was right about the food. Sunlight furnishes the energy for food-making on our earth. Life as we know it couldn't exist without the sun.

Jim could have gone on and said that without green plants we would have no food. For green plants make the basic food on which all other living things depend.

Green plants make food. You see a cross-section of a leaf in Fig. 11-1. Note that the leaf has many cells. In some of the cells is the green-colored substance, *chlorophyll* (*klor*-oh-fill). These green cells are the ones that make food. No other cells can do this.

Green plants use two materials in making basic food: (*1*) carbon dioxide; and (*2*) water. Carbon dioxide is a gas found in air and in water. Plants take it in through tiny openings or pores in their leaves. The little hairs on the roots of higher plants take in water. This water passes up through the stem and reaches the leaves.

In the green plant cell carbon dioxide and water are combined to form: (*1*) simple sugar; and (*2*) oxygen. Sunlight provides the necessary energy for this food-making. A *simple*

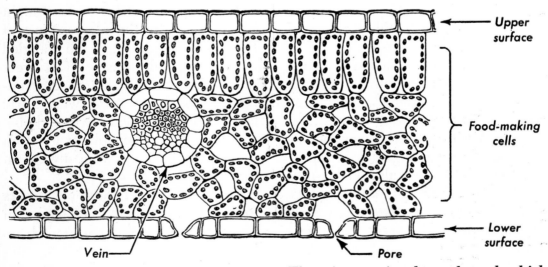

Fig. 11-1. Diagram of a leaf cross-section. The vein contains ducts through which liquids can pass.

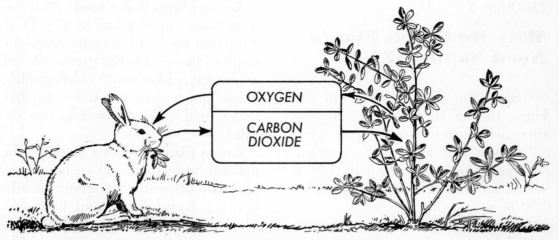

Fig. 11-2. Animals use oxygen and give off carbon dioxide. Green plants use carbon dioxide and give off extra oxygen.

sugar contains carbon, hydrogen, and oxygen.

Simple sugar is the basic food. Plants use simple sugar to provide energy for growth and repair. But green plants also use oxygen. The oxygen they don't use escapes into the air. •

Look at Fig. 11-2. Note that green plants use carbon dioxide and give off oxygen when making food. Animals, however, use oxygen and give off carbon dioxide in their breathing.

What happens to the basic food? Simple sugar is a carbohydrate (kar-boh-*hy*-drate). Green plants can change it into other sugars and into starch. A *carbohydrate* is any of the foods you know as sugars or starches.

Green plants can also make *fats* (plant waxes and oils) and proteins (*proh*-tee-ins). A *protein* is a food substance that has carbon, oxygen, hydrogen, nitrogen, and sometimes phosphorus and sulfur. Scientists don't know just how the green plant makes fats and proteins, but eventually they'll learn the secret.

So, you see you can get three important materials needed by protoplasm from green plants. You need these carbohydrates, fats, and proteins to keep your own body growing.

Sunlight and land plants. Ever think what the old forests were like back in the Indian days? You might be surprised by the facts. Most of these old forests had no tangled masses of underbrush. Tall trees raised their tops high into the sunlight. The forest floors were fairly clean except for fallen leaves and pine needles. Few green plants lived on them because they were always in shadow.

You see a few of these old forests today but mighty few. They're in places where the trees haven't been burned or cut for many years. But most of our modern forests are younger. They're made up of various trees, big and little. The forest floors aren't fully shaded. Weeds and bushes grow here and there.

You can see from this story of forests how necessary sunlight is to green plants. The growth of a forest is a real fight for life. A tree that is badly shaded is almost doomed.

For that matter, you know that many garden plants don't grow well when they're shaded. You've noticed, too, how the leaves of a plant on a window shelf turn to the light.

Sunlight and water plants. Ever go fishing along the shores of a lake? Then you've probably looked down into the water and seen pond weeds.

Pond weeds are green plants. They include those plants that make the basic food in a pond, lake, or stream. If the water is clear, these plants may grow on the bottom where it's fairly deep. But there are limits. Green plants won't grow unless they get enough sunlight to make food.

Now you'll ask: "How far will sunlight go down into the water?" The answer is: it depends on conditions. If the surface is covered with waves and the water is muddy, the light doesn't go very far. But if the surface is smooth, and the water is clear, the light goes down farther.

The fact is, most green water plants live within 50 feet of the surface. A smaller number live as much as 100 feet from the surface. A few live at even greater depths. This is true in the sea, as well as in lakes.

We'll bet you're going to ask: "What about the deep sea communi-

Fig. 11-3. Only a few small plants grow on the shaded floor of an old forest. This is because little sunlight can reach the ground. As you can see, the few plants are mostly straggling weeds.

ties? Where do they get any basic foods? And — how can they have food chains so far down in the deep ocean?"

This is a good question and it deserves a good answer. Now then, remember the plants and animals that die? They drop down from shallow water above. They form the basic supply of food for the animals that live at deeper levels. This makes a steady stream of food from above.

55

CHECK YOUR FACTS . . .

Number 1 to 6 on a sheet of paper. Select the best item in Column B *for each statement in* Column A *and write its letter on your paper.*

Column A	Column B
1. A carbohydrate	*a.* Sunlight
2. Source of energy for food-making	*b.* Oxygen
	c. Nitrogen
3. Given off by living green plants to the air	*d.* Simple sugar
	e. Protein

Column A	Column B
4. The basic food made by green plants	*a.* Carbon dioxide
5. A gas used by green plants in the process of food-making	*b.* Water
	c. Oxygen
	d. Plant oil
6. A gas produced by green plants in the process of food-making	*e.* Simple sugar

Fig. 11-4. A younger forest. Young trees and other green plants grow on the forest floor.

CHAPTER 12

There Are Barriers to Life

Ed was reading a book. "What's this thing called 'the bends'?" he asked Jim.

"Why, 'the bends,'" Jim replied, "is something divers get. You know — the men who go down to look at sunken ships."

"What gives them 'the bends'?" continued Ed.

"The pressure," said Jim. "The farther down you go, the more pressure you have."

Pressure in the water. Now, Jim had *some* of the facts, but not the whole story. Divers can get "the bends" and so can men who work under pressure building tunnels.

But let's get back to the diver and his diving gear. He has an air line through which he gets air from the surface. This air has to be under pressure. The air pressure must offset the effects of the water pressure around the diver.

You probably know that air is a mixture of several gases. Two of them are oxygen and carbon dioxide. But there's also nitrogen, and this one does the damage.

When a diver is at the surface, a

Fig. 12-1. A diver in diving gear comes up out of the water.

little of the nitrogen in the air enters his blood through his lungs. It's not enough to cause him any trouble. But when he breathes compressed air, a lot of nitrogen enters his blood and body cells.

What happens if the pressure is released suddenly? This nitrogen rushes out of his body cells and into his blood. Bubbles of nitrogen block the blood vessels and press on the nerves. Pain and cramps result. Thus, the diver has "the bends."

For this reason, a diver is brought to the surface and put in a *decompression tank*. Pressure in the tank is at first the same as that he has worked under. Then the pressure in the tank is released slowly until it gets back to

normal. The diver breathes out the nitrogen in his body slowly, and usually harmlessly.

All this reminds us that there are barriers to life. A *barrier* is an obstacle or check. One of these is pressure. We can't really get down into the deep sea.

What are the effects of air pressure? At sea level, the pressure of air on your body is 14.7 pounds per square inch. You don't notice it, because you're used to it.

You draw air into your lungs. Pressure causes some of the oxygen in this air to enter your blood. The oxygen is carried through your body and used by the body cells.

Now, suppose you go up in the air in a plane. At 20,000 feet above the earth's surface, the air pressure is greatly reduced. You get only about half the normal oxygen supply. Your body soon becomes short of oxygen. That's why oxygen is often given to passengers and the crew in airplanes. Some people need an extra amount of oxygen at only 5,000 feet. At 25,000 feet, people without an extra oxygen supply may die in a few minutes. Low pressure, like high pressure, is also a barrier to life.

Of course, people sometimes get a mile or more above sea level without flying in a plane. Some of our towns and cities like Denver, Colorado, are more than a mile high. Newcomers from low areas get tired easily at this height. After a few weeks, however, most of them get adjusted. They breathe more deeply, and changes

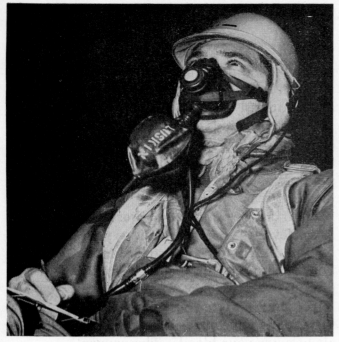

Fig. 12-2. Pilots who fly at high altitudes must have an extra oxygen supply.

take place in their blood. Then their bodies get normal oxygen supplies again.

Heat and cold are also barriers. "Are all plants and animals killed by freezing or boiling?" you ask.

Water boils at 212°F. and freezes at 32°F. Probably you begin to feel too hot when the temperature gets up around 90°F. But think of some of the simple plants that live in hot springs. They live in water at 200°F. You'll find such plants in the hot springs at Yellowstone National Park and at other famous hot springs. What's more, such plants won't stand water much colder than 200°F.

Scientists have known certain bacteria to live after being boiled. Some plant seeds, heated to 248°F., continue to live. So you see that boiling

temperatures don't kill *all* living things.

What about the effect of freezing temperatures on such an animal as a frog? Will they kill it? Yes, if the vital organs such as the heart and lungs are frozen. But if these organs aren't frozen, the frog may live.

Freezing doesn't necessarily kill many simple forms of plant and animal life. Many kinds of plants and their seeds survive the winter cold. So do the eggs of many insects which are laid on the ground. Some bacteria have been known to survive temperatures far below zero.

Most plants and animals, however, can't stand extreme heat and cold. Boiling or freezing kills many of them. That's why we say that extreme heat and cold are barriers to most living things.

Warm-blooded animals differ from cold-blooded ones. As for animals, it makes a difference whether they're *warm-blooded* or *cold-blooded*. Only the higher types of animals like birds and mammals are warm-blooded. *Mammals* are animals with backbones, whose bodies are more or less covered with hair.

Most *warm-blooded animals* have body temperatures around 100°F. As you know, your own body temperature is about 98.6°F. This doesn't change as the temperature around you changes. Many warm-blooded animals can keep active through the winter as well as in the summer.

Cold-blooded animals, on the other hand, are those whose body tempera-

Fig. 12-3. A mink and a snake with her young. The mink is active during cold weather, but the snake becomes inactive.

tures change with the changes in the temperature around them. Such animals as insects, fish, frogs, turtles, and snakes are examples. They're active only when the weather is warm. When it's cold, they become less and less active.

Some warm-blooded and most cold-blooded animals are inactive through the winter. Woodchucks and ground squirrels take refuge in their burrows. Frogs go down into the mud at the bottom of ponds. These animals live on the fat they stored up during the summer. They don't become active again until the weather warms up in the spring.

There are, however, a few types of cold-blooded animals which manage to be active in cold weather. They're mostly of small size and they hide out in various heated buildings. The rest of the cold-blooded animals either die or become inactive.

Plant life becomes far less active in cold weather, as you probably know. In fact, the winter months are the period when the food supplies of any community drop to a low point for the year. Just as the food supplies drop to a low point during these months, so do the number of active plants and animals drop, too.

CHECK YOUR FACTS . . .

Number 1 to 6 on a sheet of paper. Select the best answer for each of the following items.

1. What rushes out of the body too fast in "the bends": (*a*) oxygen; (*b*) nitrogen; (*c*) carbon dioxide; (*d*) blood?

2. Mammals are animals which have backbones and: (*a*) hair; (*b*) fins; (*c*) feathers; (*d*) scales.

3. In the following list, a cold-blooded animal is a: (*a*) robin; (*b*) cat; (*c*) snake; (*d*) dog.

4. At a height of 20,000 feet, the human body tends to run out of: (*a*) water; (*b*) carbon dioxide; (*c*) nitrogen; (*d*) oxygen.

5. In the following list, an animal that is inactive through the winter is a: (*a*) man; (*b*) dog; (*c*) woodchuck; (*d*) crow.

6. At sea level, the pressure of air around you per square inch is: (*a*) 14.7 pounds; (*b*) 2.3 pounds; (*c*) 25.3 pounds; (*d*) 110.2 pounds.

Plants and animals must meet changing conditions of life. If they don't, they won't survive.

Soil is an important part of the environment. It's made up of rock fragments and decayed remains of plants and animals. Many plants grow on or in the soil but some don't. A fertile soil must contain certain chemicals needed for plant growth. It must also hold water quite well. But it mustn't be so fine-grained that it keeps out air.

Water is necessary to active life. Ground water exists under the surface of the earth everywhere. But in some places it's too deep to be of value to plants. Desert plants are adapted to save their water supply.

Sunlight is another necessity for life. It gives the energy for food-making in green plants. The green plants produce simple sugar and oxygen. Simple sugar is the basic food. Green plants can also make plant oils and proteins.

High pressure and low pressure act as barriers to life. Extreme heat and cold also act as barriers. But some plants and animals can survive both freezing and boiling.

WHAT DO THESE WORDS MEAN?

Basic food	Ground water	Soil
Clay	Loam	Subsoil
Cold-blooded animal	Mammal	Topsoil
Cyst	Sand	Warm-blooded animal
Gravel	Silt	Water table

ASK YOURSELF . . .

1. How is soil formed?
2. Why is topsoil usually more fertile than subsoil?
3. Would all deserts be fertile and productive if they had enough water supply?
4. (a) Is a very porous soil likely to be productive? (b) Is a very fine-grained soil apt to be productive?

5. Do you think it would take a short time or a long time to form a fertile layer of topsoil a foot thick?

6. (a) What are five common types of soil? (b) Of what is each type made up?

7. (a) Where does ground water come from? (b) Under what conditions would the most water soak into the ground?

8. What materials do green plants use in making foods?

9. (a) As you go up in an airplane, does pressure increase or decrease? (b) What is the effect on the oxygen supply?

10. Why is a diver returned to normal pressure in a decompression tank?

11. (a) How do warm-blooded and cold-blooded animals differ? (b) Do you see any advantage in being warm-blooded?

GETTING THE FACTS . . .

1. Visit a cut on a roadway or a place where a deep hole has been dug. Study the types of soil you find. Learn to tell the topsoil from the subsoil. Look for proof that conditions of life change.

2. Make an exhibit of soils to include gravels, sands, clays, loams, and silts.

3. Weigh a potato. Cut it into small pieces. Dry out the small pieces in an oven or on a radiator. Weigh them again when thoroughly dry. How much weight has been lost? What does this weight loss represent?

4. Using a microscope or a microprojector, look at the cross-section of a leaf. Locate the pores or openings through which gases enter or leave the leaf. Locate a vein through which liquids move in the leaf. Identify the cells which make the foods.

5. Change the position of a potted plant on a window shelf from day to day. See whether the leaves keep turned to the light.

6. Put a mixed pond culture in a refrigerator tray. Freeze it solid. Then, let it thaw out gradually. Look at samples with a microscope. See if all the plants and animals have been killed.

7. Your teacher will help you prepare a bog terrarium. You can use a container like the one you used to make your aquarium. Put a one-inch layer of sand on the bottom. Now cover the first layer with about two inches of soil. Slope the surface so that the soil is higher at one end. You can make a tiny pond by putting a culture bowl in the soil at the base of the slope. Plant liverworts and mosses around the pool. Plant mosses, small ferns, and other plants from moist places on the rest of the soil. Water the whole thing well and keep your terrarium on a window shelf. Cover it with a glass plate to prevent rapid loss of water.

Books You May Like . . .

Andrews, Roy Chapman. NATURE'S WAYS. Crown Publishers, New York. 1951. A readable account of the adaptations and habits of various interesting animals and some plants.

Bennett, Hugh H. *ELEMENTS OF SOIL CON-SERVATION.* McGraw-Hill Co., New York. 1947. A good reference on the soil, its relationship to human welfare, and soil conservation.

Carson, Rachel L. *THE SEA AROUND US.* Oxford University Press, New York. 1947. An interesting account of oceans, which includes discussion of ocean life.

Forman, Jonathan and Fink, Ollie E. (Editors). *WATER AND MAN.* Friends of the Land, Columbus, Ohio. 1950. Selected papers by a number of writers dealing with the rela-tions of water to the soil and to human interests.

Mavor, James W. *GENERAL BIOLOGY.* The Macmillan Co., New York. 1952. A standard reference work dealing with both plants and animals. Contains a chapter on life in different habitats.

Palmer, Laurence E. *FIELDBOOK OF NATURAL HISTORY.* McGraw-Hill Co., New York. 1949. This very useful reference book includes descriptions of many plants and animals, with emphasis on distribution habits and economic importance.

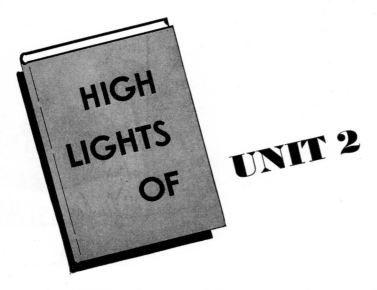

HIGH LIGHTS OF UNIT 2

The things and forces around you make up your environment. It includes plants and animals of many different species. Some are simple and some are complex. Some are tiny, and some are large.

Plants and animals live in communities. There are many important food chains in these communities. Our own problem is to live in natural communities to our best advantage.

The environment also includes factors such as soils, water, sunlight, temperature, and pressure. Many plants grow on or in the soil. Water is necessary to active life, while sunlight supplies the energy for food-making in plants.

All parts of the environment affect living things. Under favorable conditions, green plants make the basic food of the community. All other plants and all animals are dependent on these green plants for their food supply.

Factors of the environment change from season to season and from day to day. Plants and animals must meet the changed conditions of life if they're to continue to live.

Unit 3

Life

in the

Plant World

Ann's aunt took her to Florida during the week of winter vacation. When she got home she showed Ed and Jim her picture post cards. What interested them most were those of coconut palm trees.

"They're used for so many things!" Ann explained. "Of course, in Florida they're mostly planted for shade. But in the tropics they're used for clothing, firewood, shelter, and food."

"Does the coconut Mom uses to put on icings come from them?" Ed asked.

"You bet, and what's more, someone told me they get oil from these coconuts. It's used to make soaps, facial creams, and other cosmetics," Ann informed him.

"I never realized before how useful trees could be," Jim said. "Hey, Ed, don't you think this coconut palm would make a good topic for me to write up for biology class? You've got one, but I haven't. O.K. by you, Ann?"

"Sure thing, Jim," Ann told him, "and you can take these cards along, too. But remember, I'd like to have them back as soon as you are through using them."

65

Topic 1

SOME SIMPLE FORMS OF PLANT LIFE

Not all useful plants live on land. Many live in water, including the ocean.

Ever hear of the Sargasso Sea? It's an area of about two million square miles in the Atlantic Ocean off Bermuda. The water is from two to four miles deep. Masses of simple plants live at the surface of this sea. They make basic food.

Sailors after Columbus' time found the Sargasso Sea. Stories grew up about it. One said it was a graveyard for lost ships.

In the Sargasso Sea, the simplest plants make food for a shallow-water community far from shore.

AMONG THE NEW WORDS FOR THIS TOPIC

- **AGAR.** (*ah*-gahr). A food substance made from algae.
- **ALGAE** (*al*-jee). Green plants of certain simple plant groups.
- **BACTERIA** (bak-*tih*-ree-uh). Small, one-celled plants without green-coloring matter and organized nuclei.
- **EGG CELL.** A female sex cell.
- **FUNGI** (*fun*-jye). Non-green plants belonging to certain lower plant groups.
- **SPERM CELL.** A male sex cell.

CHAPTER 13

Algae Are Simple Green Plants

"You can always find your way out of the woods," said Jim, "because you know that moss grows on the north side of trees."

"Yes, but this stuff doesn't look like moss to me," Ed objected. "It's too small, and it grows on the tree like a green film."

Ed was quite right. What the boys were looking at wasn't moss at all. It was a growth of *algae* (*al*-jee). Algae are green plants which belong to some of the lower plant groups. And they're somewhat simpler than the mosses.

Also, Jim was partly right about moss growing on the north side. Both algae and mosses occur on the trunks of trees. You find them mostly on the side that is moist and shaded. Quite often this is the north side.

Many algae are one-celled. You see an alga in Fig. 13-1. This type happens to live on land. You can find

it on rocks and tree trunks near streams. Algae need a lot of moisture. Often, there are so many cells in a growth of algae that they form a green mat.

Algae like the one in Fig. 13-1 can't move about. They live and die in the same spot. Sometimes many cells live together and form a sort of colony. But each cell carries on its own life activities. When a cell grows to full size, it divides into two. Thus, new cells form.

Other one-celled algae live in the sea, or in lakes, ponds, and streams. All of them are food-makers because they're green. They make basic food on which many food chains depend. This is one reason why algae are important to us.

Not all algae are one-celled. Some are made up of many cells placed end to end. They form chains of cells.

Take a look at Fig. 13-2. It shows a common type of algae found in ponds and streams. Such algae float at or near the surface of the water. They're called *pond scums*.

The cells of this alga make food

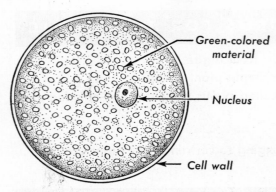

Fig. 13-1. A simple, one-celled alga. Such an alga may live on a moist rock or tree surface.

and grow. When fully grown, a cell may divide to form two cells. As a result, the chain of cells gets longer.

There are still other kinds of algae. Some other types of algae form masses of cells. Among these are the various *seaweeds*. One of these seaweeds is the rockweed, as you see in Fig. 13-3. If you've ever been to the beach, you've probably seen seaweeds. They're washed up by waves and the tide.

Some of the algae that live in the sea form huge growths. Certain types even develop lime skeletons. You know what coral reefs are. But did you know algae often form part of them? Actually, some of the reefs in the mid-Pacific Ocean are made up largely of lime that algae have deposited.

Many algae are useful. The greatest value of the algae is that they make foods in water communities. These foods support food chains. In the end we profit because we use fish and other animals from the water.

But people use some algae directly. Natives of islands in the Pacific often eat algae. In fact, they're raised for the market along the coasts of Japan. However, algae aren't very nourishing because they consist mostly of water. One form is used in making ice cream smooth and slower melting.

The substance known as agar (*ah-gahr*) comes from algae. **Agar** is a type of gelatin. People in some countries actually eat it. But scientists use it mostly in laboratories as a good food on which to grow bacteria.

Algae can be a nuisance. In the wrong places, algae can be pests. In warm weather they're too common in reservoirs where cities store drinking water. When you drink water from reservoirs which have lots of algae in them, the water smells bad. Algae also get into swimming pools and form scums on the surface.

CHECK YOUR FACTS . . .

Number 1 to 6 on a sheet of paper. Mark each of the following items True *or* False.

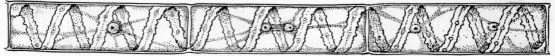

Fig. 13-2. An alga from a pond which grows as a chain. Each chain of cells is made up of a number of cells placed end to end.

a germ is a small living thing that causes disease
all Bacteria are small
alive, But not all bacteria causes
disease there
fore
not all
Bacteria
are germs

Fig. 13-3. Seaweeds growing upon rocks along the shore. Such plants are many-celled algae.

1. Algae make basic foods on which many food chains depend.
2. Agar is a substance made in the laboratory from bacteria.
3. Lime deposited by algae makes up a part of some ocean reefs.
4. Algae are raised for food in some parts of the world.
5. All algae are one-celled plants.
6. Some algae live on the land.

CHAPTER 14

Bacteria Are Tiny Non-Green Plants

When you think of bacteria you probably think: " Those germs! "

Here's something to remember: not all germs are bacteria. And not all bacteria are germs!

Bacteria (bak-*tih*-ree-ah) are very simple forms of living things. They haven't any green-coloring matter in their cells. Thus, they're not food-makers like algae. They're not really animal cells like Amoeba, either. They consist of only one cell. Biologists usually group them with the simple plants.

There are three general types of bacteria. Take a look at Fig. 14-1. Note the three types of bacteria. One type is rod-shaped. The second type is round like a ball. The third type is twisted or spiral-shaped. Some have tiny, hair-like whips sticking out from

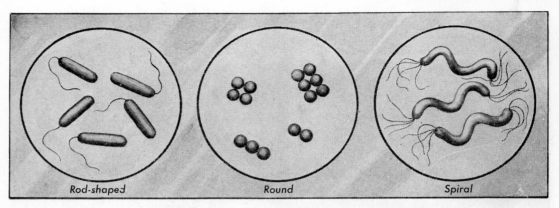

Rod-shaped   Round   Spiral

Fig. 14-1. Three general types of bacteria. All of them are very small in size.

the cell bodies. The bacteria can lash these back and forth and thus make the cell move around. They act like the oars of a boat.

The first thing you learn about bacteria is their size. They're so tiny you can't see many of them through the ordinary high-power lens on a microscope. It takes a special kind of lens to do the job.

Another odd thing about the bacteria is that they seem to have no real nucleus. Each one has a cell wall, of course. And inside the wall is the living substance, protoplasm. Actually, the material that makes up the nucleus probably is scattered through the cell. It isn't grouped into a real nucleus, but it's there just the same.

Bacteria grow and divide like other cells. Although they can't make their own food, they can and do take in food through their cell walls. They can grow very rapidly. In fact, one of them may grow to full size in 30 minutes. Then, it divides to form two new bacteria cells. At this rate one cell can give rise to over 500 new bac-

teria in as little time as four hours.

Sounds crazy? Try figuring it out yourself on a sheet of paper. Figure out what can happen in just one day alone!

"Well, if they grow and divide so fast," you say, "why don't they eat up everything on earth?"

They can't grow and divide at full speed all the time. The temperature must be just right. The right kind of food must be where they are. Often

Fig. 14-2. A colony of bacteria growing in the laboratory.

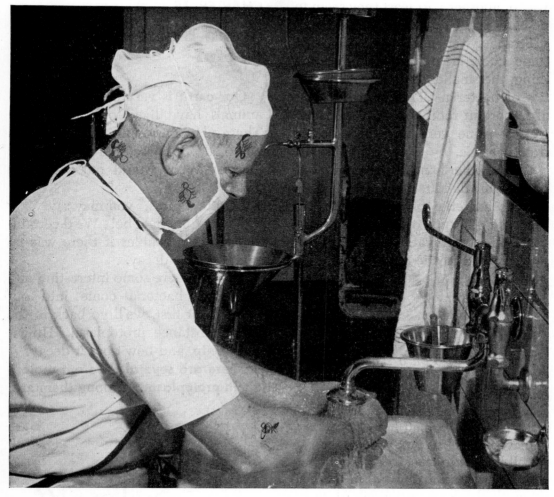

Fig. 14-3. Before operating, the doctor scrubs his hands thoroughly to prevent germs from coming in contact with his patient.

they don't find these conditions. Also, a mass of bacteria growing together may poison themselves with their own waste products.

Bacteria are all around us. Suppose you wanted to live in a place that was free of bacteria. Many people, frightened by the mere thought of germs, have had this idea. But where could you find such a place? You just couldn't.

Bacteria are everywhere. They're in the air, in water, on land, and in the soil. They're even in the bodies of plants and animals and in your own body. But don't get worried, they won't usually make you sick. Of course, the wrong kinds may, for they cause disease.

Some bacteria are useful and some are harmful. Quite a few don't really seem to be of much importance one way or another.   At least they seem to be harmless so far as we're concerned.

Strangely enough, we know that some bacteria are useful.   For one thing, the smaller animals eat quantities of bacteria.   Thus, they're parts of important food chains.   Then too, we get some very useful medicines from bacteria.

On the other hand, a fair number of bacteria are definitely harmful.   These are the bacteria that cause diseases. They are one type of germ.   The diseases affect cultivated plants.   They also affect domestic animals and your own body.

CHECK YOUR FACTS . . .

Number 1 to 6 on a sheet of paper. Choose the best answer for each of the following items.

1. Bacteria are alike in that they: (*a*) make foods; (*b*) are all harmful to man; (*c*) have no nucleus that you can see; (*d*) are all helpful to man.

2. Bacteria are found: (*a*) in the sea; (*b*) on the land; (*c*) in the soil; (*d*) in all of these places.

3. All bacteria are: (*a*) small in size; (*b*) rod-shaped; (*c*) able to make food; (*d*) injurious to your best interests.

4. Some bacteria can grow to full size in about: (*a*) 30 minutes; (*b*) one minute; (*c*) 5 minutes; (*d*) 30 seconds.

5. In the following list, a structure that all bacteria have is a: (*a*) mouth opening; (*b*) cell wall; (*c*) digestive canal; (*d*) hair-like whip.

6. Various bacteria are: (*a*) ball-shaped; (*b*) rod-like; (*c*) twisted or spiral; (*d*) all of these shapes.

CHAPTER 15

Some Bacteria Are Useful

Our earth is very old.   Plants and animals have lived on it for ages. These plants and animals have lived and died.   Suppose their bodies didn't decay.   What would our world be like?

" Quite a mess," you may say.

How right you'd be!   We'd certainly have our troubles if there was no such thing as decay.

This is where some interesting and important bacteria come into our story.   But first, we'll go back to the living substance, protoplasm.   How is it built up, and how does it decay?

There are several different materials in protoplasm.   Among them are:

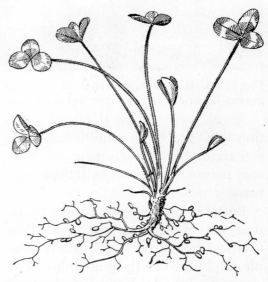

Fig. 15-1. Diagram of bacteria colonies on the roots of a clover plant. These bacteria make nitrogen compounds.

(1) carbohydrates; (2) fats; and (3) proteins. We call these materials *foods,* because they build up the living substance.

Carbohydrates and fats are alike in some ways. Each of them contains three elements. These are: (1) carbon; (2) hydrogen; and (3) oxygen.

Proteins are different. In addition to carbon, hydrogen, and oxygen, proteins also contain nitrogen, and sometimes, sulfur and phosphorus.

You've learned that nitrogen is one of the gases of the air. In fact, it makes up a large part of air. Where do green plants get the nitrogen they use in making proteins?

Air is all around the leaves of green plants. It's also present as air bubbles in water and in the soil. In that case, you may think green plants get nitrogen from the air. But they don't. Green plants simply can't use this pure nitrogen in the air.

"It's like the old saying: 'water, water, everywhere but not a drop to drink,'" you'll say. Well, it would be very much like that except for one useful group of bacteria.

Some bacteria enable plants to get nitrogen. Small clumps of these bacteria often grow on the roots of plants belonging to the bean and pea family. You can see a clump of these on the roots of a clover plant in Fig. 15-1. These bacteria unite pure nitrogen with other chemicals to make nitrogen compounds. *Nitrogen compounds* contain nitrogen and other elements. The roots of the green plants can take in these nitrogen compounds. That's

Fig. 15-2. A field of alfalfa. What relation does this crop have to nitrogen in the soil? List some other crops farmers plant which serve to help them to raise crops for bigger profits.

how green plants get nitrogen for making proteins.

Now you'll see why these bacteria are important and useful. Farmers often plant clover, alfalfa, beans, cow peas, or soybeans in their fields. The useful bacteria grow on the roots of these crop plants. They make the nitrogen compounds. Some of these compounds stay in the soil. So the soil becomes more fertile. Then, farmers can raise other crops with bigger profit.

Nitrogen is indeed necessary to the life of all plants, animals, and man.

How are proteins used? The story of proteins begins with this useful group of bacteria. They make the important nitrogen compounds. Green plants use the nitrogen compounds to make proteins.

Here's an interesting fact. Animals

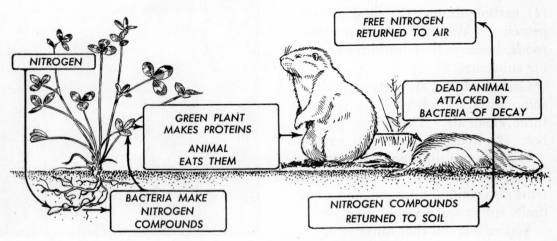

Fig. 15-3. A diagram to show events in the nitrogen cycle.

and man can't make proteins. Only the green plants can do this. Animals and man have to get their proteins by eating plants or various other animals. You get quite a few of your proteins by eating these plants. You get the rest by eating meat, including fish and other seafoods. Proteins are also present in eggs and milk. But don't forget that you can trace all of them back through food chains to green plants. The making of proteins is the first stage in what we call the *nitrogen cycle*. Animals get proteins from plants, which is the second stage. But sooner or later both plants and animals die. What happens then?

The decay process. We say that living things decay, but what does it mean? It means that various small living things feed on the dead bodies. Among these eaters of dead materials are another useful group of bacteria. They're the bacteria of decay.

Some bacteria of decay break down the proteins in dead cells. Nitrogen compounds are then set free. These compounds soak down into the topsoil during rains. Now, the green plants can use them again.

The return of these compounds to the soil is another step in the nitrogen cycle. Look at Fig. 15-3. It tells the story better than words do.

You can see that decay isn't just a matter of getting rid of dead bodies. The return of nitrogen compounds to the soil keeps it fertile.

Some other bacteria of decay even break down nitrogen compounds. Nitrogen, in the form of a gas, is thus returned to the air. This completes the nitrogen cycle.

What would the world be like if there weren't any bacteria? Who can say? It certainly would be different from the world you know.

CHECK YOUR FACTS . . .

Number 1 to 6 on a sheet of paper. Answer each of the following items.

1. What material in protoplasm contains nitrogen?

2. Pure nitrogen of the air can be taken in and used by green plants. *True* or *False?*

3. Animals can make their own proteins. *True* or *False?*

4. Name one plant on whose roots you might find groups of bacteria that can make nitrogen compounds.

5. Some bacteria are necessary to our welfare and comfort. *True* or *False?*

6. Some bacteria free nitrogen from nitrogen compounds. *True* or *False?*

CHAPTER 16

Yeasts and Molds Are Fungi

Ed and Jim were out in a vacant lot. Ed had an empty can and Jim had a spade. The boys were looking for worms for fishing.

Ed kicked a chunk of rotten wood out of an old log that was half-buried in the soil. To his surprise he saw a couple of worms and several grubs.

"What's wrong with using these?" Ed asked Jim.

"Not a thing," Jim replied as he pulled the rest of the log apart.

In the rotting wood were many odd things. There were insects, including ants. There were other small animals that the boys didn't know. Of course there were bacteria of decay, but these were too small for the boys to see.

What are fungi? "See these funny looking gray webs?" Jim asked, pointing at one of them. "Know what they are?"

"Why, I think they're molds, aren't they?" Ed questioned. "Same sort of thing you find on stale bread. They're called fungi (*fun*-jye)."

"Are they animals?" Jim wanted to know.

"No, I don't think so," Ed told him. "They're some simple sort of plant that lives on dead or decaying things."

Ed was almost right. Molds are fungi. *Fungi* are plants, but they have no green-coloring matter so they can't make foods. Many of them feed on dead materials, to be sure. But some of them feed on living plants and animals as well.

The fungi include a great number of small, and sometimes, very important plants. Among them are the yeasts, molds, rusts, smuts, mildews, and mushrooms.

The yeasts. The yeast cells you see in Fig. 16-1 are among the simplest

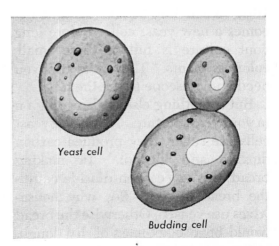

Yeast cell

Budding cell

Fig. 16-1. Diagram of yeast cells. Such cells reproduce by forming buds.

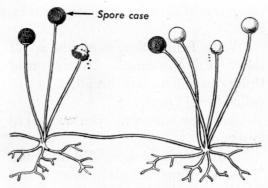
← Spore case

Fig. 16-2. Diagram of one type of mold. Spores come from the spore cases. A spore can develop into a new mold plant.

fungi. If you have a cake of yeast or some powdered yeast, you can easily raise yeast cells. Here's how.

Take some fruit juice and add sugar to it. Put it in a glass. Add a small amount of the yeast and keep the material in a warm place for a couple of days.

The yeast cells take in the sugary juice. They grow to full size. Then they form buds like the one in Fig. 16-1. Each bud breaks off and becomes a new yeast cell. Before long your culture is full of these small, colorless plants. They're so tiny you need a microscope to see them.

But something else is also going on in your yeast culture. When the yeast cells use sugar, they produce carbon dioxide and alcohol. In making bread, this gas carbon dioxide causes the bread to rise. See why housewives use yeast? Otherwise the bread would be a soggy mass of dry dough.

The molds. You've probably seen mold growing on bread. Any bread

that has been in a warm, moist place is apt to get moldy.

There are many different kinds of molds. When you see them growing on bread, they look like a coating of white or gray fur. But when you look at a bit of bread mold with a microscope, you see something like Fig. 16-2.

A mold plant is made up of many cells fused together. These form a series of thread-like branches. Some of the branches go down into the bread where they take in food.

However, other branches of the mold grow straight up. At their ends are little round balls which contain spores. A *spore* is a very tiny cell that can reproduce the mold. A spore can grow into a new mold if it falls on the right substance, like bread.

Now you can see why bread gets moldy. Mold spores are blown about in the air. You find them in dust. They're on and in everything around you. Naturally, they get on bread and other foods.

"Why doesn't everything get moldy?" you may well ask.

You've noticed that things begin to mold in damp, warm weather. Not foods alone, but all sorts of things that come from plants and animals. If these things dry out thoroughly, the molds stop growing. Molds must have moisture and warmth to grow well.

Molds can be a nuisance. Some molds destroy growing crop plants. Some of them ruin clothing and other materials. We fight back by spraying

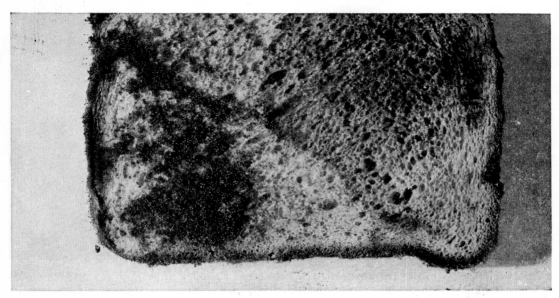

Fig. 16-3. What caused this piece of bread to get moldy?

poisonous chemicals on some of the things we want to protect. We store foods and other things in dry or cold places.

Some molds are useful. We raise them to give special flavors to cheeses. Blue cheese, for instance, contains one type of mold.

Other molds are used in making drugs. Everybody knows about *penicillin* (pen-ih-*sil*-in). It's used to fight certain kinds of diseases and infections. Scientists get penicillin from molds grown in laboratories. We also get some other useful drugs from molds. Like penicillin, they are used to combat germs.

Many molds and other fungi feed on dead plant and animal materials. They speed up the decay of these materials. The decay products are returned to the soil, which then becomes more fertile.

CHECK YOUR FACTS . . .

Number 1 to 6 on a sheet of paper. Mark each of the following items True *or* False.

1. Molds grow only on bread.
2. Yeast cells can make their own foods.
3. Yeasts and molds are two types of fungi.
4. When they use sugar, yeast cells set free carbon dioxide and alcohol.
5. Molds grow best in dry, cold places.
6. Certain molds are used to give special flavors to cheeses.

CHAPTER 17

Some Fungi Cause Trouble

" Look what I found in the back yard! " exclaimed Grace as she burst into the kitchen. She held a dozen or

Fig. 17-1. A poisonous mushroom, the so-called "death angel" (left), and an edible type (right). Only the real expert can be sure of the one it is safe to eat.

more mushrooms in her hands. Grace lived next door to Ed, Jim, and Ann and was in the boys' biology class.

Grace's mother looked, but didn't seem to be overjoyed by what she saw.

"Yes, mushrooms," she said quietly, "but we won't eat them."

"Not eat them?" asked Grace. "After all my work! They look a lot like the mushrooms you get at the store."

"Yes, Grace, they do," her mother agreed. "And that's why it's dangerous to eat mushrooms you find outdoors. The poisonous ones look a lot like the ones you can eat safely."

Mushrooms as food. Grace's mother certainly knew what she was talking about. Take a look at Fig. 17-1. On the left is a deadly poisonous mushroom. On the right, however, is one you can eat safely. Many people have been poisoned and even killed by eating the wrong kinds of mushrooms. Only a real expert can tell which types are safe to eat.

All mushrooms you buy at the store are raised on farms especially for the market. The farms are often in caves, old mine tunnels, and basements. In such places, temperatures stay much the same regardless of weather. This favors the growth of mushrooms. They do well in a damp, dark, and fairly warm environment.

Mushroom farms must be run with great care. Experts see to it that only edible mushrooms go to the store. Also, these fungi aren't easy to raise. Even the soil and fertilizer must be of a special type.

You eat mushrooms to add flavor to your food. Actually they're about nine-tenths water. The other part has little food value.

Where are mushrooms found? You're apt to see mushrooms and other fungi like them in the fields or woods.

Fig. 17-2. Bracket fungi growing on the trunk of a tree. They do not make foods, but get them from the tree.

They often grow in shady places. Not being food-makers, they don't need sunlight. Many, like those in Fig. 17-2, grow on decaying wood. They speed up the breakdown of dead plant materials.

Mushrooms can reproduce. Did you ever find an old puffball growing in a field? It's one type of mushroom. When you break it open, you see a black or brown cloud of dust come out. This dust is made up of spores — millions of them. A *spore* is a cell which can reproduce the plant. These spores may fall to the ground. Or, the wind may carry them for miles. One of these spores grows into a new puffball if it falls in the right place.

What are rusts? Ever heard of wheat rust? The rusts are another type of fungi. Some of them are pests because they attack crop plants, such as wheat and apples.

A farmer once cut down all the cedar trees on his farm. People thought he was crazy and one of his neighbors asked him why he did it.

"Well, looks foolish, I admit," the farmer said. "But I've got a fine apple orchard here. Apple rust is a disease which ruins my fruit."

"But how do the cedar trees come into the picture?" his neighbor asked.

"During the winter and early spring this apple rust lives on the twigs of cedar trees. It forms small balls which are full of apple rust spores. During the late spring, just about time the little apples are formed, these spores escape. The wind carries them from the cedar trees to my apple trees. They'll ruin my entire crop unless I cut down the cedars. Then the disease won't be able to live over the winter."

"What about the cedar trees on my farm and all our other neighbors?" his friend asked.

"You've got just as good an orchard as I have. I hope we can get everyone around here to do the same thing."

Now you can see why cutting down cedar trees makes sense. No cedar trees — no apple rust.

What would you call apple rust? A parasite? Yes, because it lives at the expense of other plants — in this case, cedar and apple trees. The cedar trees and apple trees are the hosts of

Fig. 17-3. Forest trees are now raised like crop plants. Here you see a growing forest of pine trees.

this parasite. A *host* is the living thing from which a parasite gets its food.

Since apple rust has to have two hosts, farmers can control it. All that is necessary is to raise either cedar trees or apple trees, but not both.

Another rust pest is the blister rust of white pine trees. You probably know that white pines are valuable trees. We even plant them and raise them like other crops.

Blister rust kills white pine trees. It's another rust that has to have two hosts. One of them is white pine. The other can be either gooseberry or currant bushes.

So farmers can control the blister rust by getting rid of all gooseberry and currant bushes. But this isn't as easy as it sounds. In many forest areas these bushes grow wild. Getting rid of them calls for a lot of work.

Other fungi as pests. Many other fungi are pests for one reason or another. Certain fungi cause skin diseases like ringworm, and athletes' foot. Fungi also cause rots and blights of many field and garden crops.

CHECK YOUR FACTS . . .

Number 1 to 6 on a sheet of paper. Answer each of the following items.

1. What other tree is a host of apple rust?

2. What tree is attacked by a rust which also lives on currant and gooseberry bushes?

3. Mushrooms must be raised in a warm, well-lighted place. *True* or *False?*

4. The "death angel" is a poisonous type of mushroom. *True* or *False?*

5. About how much of an edible mushroom is water?

6. What do we call the small cells developed by a mushroom that produce other mushrooms?

CHAPTER 18

Mosses and Ferns Are Green Plants

How would you like to eat bread made partly from ferns? Sounds odd, doesn't it? But people eat all sorts of things in different parts of the world. Among them is a flour made from one kind of fern. The underground parts of this fern are dried and ground up to make the flour.

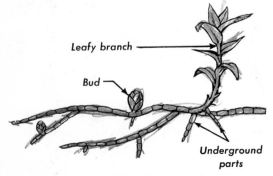

Fig. 18-1. Diagram of a moss plant. A new leafy branch can grow from a bud.

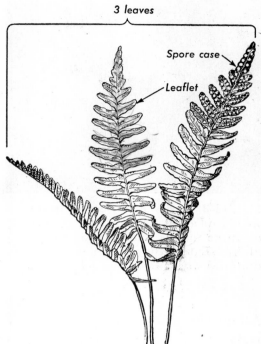

Fig. 18-2. Fern leaves or fronds. Each leaf is made up of a number of leaflets.

The mosses are green plants. No doubt you've seen mosses in the woods, especially near streams. This is because they grow best in fairly moist places.

If you have a clump of moss, examine it with a hand lens. You'll see that it's made up of many small moss plants. Usually, these plants will be attached to one another. Fig. 18-1 shows a single moss plant.

The leafy branch of a moss plant grows above ground. This part of the plant has green parts that make food. Underground, the moss is made up of a branching, thread-like growth. It has no true roots. This part of the plant takes in liquids from the soil.

Do you see the bud in Fig. 18-1?

Fig. 18-3. Ferns often grow in moist woodland areas. At one time they made up large forests and grew 30 to 40 feet high. Later they formed layers of material which became coal.

A bud like this can grow into a new leafy branch. You now see why so many moss plants grow joined together.

How does a moss reproduce? Mosses have another way of reproducing. They form tiny male sex cells, called *sperms.* They also form special female sex cells, or *eggs.* These are in between leafy clusters at the top of the moss plant.

In wet weather a sperm moves through the dew on a moss stem. It unites with an egg cell. This egg cell then forms a structure which produces spores. The wind scatters moss spores far and wide. When they fall in favorable spots, new moss plants develop from them.

Mosses have some value. However, they perhaps don't have as much value as some other plants. But they do form parts of various food chains. They form cover, or places of safety for many small animals. In cold countries mosses provide food for stock animals.

The ferns. The ferns you see in the woods have leaves. You can see these in Fig. 18-2. They're made up of a number of green leaflets. These are food-making centers.

Below ground a fern has a system of true roots. These take in liquids from the soil. The liquids follow regular tubes or ducts through the stems to the leaflets. All the higher plants have ducts of this type.

The stems of ferns grow partly underground. Here they may live from year to year. New leaves push up through the soil in the spring. They are often coiled, and when young are usually fuzzy.

Did you ever see rows of brown spots on the underside of a fern leaf? These spots are *spore cases* where spores are formed. Not all ferns have spore cases on their leaves. Some develop spore cases on special stems.

When ripe, the spores fall from the parent plant. If a spore falls in a likely spot, it begins to grow. A special structure which bears eggs and sperms comes from the spore.

The sperm cell unites with an egg cell. Then the egg cell begins to divide. And that's how a new fern plant starts.

Ferns also have value. Ferns have value for much the same reasons that mosses do. They're parts of various food chains. They also form a protective cover for many small animals.

People in some parts of our country

Fig. 18-4. The swamps of long ago probably looked like this. Plant remains, buried in the mud and mire, finally became coal.

use the young shoots of certain ferns as green vegetables. When cooked these taste like asparagus.

Ferns and related plants probably have more of a past than a future. Long ago when the earth was much younger, there were no seed plants. There were, however, many types of fern-like plants.

Some of these fern-like plants were giants compared to the ferns today. They formed huge forests in the swamps. As the plants died, they fell down into the muck and ooze. Here they were partly preserved. Slowly, but surely, their buried remains were

pressed together and formed layers of coal.

Not all of our coal deposits came from fern plants, however. Some came from other plants. Scientists think that oil deposits also come from the remains of ancient plants.

CHECK YOUR FACTS . . .

Number 1 to 6 on a sheet of paper. Mark each of the following items True *or* False.

1. The leafy part of a moss plant grows above ground.

2. Coal deposits are formed from the

remains of ancient plants that became buried in swamps.

3. A sperm is a female sex cell.

4. Both mosses and ferns can make their own foods.

5. A fern leaf is made up of roots and stems which always grow under the ground.

6. Ferns have special ducts for carrying liquids to all parts of the plant.

Some algae are one-celled. Others live as chains of cells or masses of cells. People use some algae for food. Many types are parts of important food chains.

Bacteria are small one-celled plants, perhaps with nuclear material scattered through the protoplasm. Bacteria grow and divide rapidly. They're everywhere, and even in your own body. Some bacteria cause disease, but other types are useful.

One group of useful bacteria combines nitrogen with other elements and forms nitrogen compounds. Plants then use these nitrogen compounds to make proteins. The bacteria of decay break up dead plants and animals and return them to the soil. Some bacteria even break up nitrogen compounds and return pure nitrogen to the air. Bacteria, yeasts, molds, rusts, and mildews are simple types of plants. None of them has any green-colored material and none can make its own food.

Mosses and ferns are green plants. They make their own foods. Mosses have branching parts under the ground. They also have green leafy branches above the ground. Ferns have underground stems. They have green leaves or fronds above ground. They develop special ducts through which liquids pass to all parts of the fern plant. From fern forests of long ago come some of our coal deposits. Some oil deposits may have come from them also.

WHAT DO THESE WORDS MEAN?

Agar	Food	Nitrogen compound
Algae	Fungi	Nitrogen cycle
Bacteria	Host	Rust
Egg cell	Mold	Sperm cell
Ferns	Moss	Spore

ASK YOURSELF . . .

1. What are the green, film-like plants you often find on trees or rock surfaces?
2. (*a*) Why aren't algae very good food? (*b*) Compare algae with fungi, such as mushrooms, as sources of food.
3. How do we get agar and for what purposes do we use it?
4. Why is it possible for air to contain disease-producing bacteria?
5. Why can't you keep entirely away from germs?
6. Discuss the ways in which green plants get useful nitrogen compounds.
7. What is the importance of the nitrogen cycle?
8. (*a*) What kind of plants would you expect to grow on a soil which lacked nitrogen compounds? (*b*) Why?
9. From what sources do you get proteins needed to build up your body cells?
10. (*a*) What is added to the soil when dead plants and animals start to decay? (*b*) Why is this important?
11. What uses do we make of yeasts? — *75–76*
12. What uses do we make of molds? — *77*
13. In what ways are molds pests and how can you control them? — *76*
14. Why are some rusts serious pests and how can you control them? — *79–80*
15. What are some ways in which mosses and ferns are of value?
16. How have some coal deposits been formed in past ages?

GETTING THE FACTS . . .

1. Get a pond culture which contains some algae. The pond scums which float on the surface in shallow water are made up of algae. One-celled algae are also common in pond water. Examine samples of the culture with a microscope or a microprojector. Report on what you see, or make drawings if you wish.

2. Break off a small piece of bark that is covered with algae. Scrape off a little of the green mass. Put it on a microscope slide. Add a drop of water and put on a cover glass. Now look at the specimen with a microscope. Describe what you see, or make a drawing.

3. Algae are simple plants, but some of them grow to great size. Look up the *kelps* in a botany book or in an encyclopedia. Report on them to the class, telling as much as you can find.

4. Mix nutrient agar and water according to the directions on the package. Pour this mixture into several Petri dishes and let it set. It will form a medium on which bacteria will grow. Put a little dust on one agar surface, and a little material scraped from the side of a tooth on the other. Cover both samples and keep them in a warm, dimly-lighted place. Look at them each day for sev-

eral days. See whether colonies of bacteria have developed.

5. If you live in the country or go on a field trip, you may find some clover, alfalfa, or soybean plants. Sometimes they grow along roadsides. Dig one of them up carefully. See if you can find any bacteria colonies on the roots.

6. If you go on a field trip, find a well-decayed log. Break it apart and see what types of plants and animals are speeding up its decay.

7. Look up the black stem rust of

wheat in a botany book or an encyclopedia. Report on this pest to the class.

8. You can easily raise molds in the classroom. First, put a piece of moist blotter in a Petri dish. Put a half slice of bread on the top of the blotter. Now scatter a pinch of dust over the bread. Put the cover on the Petri dish and let it stand in a warm place for a few days.

9. Study specimens of mosses and ferns taken from your terrarium. Get to know the parts as described in Chapter 18.

Topic 2
THE SEED PLANTS

Is there anything in this picture that isn't related to plants? Look carefully.

The trees, bushes, and grain are plants. The lumber in the house and fence posts came from trees. Part of the soil came from decayed plants.

What about the other things? The young boy eats plants, of course. The car and plane run on gasoline. Gasoline comes from plant materials that lived ages ago.

Now perhaps you see how important seed plants are today. We eat some, from others we get lumber and fibers to make paper and cloth. And from some, we get drugs, oils, and even plastics.

AMONG THE NEW WORDS FOR THIS TOPIC

- **ADHESIVE** (ad-*hee*-siv). A glue-like substance used to bind two objects together.
- **CEREAL** (*seer*-ee-ul). An edible grain, including wheat, corn, rice, oats, rye, barley, etc.
- **DRUG.** A medical preparation.
- **LATEX** (*lay*-teks). The partly dried sap of a rubber tree.
- **OVARY.** A female sex organ.
- **PETALS.** Certain colored part of a flower.
- **POLLEN** (*pah*- len). A substance produced by a flower. From it come the male sex cells.
- **ROOT CAP.** A mass of cells which more or less covers a root tip.
- **ROOT HAIR.** A hair-like growth from a single root cell.
- **SEED PLANT.** One which produces seeds.

CHAPTER 19

Roots and Stems Are Parts of Seed Plants

Man used seed plants long before he wrote history. He even began to raise the more useful plants in his gardens. *Seed plants* bear flowers, fruits, and seeds. Most of them have roots, stems, and leaves, too.

If you lived long ago, say in the Middle Ages in Europe, you would only have certain seed plants to eat. You'd have turnips, cabbage, peas, and probably onions. Your bread would be made from rye or wheat.

You wouldn't know about corn, lima beans, or potatoes. You would never have tasted peanuts, squash, or pumpkins. These are plants of North or South America, not Europe.

The early explorers did more than find new lands. They also found new

Corn   White potato   Sweet potato   Lima bean   Squash

Fig. 19-1. All of these foods come from plants first raised in the Americas.

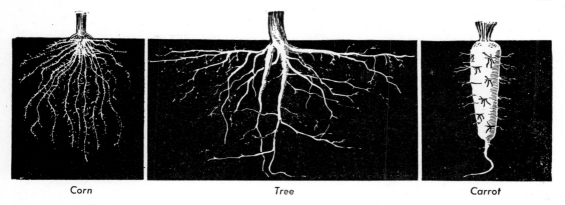

Corn   Tree   Carrot

Fig. 19-2. Three different types of root systems. Roots anchor the plants to the soil, and absorb liquids from the soil.

plants. They took some of the seeds and brought them back to Europe. In the same way, the early settlers in America brought the seeds of some European plants to this country.

Roots usually grow under the ground. Look at Fig. 19-2. It shows the root system of a corn plant. From this plant we get many food materials. We also get many other products used in industry.

You can see that the root system of a corn plant branches a lot. It anchors the plant to the soil. But the root system of a tree is different. In this case there's a long tap root which grows deep down into the soil. Look at Fig. 19-2 to see this. You can also see a third type of root in Fig. 19-2. It's a carrot, which has a thick tap root.

What do roots do? Of course, they anchor the plant to the soil. But that's only one part of the story. Roots also take in liquids.

The liquids taken in are mostly water. But nitrogen compounds are dissolved in the water. There are also compounds of other chemicals. These

are called **mineral compounds**. The green plant uses water and its dissolved mineral compounds to make proteins, and some of the other foods.

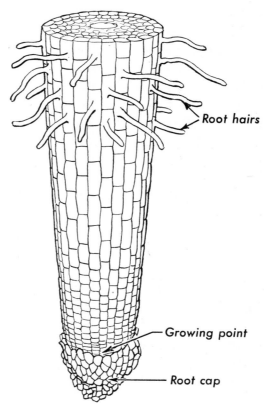

Root hairs

Growing point

Root cap

Fig. 19-3. Diagram of a young root tip.

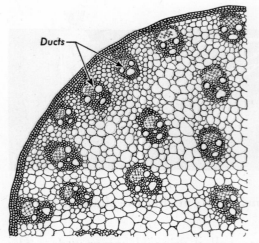

Fig. 19-4. Two types of plant stems.   Note that the arrangement of ducts is different in the two types.

When you look at the tip of a young root through a microscope, you'll see something like Fig. 19-3.   That mass of loose cells at the end of the root tip makes up the *root cap.*   Some of these cells are rubbed off as the root grows down deeper into the soil.

Just behind the root cap is the actively growing part of the root.   Note the tiny root hairs in Fig. 19-3.   Each *root hair* is part of a single cell.   The root hairs are the parts that take in the water and the mineral compounds dissolved in it.   These liquids pass from cell to cell until they reach the tubes or ducts in the root.   Then they rise in these root ducts up to the stem.

Stems have ducts like those in roots. Liquids go up in these ducts and reach the leaves and flowers.   As you know, leaves are the food-making centers in most seed plants.

" How do liquids rise in the ducts? " you ask.

Well, it's a case of liquids passing from one cell to another cell.   To do so, the liquids must pass through cell walls.   Some liquids will go through these walls; others won't.

The arrangement of ducts in stems varies in different seed plants.   The cross-sections of stems you see in Fig. 19-4 show two general types.   In one case, the ducts are scattered through the stem.   In the other case, they're grouped near the outside of the stem.

The roots and stems of many seed plants are useful.   The white potato, for example, is an underground stem. The part of the carrot you eat is the root.   Turnips, radishes, and beets are also roots.   Roots are often rich in stored foods.

You also eat many other roots and stems.   Some are food for animals. And, of course, you get other materials from these plant parts, too.   The dried stems of various plants are woven into hats, baskets, and handbags.   Woody stems become lumber and firewood.

Read on, in Chapters 20 to 26, and find out some more things you get from plant roots and stems.

CHECK YOUR FACTS . . .

Number 1 to 6 on a sheet of paper. From Column B *choose the best answer for each item in* Column A.

Column A	Column B
1. Duct	a. The tap root of a garden plant
2. Root hair	b. Of no importance to man
3. White potato	c. An underground stem
4. Root cap	d. A mass of cells at the tip of a growing root
5. Carrot	e. A part of a single root cell
6. Corn plant	f. Passageway through which liquids pass in a plant stem
	g. A source of rubber
	h. Has ducts scattered throughout the stem

Fig. 20-1. Here plants are being grown in tanks of water. Certain chemicals are in the water.

The water contains chemicals which the plants need. The carbon dioxide needed by the plants comes from the surrounding air.

Some plants grow well in this kind of garden. It's striking that they grow entirely without soil. They have all the parts: roots, stems, leaves, flowers, fruits, and seeds. In fact, you wouldn't be able to tell them from plants that grow in soil.

You use different parts of plants. You've seen how you use some roots and stems of various plants. You use other parts, too. You can think of many leaves and seeds you eat. For

CHAPTER 20

Flowers Form Fruits and Seeds

Ever hear of gardens without soil? Well, there are such things. One kind appears in Fig. 20-1. Here, plant roots grow in a tank filled with water.

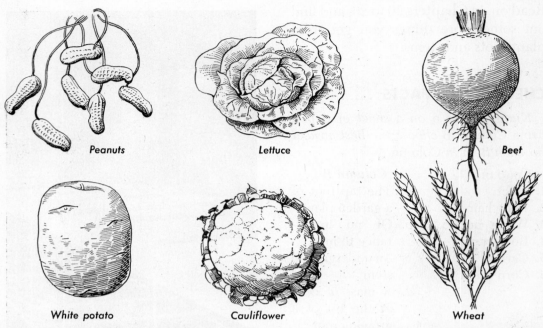

Peanuts

Lettuce

Beet

White potato

Cauliflower

Wheat

Fig. 20-2. We eat the stems, leaves, roots, flower buds, and seeds of various plants.

instance, lettuce and cabbage are leaves. You eat the seeds of corn, wheat, beans, and peas. Oranges, apples, lemons, melons, and squash are fruits. You even eat some flowers.

" Flowers? That's a new one! " you'll say.

What about cauliflower and broccoli? Have you ever eaten these? They're flower buds.

Useful things such as medicines and plant oils also come from flowers, fruits, and seeds. And then, of course, seeds are important because they produce new plants.

Leaves are the food-making regions of most seed plants. The veins of the leaves connect with ducts in the stems. Liquids taken in by the roots come up the stem to the leaves through these ducts. Some of the water that gets to the leaves is used in food-making. But a great deal passes out through the leaf pores into the air.

All seed plants form flowers. Some of the flowers are so small you can hardly see them. Others are large and showy.

Look at the parts of a flower in Fig. 20-3. Usually, there are some green, leaf-like parts at the base of the flower, the *sepals* (*see*-pals). Then come the *petals* which are the colored parts. Sometimes they're white. In other flowers they're blue, red, yellow, orange, or purple, or a mixture of several colors. Petals are what make flowers pretty.

Inside the ring formed by the petals you'll find even more flower parts. These are the ones which produce the male and female sex cells. The *sta-*

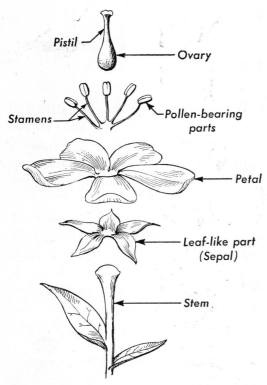

Fig. 20-3. Diagram to show the parts of a flower.

mens (*stay*-mens) are the parts with colored tips — usually yellowish or orange. They bear the *pollen* (*pah*-len) *grains* which contain the male sex cells. Many plants produce pollen in late summer. When you brush against them, the pollen falls like yellow dust.

The female part of a flower bears the *pistil.* Some flowers have only one pistil; others have several. The pistil has a swollen base which is the *ovary* (*oh*-var-ee). This ovary contains the female sex cells.

Each seed contains a young plant. One or more seeds is formed in an ovary. You've seen seeds, of course. But do you know what they are? If you cut open a seed and look at it with a hand lens, you'll see the young plant inside it. Look at Fig. 20-4. It shows you the parts of a bean seed. This seed has just begun to sprout. You can see that there are two little seed leaves. These are full of stored food used in early growth. A young root pushes down into the soil. And a young stem pushes up through the soil.

" But what about fruits? " you say.

Well, fleshy fruits like apples, pears, and berries are formed on some plants. These fruits grow mostly from the walls of the ovary at the bottom of the pistil. They have seeds inside.

Other fruits dry out, like pea and bean pods and nuts. They have seeds inside them, too. You can think of a *fruit* as the ripe ovary with its different parts. The most important of these parts are the seeds. New plants come from the seeds. The seeds must fall in places where they can grow. Then a new group of plants is produced.

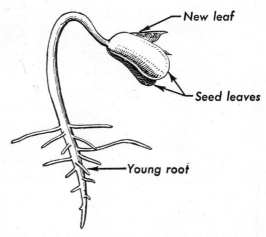

Fig. 20-4. Diagram of a sprouting bean seed.

CHECK YOUR FACTS . . .

Number 1 to 6 on a sheet of paper. Choose the best answer for each of the following items.

1. Fruits develop from: (*a*) petals; (*b*) stamens; (*c*) ovaries; (*d*) pollen grains.

2. Pollen contains: (*a*) young plants; (*b*) male sex cells; (*c*) useful medicines; (*d*) female sex cells.

3. The main food-making regions of most seed plants are the: (*a*) leaves; (*b*) stems; (*c*) roots; (*d*) flowers.

4. A seed leaf is full of: (*a*) green-colored cells; (*b*) male sex cells; (*c*) stored fruits; (*d*) stored foods.

5. Seeds are formed: (*a*) by roots; (*b*) in ovaries; (*c*) on petals; (*d*) in leaves.

6. A bean pod is best described as: (*a*) flower; (*b*) seed; (*c*) stem; (*d*) fruit.

CHAPTER 21

Crop Plants Provide Food

In the wide open spaces cattle and sheep graze on wild grasses. In the West, there are still large areas of natural grassland. Often people ask: "Why not use these lands to raise other crops?"

Perhaps you can give the answer. In many areas the soil is rich enough, but too dry for growing vegetable crops. However, the wild grasses do quite well there. These grasses are a good food for cattle and sheep. And we have many uses for such animals.

Fig. 21-1. We don't eat the grasses, but we do eat animals that feed upon them.

Fig. 21-2. Spraying a field of grass to control insect pests.

What are crop plants? Wild grasses are one group of seed plants. Clover and alfalfa are other types which make good food for grazing animals. We also raise certain grasses to get hay. The grass, clover, and alfalfa plants are called *forage crops.* They're just as important to one farmer as vegetables are to another. Livestock eat them. And we eat the meat of the livestock. There are other kinds of crop plants. Among them are the *cereal grains.* Cereals include wheat, corn, oats, rice, and barley. They're among our most important foods. You eat them yourself, and farmers feed them to cattle, sheep, pigs, chickens, and ducks.

Crop plants need good care. When farmers raise plants, they try to get the best results. They cultivate the soil. They kill the weeds. Then the crop plants have better living conditions. They get more sunlight, more soil moisture, and more mineral compounds.

Farmers also try to protect crop plants against insect pests and plant diseases. They have to spray and dust to keep these under control. Then, too, the farmer tries to pick out the best varieties for growing crops. The purpose of all this is: (1) to increase production; and (2) to improve the quality of the crop.

Wheat — the world's favorite. You usually think of wheat as a source of flour. And so it is. But there are many by-products of wheat which are also important. Bran is one. Even the dried stems (straw) are useful as packing material.

Fig. 21-3. Machines do much of the work in harvesting wheat that men and horses once did.

Why should wheat be such a world favorite? For one thing, wheat can be stored for months or even years. For another, different varieties of wheat will grow in many parts of the world. Wheat is raised in the tropics and also in cold countries. Some kinds are planted in the fall and others in the spring. A farmer can raise certain kinds of wheat crops in a few weeks. But best of all, wheat is high in food value.

Corn is an American favorite. In this country " corn is king." Scientists believe that corn came from one or more wild grasses. Probably natives

of Mexico or Central America first raised it. Corn was a food crop of various Indian tribes.

Many different varieties of corn have been developed. These are suited to different climates, but the Midwest is the greatest corn area today.

Farmers feed a good deal of the corn raised each year to pigs, cattle, and other livestock. Another large part is made into corn meal and breakfast cereals. Some corn is used to make cornstarch and corn sugar. Then, there are sweet corn and popcorn which you know so well.

Fig. 21-4. Improved varieties of corn yield bigger and better crops today.

Rice — an Oriental favorite. Rice, like wheat, is a cereal crop from the Old World. It was raised in the Orient hundreds of years ago.

There are many varieties of rice. You'll find that this is usually true when a food plant has been raised for a long time. Most rice plants are grown on low ground that is flooded or can be flooded easily. A few kinds of rice can grow on higher ground.

Man uses a large part of the world's rice crop as food. Some rice goes into breakfast cereals and flour. Like other cereal crops, rice has by-products which we use in many ways.

Forage and cereal crops are the most important food crops of the world. They provide food for man and animals.

CHECK YOUR FACTS . . .

Number 1 to 6 on a sheet of paper. Mark each of the following items True or False.

1. A plant that has been raised for a long period of time usually has many varieties.

2. Scientists believe that corn has been developed from wild grasses.

3. The ancient Greeks and Romans first raised corn.

4. Wheat can be raised successfully only in the temperate zone.

5. Some varieties of rice can be grown on lands that aren't flooded.

6. The control of insect pests improves crop production.

CHAPTER 22

Vegetables and Fruits Are Foods

"How do you tell whether a plant is a weed?" Jim asked his father.

His father laughed.

"Well, now," he said, "I guess one man's weed is another man's crop plant."

Quite true. Look at sunflowers. To some farmers they're pests like a lot of other weeds. Other people raise them in their flower gardens. Still others grow sunflowers, and feed the seeds to poultry. A *weed* is any plant which grows where you don't want it.

The tomato has a strange history. The early explorers found tomatoes growing in the New World. They took some seeds back to Europe. But the Europeans were afraid to eat tomatoes, because they thought they were poisonous. They raised them because the fruit looked attractive.

Fig. 22-1. Not all of the plants we raise are used as foods. Flower gardens and borders make our homes more attractive.

The habit of eating tomatoes developed only about 100 years ago. At that time someone found that he could can tomatoes easily. Today, these plants are garden favorites.

White potatoes and tomatoes belong to the same plant family. The white potato is a native of the New World. Explorers brought potatoes to Europe soon after the voyages of Columbus. In Europe, and later in Ireland, these plants became popular. The Irish people liked them and grew them in great quantities.

Potatoes will grow on various soils. They can be raised in warm countries and in cold countries. What you eat is one of several swollen underground stems of the plant. They have "eyes" which are really buds. The buds produce new potato plants.

Beans and peas have been used for years. Some are native to the Old World. Others came from North or South America. They've long been part of man's diet. Farmers grow them for food for their livestock.

Actually, beans and peas rank next to cereal grains in importance. Not only are they eaten but they're used in industry. The seeds of some varieties contain large amounts of protein and oil.

There are over 300 different products that come directly or indirectly from beans and peas. Among them are certain types of soaps, salad oils, cosmetics, candy, and paint. You've eaten peanuts many times. Not only do we get peanut butter and peanut oil from the peanut, but many other

Fig. 22-2. The soybean plant is becoming a very important crop plant. Besides the use of soybeans as food for animals and man, we also get adhesives and oils.

products we use in our daily life.

Remember, too, that useful bacteria live on the roots of bean and pea plants. They're the bacteria that form nitrogen compounds that green plants use.

Citrus fruits are popular today. When you talk about fruits, you're apt to think of oranges, grapefruits, lemons, and limes. These are citrus fruits.

Many people think that raising citrus fruits is something new. It isn't. As a matter of fact, oranges were raised in China centuries ago.

Today, we grow citrus fruits in Arizona, California, Florida, and Texas. The fruits are noted for their vitamin C content. As you know, you can eat them fresh, or drink the juice.

Apples, pears, and peaches are Old World favorites. Many different varieties have been developed today. The early settlers brought apple trees

Fig. 22–3. A grove of citrus trees. We raise a number of citrus fruits in the warmer parts of our country.

and seeds to America. Peaches and pears were grown in Europe for years and came to us from across the Atlantic.

Apples and pears do well in cool climates, but peaches need warmer climates. Peaches bloom early, and if frosts occur during flowering there is no fruit. Peach trees last only about 20 years whereas apple and pear trees live much longer.

Grapes have a long history. Records show that the ancient Egyptians raised grapes at least 5,000 years ago. They're one of the oldest fruits known. Wild grapes grew in America long before the coming of the white men and still do.

The early settlers brought certain kinds of grape vines from Europe. Others, like the Concord grape, came from native American wild grapes which were specially developed.

There are many other important fruits. We can't tell you about all the fruits, but here are some interesting examples.

Olives came from southern Europe and Asia, and are grown today in southern California. Many of the olives you buy in the store have been grown there. They're a rich source of oil which was once used in lamps. Today we use it as a salad oil.

Figs and dates were brought over from Europe by the early settlers. Today you'll find them growing in the warm states. California grows most of those you buy.

Bananas first grew in Asia. Then early settlers brought them to tropical Mexico and Central America where

Fig. 22-4. A vineyard. Men have raised grapes for centuries.

they're grown almost entirely today. Most of our own country is too cold for them. However, quite a few people in southern California, Florida, Arizona, and Texas grow them in their yards for fun. The pineapple is another tropical fruit, now raised on a large scale in Hawaii.

There are many useful nuts. When the explorers came to North America, they found hickory nuts, pecans, walnuts, and hazelnuts. Pecan orchards were planted in the South at an early date. Raising them is now an important industry there. People also plant a lot of black walnut trees, but as much for the lumber as for the nuts.

From the Old World we have brought in English walnuts, filberts, and almonds. We now grow large quantities of these nuts on the West Coast.

CHECK YOUR FACTS . . .

Number 1 to 6 on a sheet of paper. For each item in Column A *choose the best answer from* Column B.

Column A
1. Potato
2. Pecan
3. Olive
4. Soybean
5. Orange
6. Grape

Column B
a. A citrus fruit
b. A fruit which is a source of oil
c. Contains no vitamins
d. A nut native to North America
e. Belongs to the same plant family as the tomato
f. Bacteria on its roots form nitrogen compounds
g. Some varieties from Old World and some from New World

Fig. 23-1. One step in making finished lumber. A power saw is being used to cut rough boards from a log. Later, these boards will be thinned and planed. Then they will be finished lumber.

CHAPTER 23

How We Use Lumber and Plant Fibers

Have you ever seen a rustic cabin? Perhaps you've noticed that these cabins are often built from rough logs and slabs.

Men built such shelters for homes centuries ago. Natives in some parts of the world still use them.

Today lumbering has become one of our largest industries. We depend on lumber for thousands of products used in our daily lives. We even depend on wood for some of our fabrics.

Lumber comes from trees. For the most part, we now use finished lumber. It goes into homes, furniture, and thousands of other things. Trees are cut, and the lumber is sawed into boards and other useful shapes.

Are trees getting scarce in our country? Hardly that — yet. But as you might expect, some of the better types are getting more and more scarce. There are still plenty of trees. But a lot of them aren't very good for lumber. That's why the raising of useful trees is so profitable.

What is a plant fiber? Meanwhile, we've learned how to use wood in other ways. You know that a plant cell has a cell wall. When a piece of wood dries out, the cell walls in it remain. They make up about three-fourths of the woody material. Wood is composed mostly of dried up ducts of the plant.

Fig. 23-2. Logs are often floated down rivers to the mills where they are used.

Machines can chop up this woody material. What results is *plant fiber.* Cotton and linen are also plant fibers. Linen fibers are ducts of the flax plant. Cotton fibers are seed hairs that grow on cotton seeds.

Paper comes from plant fiber. Centuries ago, the Egyptians made a crude writing material. They took strips from rushes and crisscrossed and pressed them together. The result was a flat sheet on which they could write.

Some time later, but still long ago, the Chinese improved on this method. They chopped up mulberry bark. Then they pressed the fibers into thin, matted sheets which became paper when dry.

Trees that don't have a lot of gummy substance make the best pulp. Spruces and aspens are used for good quality paper. The pines in our southern states make a pulp that is used mostly for paper bags and boxes.

In making paper, the wood is first broken into separate fibers. This is done by grinding the wood or by treating it with chemicals. Often the two processes are combined. When broken down, the wood becomes *wood pulp.* Wood pulp is pressed or rolled into sheets of paper. It can also be pressed into sheets of wallboard.

What is plywood? You've no doubt seen plywood. It's an unusually strong material for its light weight.

Fig. 23-3. Here you see panels of plywood being glued and assembled.

Plywood is used to make some furniture. It even goes into some types of airplanes and speed boats.

In making *plywood,* thin sheets of wood are cut from a log. Then a sheet of this wood is put into a large press. Its upper surface is coated with an adhesive, which is a glue-like material. Another sheet of wood is put on top of it so the grain runs at right angles to the grain of the first sheet. Now comes more adhesive and another sheet of wood. This makes a sort of sandwich. The process goes on until the right thickness has been built up. Then the sandwich of wood and adhesive is pressed together. When dry, it's plywood.

Cloth comes from plant fibers, too. Plant fibers don't come from trees alone. You can get them from many plants, both large and small. Cotton plants, for instance, have long been a source of fibers.

There are about 50 different varieties of wild and cultivated cotton. Their seed hairs are the cotton fibers. Each seed hair is a part of a single cell. Cotton cloth is woven from these fibers.

Linen is another cloth which is made from plant fibers. In this case, the fibers come from flax plants. The fibers aren't single cells but are whole ducts in the stems of the flax plant. They're longer and stronger than cotton fibers. Now do you see why linen wears so well?

CHECK YOUR FACTS . . .

Number 1 to 6 on a sheet of paper. Answer the following items.

1. Which of the following is a tree that makes good paper pulp: (*a*) red oak; (*b*) pitch pine; (*c*) elm; (*d*) spruce?

2. Which of the following is a single plant cell: (*a*) cotton fiber; (*b*) plywood; (*c*) wood pulp; (*d*) linen fiber?

3. From what plants did the Egyptians make a paper-like material?

Fig. 23-4. Cotton plants. The white masses you see here are made up of seed hairs or fibers.

4. What people first made paper from wood fibers?

5. On some land it's profitable to raise tree crops. *True* or *False?*

6. A plywood board is usually stronger than a plain board of the same size and shape. *True* or *False?*

CHAPTER 24

How We Use Plant Saps and Oils

Maple syrup comes from the sap of maple trees. A tree is tapped by boring a small hole in its trunk. The sap flows out, and it's boiled down to make maple syrup and sugar.

We also get sap from many other trees. In some cases, however, we're not seeking food, but materials of commerce.

Rubber comes from latex. *Latex* (*lay*-teks) is the sap of the rubber tree. Early explorers of Central America found natives playing games with balls of latex. They brought latex back to Europe, but at first it had little value. They only used it to erase pencil marks. Then an American found a way to cook latex with sulfur and thus to get vulcanized rubber.

At first latex was taken from a number of different rubber trees. It was soon found that some types of trees had better latex than others. The British and Dutch planted seeds from some of the better trees in the East

Fig. 24-1. Sap being collected from a rubber tree. When the sap is boiled down, it becomes latex.

Indies. Before World War II, most of the world supply of latex came from these plantings. Later, rubber trees were taken to other parts of the world.

Rubber trees are tapped by cutting out a narrow strip of bark. Sap flows from the wound and is collected. When excess water is removed, this sap becomes latex. We can also get latex-like fluids from several other plants, such as the milkweed. They're not as good sources as real rubber trees, and aren't used now.

What is synthetic rubber? *Synthetic rubber* is made from such materials as coal and alcohol. Actually, it isn't rubber, but a rubber-like material. Synthetic rubber is better than real rubber for some purposes. However, for other purposes, real rubber is best. But notice one thing. Coal and alcohol come from plants. So if you trace synthetic rubber back far enough, it also comes from plants.

You use plant oils every day. Ever hear of plant oils? One of the most important is cottonseed oil.

About 1860, a way was found to extract the oil from cotton seed. Since that time, cottonseed oil has been used in many food products. It goes into butter substitutes. It becomes cooking fat or oil. It's also used in making soaps.

After the oil has been taken out of the cotton seed, the solid material is pressed into cakes. These cakes are used to feed cattle. Some cotton growers make more money from cotton seed than they do from the cotton fiber.

Another useful oil comes from coco-

Fabric   Butter substitute   Frying oil   Soap   Candy

Fig. 24-2. All, or large parts of these things, come from cotton plants.

nuts. This oil has many uses in industry. Much of it is used in making soap, shampoos, candies, and cosmetics. Peanut oil, from peanuts, is another plant oil which is valuable.

Paints and inks. What have plants to do with paints and inks? Let's take turpentine as an example. It's an oil which comes from certain species of pine trees. One of these is the long-leaf pine of our southern states.

To get turpentine, trees are tapped in the spring. Their sap is collected and distilled. The part that is driven off as a vapor is *turpentine*. The rest hardens and becomes *rosin*. Turpentine is used mainly in varnishes and paints. Rosin also goes into varnishes and into soaps.

A newcomer among the trees raised in the South is the tung tree. It's a tree which grows wild in the Orient and produces tung nuts. Oil from tung nuts is very useful in making printer's ink.

Of course you've heard of linseed oil. It comes from the seed of flax plants. Linseed oil is used in paints. It's also useful in making linoleum, oilcloth, and patent leather.

Fig. 24-3. Nuts of the tung tree yield a very useful oil. This oil is used in waterproof fabrics and paper, high grade varnishes, lacquers, and enamels, as well as printing ink.

3. Cottonseed oil can be used in making: (*a*) butter substitutes; (*b*) cooking oils; (*c*) soap; (*d*) all of them.

4. In which of the following would you expect to find tung oil; (*a*) soap; (*b*) candy; (*c*) printer's ink; (*d*) cosmetics?

5. Linseed oil is obtained from the seed of the . . .?. . . plant.

6. We get rosin from the sap of pine trees. *True* or *False?*

CHAPTER 25

How We Use Other Plant Products

Did you ever go camping in the woods? If you know how, you can build a fairly good lean-to. It will keep out the rain and most of the wind. You don't mind sleeping in it

CHECK YOUR FACTS . . .

Number 1 to 6 on a sheet of paper. Answer each of the following items.

1. The partly dried sap of rubber trees, from which rubber is made, is called . . .?. . .

2. From which type of plant do we get turpentine: (*a*) flax; (*b*) oak trees; (*c*) pine trees; (*d*) cotton?

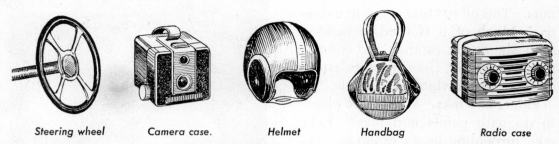

Steering wheel   Camera case.   Helmet   Handbag   Radio case

Fig. 25-1. Some of the many things that are often made from plastics today.

if you have to do so for just a night or two.

But as a steady thing you'd probably want something better. Of course, your ancestors took the products of field and forest, and used them as they found them.

However, man is always trying to improve on raw products. Not satisfied with ordinary lumber, he has learned to make plywood. He has learned to extract sugar from plants,

Fig. 25-2. Inside a modern factory. Into this mixer go the cotton fibers to make plastics.

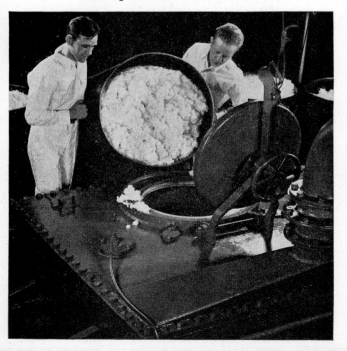

to make rubber from plant sap, and to make paper and fabrics from plant fiber. So you see man has made great progress.

Plastics and adhesives. It's not surprising that we now have many plastics and adhesives. *Plastics* include various substances made in the laboratory. They can all be molded or cast into desired shapes. *Adhesives* are glue-like materials used to fasten things together.

You see plastics and adhesives every day. Some of them are made from non-living things. Others come entirely or partly from various plant products.

What was the first plastic? In 1868, a printer was trying to make billiard balls out of cotton fiber. He tried various chemicals on the cotton fiber. The printer got no billiard balls, but he did learn how to make *celluloid*.

For a time celluloid was popular. Many small articles were molded from it. It was even used to make collars for men. Today, however, we have a choice of many plastics. Some are good for one thing and some for an-

Fig. 25-3. This is how synthetic rubber looks as it goes through a tuber. A tuber is a machine like a meat grinder that squeezes large chunks into smaller pieces. This removes water from the product.

other. You can see some uses of plastics in Fig. 25-1.

Uses of plastics. Manufacturers use cotton fibers to make many plastics. They also make plastics from other plant products, such as wood pulp. But don't get the idea that plastics come entirely from plant products. A good many of them are made from non-living things.

We're learning to use plastics in new ways. Go into any 5 & 10¢ store. Look around for things made from plastics. You'll be surprised at what

a number of things you will find.

From plastics we now get building materials, fabrics for suits and dresses, football helmets, handbags, suitcases, household articles including dishes, aprons, window shades, radio and television parts, lenses and camera parts, musical instruments, raincoats, shoes, soles of shoes, stockings, tires, tubes, and many other things that you use every day.

Plastics have replaced metals and wood to a large extent. This is because cheap sources of some metals

Fig. 25-4. Sugar beets on their way into a sugar beet factory. Here sugar is extracted from them. Today beets rank next to cane as a source of sugar.

and wood have become scarcer. But remember, too, that manufacturers can mold plastics into many shapes. This makes manufacturing simpler and cheaper.

Alcohol is a plant product. *Wood alcohol* (a deadly poison) is another product which is made from plants. It's made by boiling chips of wood. *Grain alcohol* can also be made from many plant materials.

Alcohol has many uses in commerce and industry. You use it to keep the radiator of your automobile from freezing. But this is only one small item. We also use it in many toilet

and drug preparations, in explosives, and as a preservative.

As you've read, alcohol is a raw material for making synthetic rubber, a product used to make many things. In addition, alcohol is a fuel. It will run various engines. Some day our oil supplies may be gone. But we know we shall always be able to use alcohol. Since it comes from plants, a new supply is in prospect each year.

Where does sugar come from? *Sugar* is a refined product which comes from plants. We get maple sugar from the sap of maple trees. Most of our sugar supply, however, comes from sugar cane or from sugar beets.

These aren't the only possible sources of sugar. For sugar is found in many plant tissues. It may even be extracted from the wood pulp of forest trees.

CHECK YOUR FACTS . . .

Number 1 to 6 on a sheet of paper. Mark each of the following items True *or* False?

1. Manufacturers sometimes use adhesives to make plywood.

2. Many different plant materials can be used to make commercial alcohol.

3. All our modern plastics are made from plant products.

4. Celluloid is made from coal, air, and water.

5. One type of synthetic rubber is made from alcohol.

6. We use wood pulp to make various plastics.

CHAPTER 26

Some Drugs Come From Plants

In the days of the early settlers of our country, the Indian tribes had medicine men. Native tribes in other parts of the world had witch doctors. The methods of these medicine men and witch doctors were mostly nonsense. But some of them did know a few things about plant drugs.

The use of plant drugs is very old — as old as man himself. Medical men of ancient Greece and Rome studied plants. They collected plants in field and forest, and raised them in gardens.

When tobacco was first brought to Europe, people thought it was a medicine. About the same time, Europe imported spices from the Orient in the hope that they would cure diseases. However, this did not work out as they had hoped.

Quinine is a valuable drug. Not all the old plant drugs were worthless by any means. For a long time the problem was to find what was good and why.

One forward step was taken when South America was first explored. The disease malaria had been common in Europe for centuries. Explorers noticed that South American natives seemed to cure malaria by chewing the bark of a tree.

So the explorers brought some of the bark back to Europe. A couple of kings who had malaria chewed the

Fig. 26-1. A pair of native witch doctors.

bark. Their fever went down quickly. Soon other people began to try the same cure.

It was some time, however, before the full story was known. Then someone found that the bark contained the drug *quinine* (*kwy-*nyne). Quinine kills the malaria germs which are found in the blood.

It was also found that quinine-producing trees could be raised in the East Indies. For many years the world supply of quinine came from this area. Today we have other drugs related to quinine which cure malaria. These drugs don't come from plants but are made in chemical laboratories. And in some ways they are more useful than quinine.

111

Fig. 26-2. A grove of young cinchona trees. The bark of these trees yields the drug quinine.

The drug ergot. Europe wasn't a very safe place to live 500 years ago. There were too many diseases. One of them was a queer disease that crippled or killed many people. The disease was quite a puzzle for a long time. Then someone found that a fungus which grows on rye caused it. People who ate bread made from spoiled rye flour got the disease. Good rye flour, however, was perfectly safe to eat.

Many years passed. Finally, the drug *ergot* (*er*-got) was extracted from a disease-producing fungus on rye. Strangely enough, ergot proved to be a useful drug. It checks bleeding. We still get ergot from the fungus which grows on rye.

The poppy plant. One very old drug comes from the unripe fruits of the poppy plant. This is *opium* (*oh*-pee-um). Before the days of ether, opium was often used to deaden pain in operations.

Opium itself is a source of other drugs. Like opium, these drugs can be habit-forming. However, they're useful medicines *only when taken under a doctor's direction.*

Other plant drugs. Have you ever heard of the *coca* (*koh*-kuh) plant? It's a shrub from South America. Now it's grown in other parts of the world as well. Its leaves yield the drug *cocaine* (koh-*kayn*). Years ago it was found that a cocaine compound would deaden pain. *Novocaine* (*noh*-vuh-kayn) is a man-made substance similar to cocaine. It's widely used today by doctors and dentists in minor operations.

From an Oriental tree we get *strychnine* (*strik*-nin). We use this drug in very small amounts as a medicine for heart disorders. It's quite poisonous, however. In larger amounts the drug is used to kill rats and other pests.

The above are by no means all of the useful plant drugs. In Chapter 65, for instance, you'll read about some other useful medicines that come from fungi.

Today a great many of our modern drugs which we use are made in the laboratory. It is fortunate that we can do this because we can then make all we need. And, too, often we are able to make these drugs at a low cost. However, even today, there are some medicines that come only from various plants.

CHECK YOUR FACTS . . .

Number 1 to 6 on a sheet of paper. Match the items in Column A *with the best answers in* Column B.

Column A	Column B
1. Poppy fruits	a. Source of ergot
2. Bark of a tree	b. Sometimes used to kill rats
3. Coca plant	

4. Fungus on rye
5. Oriental tree
6. Strychnine

c. Source of antibiotics
d. Source of strychnine
e. Source of quinine
f. Source of cocaine
g. Source of opium
h. Source of ether

Roots anchor a seed plant to the soil. The roots also take in water and dissolved mineral compounds from the soil. Liquids pass up ducts in the roots and stems to the leaves which are food-making centers. Flowers form fruits and seeds.

Wild grasses are valuable because they're food for cattle and other animals. Cultivated grasses include cereal grains such as wheat, corn, oats, rice, and barley.

Potatoes, beans, peas, and tomatoes are among the favorite vegetables. Citrus fruits, apples, pears, peaches, grapes, olives, dates, figs, and bananas are important fruits.

We get lumber, firewood, plywood, and plant fibers from trees. Plant fibers are used to make paper, cloth, and plastics. Latex from rubber trees is used in making rubber.

Large amounts of plant oils are extracted from cotton seed, peanuts, and coconuts. Among the more important drugs which come from plants are quinine, ergot, opium, cocaine, and strychnine.

WHAT DO THESE WORDS MEAN?

Adhesive	Opium	Root cap
Cereal	Ovary	Root hair
Citrus fruit	Petal	Seed plant
Drug	Pistil	Stamen
Forage crop	Plant fiber	Synthetic rubber
Fruit	Plywood	Weed
Latex	Pollen	Wood pulp

ASK YOURSELF . . .

1. What functions do plant roots, stems, leaves, and flowers perform?
2. What are gardens without soil?
3. (a) What parts of plants do we use?   (b) Do we use them as foods alone?
4. How are fruits and seeds related to flowers?
5. (a) What plants make good hay crops?   (b) Why are such crops important?
6. In what ways do we try to improve the plants we raise?
7. (a) Why is wheat raised so commonly?   (b) How do we use our wheat and corn crops?
8. Where were the following plants first cultivated: corn, white potatoes, cabbage, turnips?
9. Why are bean and pea crops of special importance?
10. (a) Name some tropical and semi-tropical fruits we now raise in this country.   (b) Where are they grown in the United States?
11. (a) Where might it be profitable to raise tree crops?   (b) What trees would you select?
12. What are plant fibers and how are they used?
13. What is plywood and how is it made and used?
14. (a) What part of the cotton plant is used in making thread and cloth?   (b) What part of the flax plant is used in making cloth?
15. (a) From what is real rubber made?   (b) Synthetic rubber?
16. If we needed large amounts of alcohol for fuel, from what sources might the supply come?
17. (a) What uses are made of plant oils?   (b) From what plants do we get them?
18. From what plant sources do we get plastics and adhesives?
19. How do modern plastics affect our use of woods and metals?
20. What important drugs do we get from plants?

GETTING THE FACTS . . .

1. With a microscope or projector, look at a cross-section of a corn stem. Compare it with the cross-section of a bean stem or any woody stem. In what ways are the stems alike? Different?

2. Plant some bean or corn seeds in a tray containing moist soil. Cover the seeds to a depth of about an inch. Put the tray in a warm spot on a window shelf. After the young plants have sprouted, remove them from the soil. Study their parts as described on page 93.

3. Look at several types of leaves. Learn to recognize the stem, midrib, and the veins. Note that these parts are

arranged differently in various types of leaves.

4. Make a careful study of a flower. Locate the parts shown in Fig. 20-3 on page 93. Examine some pollen grains with a microscope.

5. Make an exhibit to show different types of fruits and seeds.

6. Prepare or examine an exhibit of different types of wood. Study the common uses of these materials.

7. Collect and exhibit samples of papers and cloth made from plant products.

8. Make a study of plant uses in your own community to show: (a) Common crop plants, their products, and how the products are used; (b) Grassland and forests, and their uses; and (c) Water supplies and their uses.

9. Make a collection of the common weeds which grow in your community. Press them between newspapers, then fasten them on white paper with Scotch tape. Try to name each one and label it, giving also the place and date on which you collected it.

10. Prepare a report or reports explaining how the following are made and used: (a) Rubber substitutes; (b) Turpentine; and (c) Cottonseed oil.

11. Get a soilless gardening set from a supply house. Follow the directions that come with the set. Make a soilless garden on a window ledge. You can use an aquarium or large battery jar to hold the liquid.

12. With the aid of your teacher, set up a demonstration to show that green plants lose water to the air. Use a well-watered plant in a flower pot. Seal off the soil in the pot by putting it in a plastic bag. Otherwise, water may enter the air from the moist soil. Cover the potted plant with a bell jar that is sealed to a piece of plate glass. Place this demonstration on a sunlit window ledge. See if moisture collects on the inside of the bell jar.

13. Sprout some bean seeds in moist, sandy soil. Remove a young bean plant from the soil. Be careful not to break up its root system. Wash the roots. Then place a small piece from the tip of a branch root on a slide. Examine it with a microscope. See if you can find some root hairs. Remember that a root hair is a part of a single cell.

14. This is a demonstration to show that green plants contain more than one kind of colored material. Your teacher will help you with the demonstration. Heat some alcohol *in a water bath.* Put spinach leaves in the hot alcohol. The alcohol will absorb colored materials from the leaves. Soon the alcohol will become dark green. At this point, *put out your fire.* Let the alcohol cool. Now pour 50 c. c. of the green alcohol in a large test tube or a tall bottle. Add 10 c. c. of water. Add 60 c. c. of benzol. Stir this mixture with a glass rod. When the liquid comes to rest again it is in two layers. One layer is green. This layer contains chlorophyll. What color is the other layer?

15. This demonstration shows one effect of gravity on plant growth. Use three young, potted plants about six inches tall. Young sunflowers are good, and can easily be sprouted. Place one potted plant in the normal, upright posi-

tion on a sunlit shelf. Suspend the second potted plant so that it is upside down. Place the third pot on its side, so that the plant is horizontal in position. Leave the plants in these positions for several days. See what happens.

Books You May Like . . .

Collingwood, G. H. and Brush, Warren D. *KNOWING YOUR TREES.* The American Forestry Association, Washington, D.C. 1941. An interesting and well illustrated book dealing with the trees of North America.

Jacques, H. E. *PLANTS WE EAT AND WEAR.* William C. Brown Co., Dubuque, Iowa. 1943. An illustrated key to the plants on which man is directly dependent for his food and clothing.

Robbins, Wilfred William and Ramaley, Francis. *PLANTS USEFUL TO MAN.* The Blakiston Co., Philadelphia. 1937. A well-illustrated text supplying information on the common crop plants of orchard, garden, and field of the United States which yield materials of commerce.

Robbins, Wilfred W. and Weier, T. Elliot. *BOTANY.* John Wiley and Sons, New York. 1950. A useful source book on the general structure and function of plants.

Schery, R. W. *PLANTS FOR MAN.* Prentice Hall, New York. 1952. An excellent volume on the uses of plants. It includes discussion of products from plant cell walls, latex, plant oils, medicines, starches and sugars, and plants used as foods.

Smith, G. M. and Others. *A TEXTBOOK OF GENERAL BOTANY.* The Macmillan Co., New York. 1942. A standard textbook of general botany which may be used as a general reference on plant structure and function.

Woodruff, L. L. and Baitsell, G. A. *FOUNDATIONS OF GENERAL BIOLOGY.* The Macmillan Co., New York. 1951. A standard textbook of biology which includes surveys of both the plant kingdom and the animal kingdom.

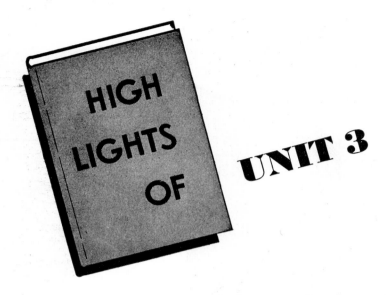

HIGH LIGHTS OF UNIT 3

Among the simple plants are the algae, which make their own foods. Some algae are one-celled; others have many cells. Algae are of value because they're necessary parts of many food chains.

Fungi are also simple plants. Some, like the yeasts, are one-celled. Others, like mushrooms, are made up of many cells. Fungi can't make their own foods. Some fungi are useful because they take part in decay and related processes. We use yeasts in baking, and molds in making cheeses. But some fungi cause diseases.

Ferns and their relatives aren't as important today as they were in the past. Together with other plants, they formed vast swamp forests millions of years ago. Our coal, and probably some of our oil, come from the products of these dead plants of prehistoric forests.

Seed plants usually have roots, stems, leaves, flowers, fruits, and seeds. We use all of these parts in various ways. From seed plants we get hay crops, cereal grains, vegetables, fruits, and seeds.

From seed plants come many other products. They include lumber, plywood, firewood, plant fibers, plant oils, plant plastics, alcohol, and certain drugs.

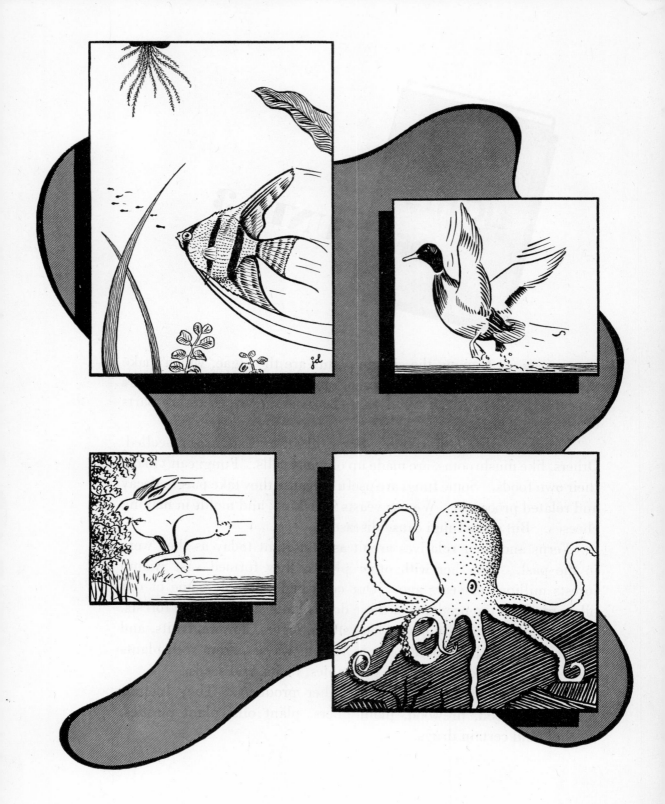

Unit 4

Life

in the

Animal World

Ann was trying to amuse two small girls whose family she was visiting one night. They had played many games, but the children were wide awake. Their father told Ann she could show them movies of some animal pictures. He even left the machine in focus ready to use. Ann decided that now would be a good time to use it.

" See these animals," she announced as the first one flashed on the screen. " See if you know what they are."

The little girls said they knew some but not all.

" There are lots of different animals in the world," she went on. " From some we get food, from some others clothing, shoes, and other things."

The girls got more and more interested as they saw the pictures.

" Now that rabbit," Ann continued as she changed slides, " eats vegetables and clover."

The girls enjoyed the pictures and were now ready for bed.

" Whew! What a time I've had," she said to herself. " My biology course last year surely came in handy tonight! "

Topic 1

ANIMALS WITHOUT BACKBONES

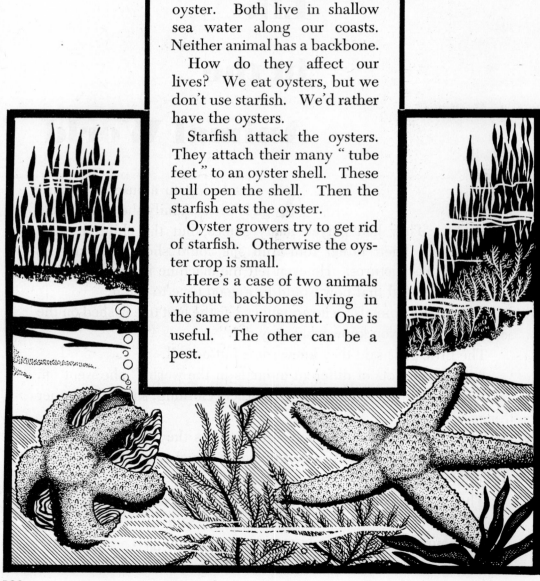

Here are two starfish and an oyster. Both live in shallow sea water along our coasts. Neither animal has a backbone.

How do they affect our lives? We eat oysters, but we don't use starfish. We'd rather have the oysters.

Starfish attack the oysters. They attach their many "tube feet" to an oyster shell. These pull open the shell. Then the starfish eats the oyster.

Oyster growers try to get rid of starfish. Otherwise the oyster crop is small.

Here's a case of two animals without backbones living in the same environment. One is useful. The other can be a pest.

- **CILIA** (*sih*-lee-uh).   Tiny, hair-like processes of a single cell.
- **FLATWORM.**   A worm with a flat body, sometimes divided into segments.
- **INVERTEBRATE** (in-*ver*-tuh-brate).   An animal without a backbone.
- **LARVA** (*lar*-vuh).   The worm-like, feeding stage of moths and other insects with similar life cycles.
- **LIFE CYCLE.**   Stages in the life of a plant or animal.
- **MOLLUSK** (*mol*-usk).   Animals which often have hard shells, like clams, oysters, and snails.
- **NYMPH.**   Early stage in the life cycle of some animals.
- **PROTOZOA** (proh-toh-*zoh*-uh).   A group of tiny animals, most of which are one-celled.
- **PUPA** (*pew*-puh).   A resting stage in the life cycle of certain insects.
- **ROUNDWORM.**   A worm with a round body that is not divided into segments.
- **SEGMENTED WORM.**   A worm with a body divided into segments and having a complete digestive canal.
   VERTEBRATE (*ver*-tuh-brate).   An animal which has a backbone.

CHAPTER 27

One-Celled Animals Are Everywhere

Our world is full of one-celled animals. You learned about one of them, Amoeba, in Chapter 5.

Most of these one-celled animals live in fresh water or in the sea. One type found in ponds is *Paramecium* (par-uh-*mee*-see-um). You see it in Fig. 27-1.

Paramecium is tiny. You can often find Paramecium in a bit of pond water. Under a good light you can barely see one as a speck in the water. Under a microscope, it's larger.

The one cell which makes up the body of this animal has an outer, flexi-

ble covering. The cell itself is almost slipper-shaped. It has a definite front end and a back end. You can tell the two ends apart because the front end is more rounded.

Most of the cell is made up of cytoplasm. Tiny, hair-like extensions of the cytoplasm come out through the cell covering. They're the *cilia* (*sih*-lee-uh) and act like little oars. A Paramecium can swim by moving these cilia. It also uses its cilia to capture foods.

Note that there is a permanent *mouth opening*. There are also two vacuoles in which extra liquids collect. These vacuoles contract and thus force liquids out of the cell.

A Paramecium always has one large nucleus. Some kinds also have one

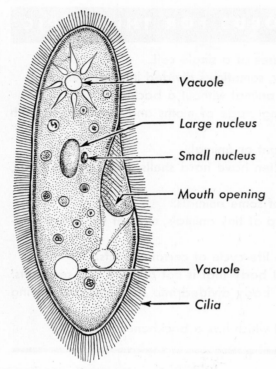

Fig. 27-1. Diagram of a Paramecium. Such one-celled animals are often found in pond water.

things. Cilia around the mouth opening make water currents. These currents sweep food particles into the cell, and vacuoles form around them. In the vacuoles, the animal digests the food particles. The food is then used for growth, repair, and to supply energy.

To release energy from food material, a Paramecium must have oxygen. It gets this oxygen from air that is in the water. Food material is broken down and the energy is used to do work, like swimming.

Paramecium reproduces. A Paramecium eats, grows, and finally becomes full-sized. Then it divides to form two new cells. It divides through the center of the cell, as you see in Fig. 27-3.

After about 50 divisions, the process of growth and division slows down. Then, two of these animals come together. They exchange some of their

small nucleus as well. Other kinds have two or more small nuclei.

Paramecium moves. If you have a chance, watch a living Paramecium through a microscope. You'll be surprised how fast it can start, stop, twist, and turn. It can move either forward or backward by using its cilia. Remember, the microscope magnifies the motion.

Paramecium reacts to heat, light, food, and to particles that get in its way. Watch some of these reactions. Then you'll see how this little animal reacts to changes in its environment.

Paramecium eats and grows. It feeds on bacteria and other tiny living

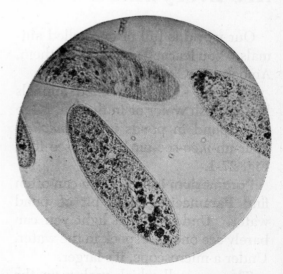

Fig. 27-2. Photograph of Paramecium taken through a microscope.

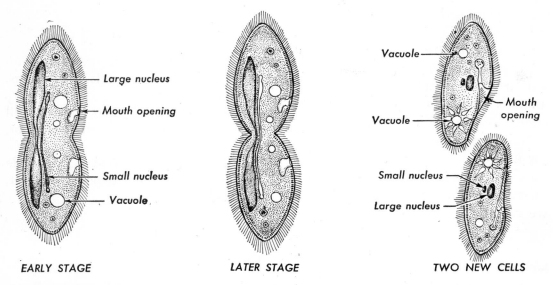

Large nucleus

Mouth opening

Small nucleus

Vacuole

EARLY STAGE

LATER STAGE

Vacuole

Vacuole

Mouth opening

Small nucleus

Large nucleus

TWO NEW CELLS

Fig. 27-3. Diagram to show how a Paramecium divides to form two cells.

cell contents. The cells then separate and can grow and divide again for about another 50 times. Then a Paramecium begins the process all over again.

One-celled animals are useful to us. Like Amoeba, Paramecium belongs to the animal group known as *protozoa* (proh-toh-*zoh*-uh). Most of these protozoa are one-celled. They have lived in fresh water and in the seas for centuries. Although they're small, they're important in our lives just the same.

For instance, some protozoa have tiny, hard, outer skeletons. Some of these skeletons are made of lime. Others are made of a glass-like material which is called silica (*sil*-ih-kuh).

Chalk deposits come from the lime skeletons of protozoa which lived centuries ago. Similarly, silica skeletons have formed deposits of flint and quartz. Chalk, flint, and quartz have many uses in modern life. Oil is now being obtained from deposits under the ocean. It may have been formed from the remains of protozoa that lived millions of years ago.

Fig. 27-4. Enlarged photograph of a single one-celled animal which has a hard, outer skeleton.

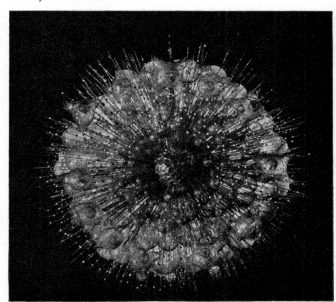

Many protozoa are valuable in another way. They serve as food for other animals that live in the water. Thus, they're an important part of various food chains. We use many animals which depend on these food chains.

Not all protozoa are useful. Some, for instance, cause diseases. One of these diseases is malaria. Other protozoa cause diseases of animals that we raise.

CHECK YOUR FACTS . . .

Number 1 to 6 on a sheet of paper. Select the best choice for each of the following items in the parentheses.

1. Paramecium and Amoeba belong to a group of animals called the (arthropods, porifera, protozoa) . . .?. . .

2. Paramecium moves by means of (cilia, nuclei, vacuoles) . . .?. . .

3. Excess liquids in a Paramecium pass out through (nuclei, cilia, vacuoles) . . .?. . .

4. Some protozoa are useful because they're parts of (coral reefs, food chains, communities) . . .?. . .

5. When a Paramecium grows to full size it may divide to form (two, four, six) . . .?. . . cells.

6. Protozoa whose skeletons are made of lime have formed deposits of (flint, chalk, quartz) . . .?. . .

CHAPTER 28

Sponges and Corals Are Interesting Animals

Not too long ago a lot of people used sponges in bathing. That was before showers were a part of most modern bathrooms. Today a sponge

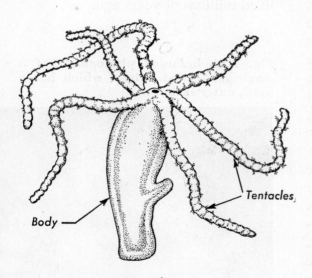

EXTERNAL VIEW

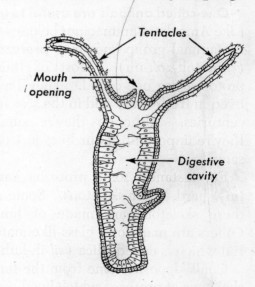

SECTION THROUGH BODY

Fig. 28-1. Diagrams of a Hydra. This little animal lives in ponds and streams.

Fig. 28-2. A Hydra with a bud. The bud breaks free in time, and becomes a separate animal.

isn't a common article in the bathroom. You probably use one in washing a car, though.

Corals (now used mostly for jewelry) and sponges belong to two groups of the animal kingdom. Most of the animals in these two groups live in the ocean. Some of the sponges are raised commercially in Florida. And some members of each group live in fresh water. Let's look at them for a moment.

Hydra lives in ponds and streams. Hydra (*hy*-drah) belongs to the same group as the corals. Fig. 28-1 shows a typical Hydra.

The slender *tentacles* (*ten*-tuh-k'ls) at one end of the body capture tiny animals which are forced into the mouth opening. The *stinging cells* on the tentacles are useful in capturing

this living food. The food is digested in the *body cavity* and taken in by the cells.

Hydra is fairly simple in structure. Its body consists of many cells, but the *body wall* has only two layers of cells.

Hydra reproduces in two ways. It forms *buds* as you can see in Fig. 28-2. A bud breaks away and eventually grows into a new Hydra. The other way the animal reproduces is by sex cells, about which you'll learn more in Chapter 67.

Bath sponges grow in colonies. These colonies are made up of many individual sponges. They have thin skeletons made of *spongin* (*spun*-jin). These useful animals live in the waters

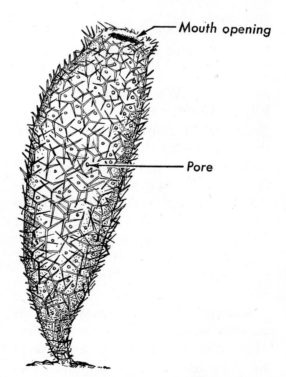

Fig. 28-3. Diagram of a simple sponge.

Fig. 28-4. Dried and cleaned sponge colonies on a pier. The skeletons of these colonies become the bath sponges you use in your homes.

around the West Indies, along the Florida Coast, and in other warm regions. They grow on the bottom of the sea in rather shallow water.

How does a sponge colony grow? It begins life as a single sponge animal. This single animal develops one or more buds. The buds grow and form the usual body parts but stay attached to the parent animal. Still more buds form and a large colony results.

Sponge fishermen get sponges in various ways. The oldest way is simply to dive out of a boat. Sometimes the diver uses a weight to pull him to the bottom. Then he tears loose part of a sponge colony and comes to the top again.

Sponge fishermen also use shallow-water diving gear. Still others spear the sponge colonies with a barbed hook at the end of a long pole. Then they bring them to the surface of the water.

The sponges are put on a pier or platform. Their soft parts thus are exposed to the sun and quickly decay. The cleaned and trimmed skeletons are then sent to market.

Corals grow in warm, shallow seas. Some of them form colonies like sponges and have hard, lime skeletons.

Ever heard of coral reefs? They're one of the dangers to ships sailing in warm seas. They begin as small coral, sponge, and algae colonies at the bottom. Then they build up until they reach the surface. In time, the reefs may grow to be islands. The Great Barrier Reef off Australia is about 1,100 miles long and up to 30 miles wide.

Corals and limestone. At times millions of years ago, vast coral reefs were formed in the shallow seas. Later, these seas became land areas. Many of the reefs were pressed down under later deposits and now appear as limestone. Not all limestone was formed in this way, but much of this useful rock comes from coral. We use it today as building stone and as a source of lime as well as crushed rock.

Some corals are used as jewelry. Suppose you were asked to name a substance more valuable than gold. Would you think of coral? Probably not, yet some delicately colored corals are worth $600 an ounce. They're used to make various types of jewelry and other ornaments. Most of these corals come from the Mediterranean area or from the Orient.

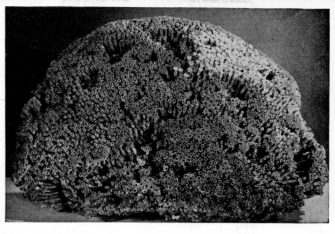

Fig. 28-5. A colony of corals. Look closely and you can see that it's made up of thousands of little skeletons all closely connected.

2. You're apt to find Hydra (in sea water, in fresh water, on the land) ...?...

3. Reefs are often formed from the skeletons of sponges, algae, and (Hydra, corals, starfishes) ...?...

4. A young Hydra that's attached to the body wall of its parent Hydra is known as a (bud, cyst, sex cell) ...?...

5. Hydras capture food through the use of their (cilia, teeth, tentacles) ...?...

6. You might expect to find bath sponges along the coast of (Oregon, Florida, Maine) ...?...

CHECK YOUR FACTS . . .

Number 1 to 6 on a sheet of paper. Pick out the best choice for each of the following items and write it on the sheet of paper.

1. The sponges of commerce have skeletons of (silica, lime, spongin) ...?...

CHAPTER 29

Some Worms Can Be Dangerous

Many people think of worms as crawling things that look much alike. Actually, there are many different kinds of worms. They live in the

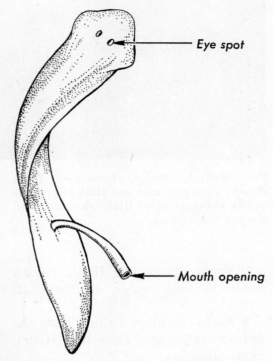

Fig. 29-1. Diagram of a planarian. This little flatworm lives in ponds and streams.

water, in the soil, and in the bodies of plants, animals, and man.

Worms that live in the bodies of other living things are *parasites*. They get their food from the living thing (*host*) on which they live. There are two important types of these worms: (*1*) *flatworms*; and (*2*) *roundworms*.

Flatworms have flat bodies. Most flatworms are parasites but a few kinds aren't. Among those which are not parasites are the *planarians* (plan-*ar*-ee-ans). They live in ponds and streams. One of them is shown in Fig. 29-1.

Such a planarian is flat and often less than one inch long. Two *eye*

spots are located on its upper surface, as you can see in Fig. 29-1. A small *mouth opening* is on the lower surface of the worm's body.

The planarian crawls around on sticks and stones in the water. Food enters its mouth and goes into a branching *digestive cavity*. There the food is digested. Solid wastes pass out through the mouth.

The body of the planarian has three cell layers. There are special sex cells, nerve cells, digestive cells, and cells to carry away liquid wastes.

Tapeworms are flatworms, too. And tapeworms are parasites. Some are less than one inch long when fully grown. Others are over 30 feet long.

There are many different kinds of tapeworms. They attack animals and some of them get into the human body.

Let's take a look at the beef tapeworm. You see it in Fig. 29-2. Young beef tapeworms form tiny cysts in the muscles of cattle. These young worms live inside their cysts. If you should eat rare beef from infested cattle, the young worms might get into your body.

In your intestines, the worms might grow to be adults. They would live there and soak up your partially digested food. They would develop eggs which would pass out of your body with waste materials. If the eggs should happen to fall on grass, cattle might swallow them. This is how cattle get the young worms in their intestines.

Soon, these young worms bore out

of the intestines and get into the cattle muscles. They form cysts in the muscles and live there.

You see, a beef tapeworm must have two hosts. The first is cattle. The second is man. The right kind of medicine will kill the worms in your intestines. But the cysts in the muscles of cattle, with the worms inside, stay right there. At least, they do until the animal is killed and its meat is eaten.

Roundworms are another group of worm parasites. You find many of them in the soil and in the waters of ponds and streams. Many live as parasites in plants or in the bodies of animals and man.

As you see in Fig. 29-3, roundworms aren't flat; they're round in cross-section. Also, their bodies aren't divided into segments.

Trichina worms. One roundworm likely to affect your welfare is the *trichina* (trih-*ky*-nuh) worm. Young trichina worms form cysts in human muscles. They also form cysts in the muscles of pigs and rats. Pigs often get the worms by eating pork scraps in garbage. For this reason farmers should always cook garbage before feeding it to pigs.

Trichina cysts in muscles are very small. You can't see them without a microscope. When you eat rare pork which contains these worms, the parasites get into your stomach and intestines.

Soon the young worms come out of their cysts. They grown rapidly and produce many young. The young

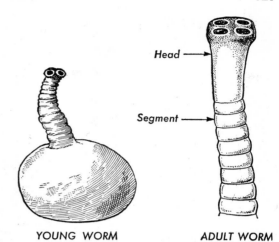

YOUNG WORM   ADULT WORM

Fig. 29-2. Diagrams of a beef tapeworm. The adult body is made up of a head and many segments.

worms bore into the muscles all over the body. Trichina worms have crippled many people and even killed some.

Now you see why it's important to eat only pork that is thoroughly cooked. The proper medicine will drive the adult worms out of your stomach or intestines. But once the young worms have bored into your muscles, they're out of reach of drugs.

Another dangerous roundworm is the hookworm. Adults of this worm live in the human stomach and intestines. They feed on blood which they get by puncturing the stomach and intestine linings. Victims suffer from loss of blood. They also are poisoned by wastes from the worms.

Inside the human body hookworms produce many eggs. These eggs pass out of the body with waste materials. If they lie on the ground in a favorable spot, the eggs hatch. Tiny young hookworms come out.

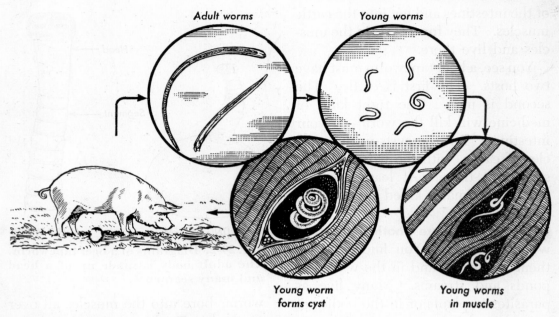

Fig. 29-3. Four stages in the life cycle of a trichina worm.

The way hookworms get into the human body is really remarkable. They usually begin by boring through the skin of the feet. Then the blood carries them to the lungs. From the lungs, they go up the windpipe to the back of the mouth. Finally they go down the food tube to the stomach and intestines. Thousands of these worms may be in a single host.

You'll find that hookworms aren't common in cold regions. But they're often a serious pest in warm areas of the tropics and subtropics. People who live in those regions should never go barefoot.

Your pet dog or cat may suffer from various kinds of parasitic worms. They can do serious damage to such a pet. A veterinarian can advise you if worms are present and tell you what to do.

CHECK YOUR FACTS . . .

Number 1 to 6 on a sheet of paper. Select the best answer for each of the following items.

1. Adult beef tapeworms live in the intestines of (cattle, sheep, people) . . . ? . . .

2. Young trichina worms usually form cysts in (muscle, liver, gland) . . . ? . . . tissue.

3. Young hookworms usually enter the human body by boring through the skin in the general region of the (hands, face, feet) . . . ? . . .

4. In the following list, the meat most likely to contain trichina worms is (beef, pork, lamb) . . . ? . . .

5. The most likely place to look for a planarian is in a (desert, pond, forest) . . . ? . . .

6. Common hookworm parasites in the stomach or intestine feed on human (blood, skin, food) . . . ? . . .

CHAPTER 30

Why Are Earthworms Important?

When you think of fishing, you probably think of earthworms. They've been used as bait for centuries. But this isn't the only way in which earthworms and their relatives are important. Actually, they're important to farmers and gardeners as you'll soon see.

Ever hear of "night crawlers"? They're nothing more or less than earthworms. On rainy nights the worms come out of their burrows and crawl around on the ground. With a flashlight, you can see these "night crawlers" rather easily.

Earthworms are segmented. Look at Fig. 30-1. You see a photograph of two earthworms. You'll see that the head end is rounder and somewhat thicker than the tail end.

You can see that the body is plainly divided into segments. Almost all of them bear short bristles. The worm

Fig. 30-1. Two earthworms. The one on the left is beginning to burrow into the soil.

uses its muscles and bristles to crawl. It braces the rear end of its body with the bristles. Then it extends the head end and fastens this with the bristles. The earthworm now pulls its tail end forward.

An earthworm's body. Did you ever wonder what earthworms eat? Actually, they eat their way through the soil. They feed on dead plant and animal materials which they get in the soil.

If you look at Fig. 30-2, you'll see that an earthworm has a *digestive canal.* This canal runs from one end

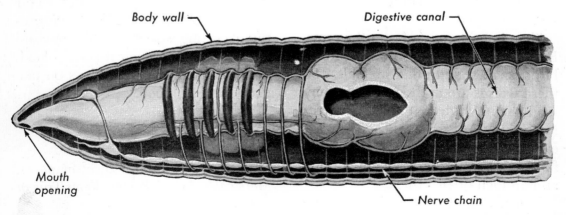

Body wall

Digestive canal

Mouth opening

Nerve chain

Fig. 30-2. Diagram to show structures in the front end of an earthworm's body.

Fig. 30-3. Photograph of a leech. The members of the leech group generally are parasites and feed upon blood.

of the body to the other. There is also a system of *blood vessels.*

An earthworm has no lungs. It gets oxygen through its outer surface. The worm does have a *nervous system.* The main part of this nervous system is a *nerve chain* which lies below the digestive canal.

The importance of earthworms. Earthworms are eaten by fish, frogs, birds, snakes, and other animals. So these worms are useful parts of many food chains. For that matter, natives in some parts of the world actually eat earthworms. Certain earthworms in foreign countries are five feet long and an inch or two thick.

In addition, earthworms have value because they loosen and turn the soil. Their borings make the soil porous. They bring deep soil to the top and leave it there in little heaps. Slowly, but surely, rocks on the surface are covered up. Then the soil is better for farming or gardening.

On the other hand, earthworms may carry some parasites. When domestic animals eat these worms, they get these parasites.

You may know, too, that earthworms are a minor nuisance on golf greens. The little piles of dirt they bring up make the surface uneven.

Leeches are parasites. The *leeches* are related to the earthworms. They live in ponds and streams, and are adapted to live as parasites. They're often called " bloodsuckers," because they attack fish, water birds, and sometimes man.

Look at a leech in Fig. 30-3. You can see a *sucker* at each end of the body. Maybe a leech has attached itself to your skin when you were swimming or wading.

A leech uses its suckers to hold on to its living host. The front sucker contains a mouth opening and a pair of cutting structures. The leech uses these cutting structures to puncture the host's skin. Then it sucks blood. A leech can live several days on one good meal of blood.

CHECK YOUR FACTS . . .

Number 1 to 6 on a sheet of paper. Mark each of the following items True *or* False.

1. An earthworm's digestive canal

runs from one end of the body to the other end. *TRUE*

2. An earthworm is an example of a roundworm parasite. *FALSE.*

3. Leeches attack fish and water birds, but aren't known to attack man. *TRUE,*

4. In the process of boring, earthworms tend to make the soil more porous. *FALSE.*

5. You'd expect to find large numbers of earthworms in a soil which didn't contain plant and animal remains. *TRUE.*

6. Domestic animals may get certain parasites from earthworms. *TRUE.*

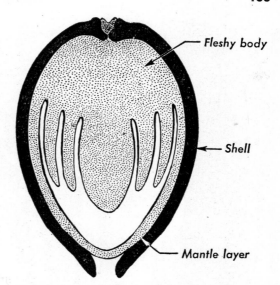

Fig. 31-1. Diagram of a clam. A hard shell surrounds the fleshy body.

CHAPTER 31

Oysters and Clams Make Pearls

Ever find clams along the seashore? Or in the shallow waters of a stream? Such animals are called *mollusks* (*mol*-usks).

Clams and their relatives, the oysters, live in such places. They have hard, limy shells. Each shell is made up of two *valves,* hinged together. The shell surrounds and protects the soft, fleshy body inside.

People have eaten oysters for centuries. The Indians once gathered them along our eastern coast. Some of the Emperors of ancient Rome raised oysters for their banquets.

Oysters live on the bottom in shallow sea water. One of their valves is attached to a rock or some other solid object. When very young, oysters swim or float at the surface of the sea.

Soon they drop to the bottom, begin to grow shells, and become fixed in position.

Because they can't move around, adult oysters may be killed by shifting sand or mud. They feed on tiny plants and animals. What they need is sea water that contains food, but not a lot of moving sand or mud.

Starfish also kill large numbers of oysters. As you've already read on page 120, a starfish can open an oyster shell. Then it feeds on the exposed fleshy mass. Some types of snails and certain fish also destroy oysters.

We get oysters by dredging them up from the bottom. We now eat most of them fresh, but some are canned. At one time the supply of oysters seemed unlimited. But it began to decrease along our East Coast about 1880. Today about half the

Fig. 31-2. These men are dredging up the oysters from the bottom of the shallow sea. The iron frame with its cotton-twine bag is being pulled up from the bed of oysters.

oyster supply comes from "oyster farms." These are places where beds of oysters are raised in shallow bays.

Clams for chowder. The *soft-shell clam* (also known as the long-neck clam) is found along our sea coasts. It lives buried in the mud or sand near the shore. You can capture it at low tide by using a special fork or hoe. Off shore in deeper water you'll find *little-neck clams* (also called hard clams and cherrystone clams). You can fry both of these clams, and also use them to make clam chowder. Little-neck clams, like oysters, are also eaten raw.

Scallops are good to eat, too. You've probably eaten scallops at one time or another. They're clam-like animals which live in the shallow sea.

You don't eat the entire body of a scallop. Rather, the scallop that appears on your plate is just a large muscle. It's the muscle which holds the two valves of a scallop's shell together.

What are pearls? If you've ever opened the shells of fresh-water clams, you know that some of them contain pearls. Most of these pearls are stuck fast to the shells and have little or no value. Certain species of pearl oys-

Fig. 31-3. On the left-hand side of the photograph you can see a little-neck clam. This type of clam is often eaten on the half-shell. On the right-hand side is a cluster of American oysters.

ters produce precious gem pearls as well as the most valuable mother-of-pearl.

"How do clams form pearls?" you ask.

Well, the story begins with the clam shell. Around the fleshy body of the clam there's a membrane called the *mantle*. It's this mantle layer that builds up the shell. The inside of the shell is lined with a smooth and shiny deposit called *mother-of-pearl*. Mother-of-pearl is secreted by the mantle layer.

Now if a grain of sand gets into a clam shell, it irritates the mantle layer. The mantle then secretes mother-of-pearl to cover the sand grain. Thus, a pearl begins to form but it's usually cemented to the shell.

True gem pearls aren't fastened to the shell. They're likely to form when a grain of sand gets embedded in the mantle layer itself; or more likely,

when a worm parasite forms a cyst in the mantle layer. The mantle layer then secretes mother-of-pearl around the irritating particle. In time, a gem pearl is formed.

Many gem pearls have been taken from fresh-water clams. We find these clams in the rivers of North America and Asia. Most of our

Fig. 31-4. A group of gem pearls. Not all of them are perfectly rounded.

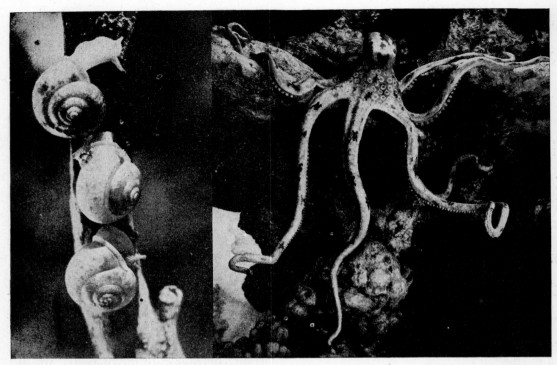

Fig. 31-5. A group of snails (left), and a small devil fish. A devil fish is also called an octopus.

pearls, however, come from the pearl oyster. This isn't the oyster that we eat, but a much larger type. It's found in waters off coasts of Central America, the South Pacific, the Indian Ocean, and the Red Sea. The pearl oysters lie on the hard sea bottom at a depth of from 50–150 feet.

Fig. 31-6. A squid. These little sea animals are used as bait in catching fish. People eat them in some parts of the world.

Pearls are among the most valuable of jewels. Large, perfectly shaped pearls rank with the most precious stones, like diamonds and emeralds.

Cultured pearls. Perhaps you've heard of cultured pearls. If so, you probably have wondered how they're formed. One method is to graft a small ball of mother-of-pearl into the mantle layer of a pearl oyster. The oyster is then returned to the water for a few years. The ball of foreign matter is gradually coated with mother-of-pearl.

Some shell products. Clam and oyster shells actually are more valuable than the pearls that come from them. Such shells are cracked up and used to supply lime in chicken feed.

Crushed shells are also used in making road-building materials. Then too, the shells are a source of material for making buttons.

Some other important mollusks. Other members of the mollusk group include snails, squid, and devil fish. We use some of these animals as food. In fact, raising snails for the market is an old industry in southern Europe.

CHECK YOUR FACTS . . .

Number 1 to 6 on a sheet of paper. Answer each of the following items.

1. What seafood item is really a muscle taken from a mollusk? snails 3 squid. devilfish,

2. An adult oyster can move about and avoid being covered by shifting sand. *True* or *False?*

3. What living layer of a clam or oyster secretes the shell? MANTLE

Match Column A *with* Column B.

Column A	Column B
4. Cultured pearl	a. Nucleus around which a pearl may form in some cases
5. Mantle layer	b. Always cemented to the shell of a clam
6. Cyst of worm parasite	c. Secretes mother-of-pearl
	d. Manufactured by chemical means in factories
	e. Formed about a solid object that has been grafted in an oyster

CHAPTER 32

You See Joint-Legged Animals Every Day

The joint-legged animals are a large group of living things. You see some of them every day. They include such types as insects, spiders, and centipedes. Crayfish, crabs, shrimps, and lobsters also belong to this group.

Let's consider a crayfish first. You have, no doubt, seen crayfish in ponds, ditches, creeks, and lakes.

Fig. 32-1. A crayfish. These animals are common in and about ponds and streams.

Fig. 32-2. On the left of the photograph you see a crab and on the right is a lobster. Both are important seafoods. They are closely related to the crayfish and shrimps. Both are found along the Atlantic Coast.

Often they're very common. Perhaps you have one or two in your school aquarium.

Habits and structures of crayfish. Crayfish are closely related to lobsters, crabs, and shrimps. All these animals have hard *external skeletons,* or coverings. These hard coverings are shed every so often. Then the animals grow rapidly before new coverings harden.

You've heard of " soft-shell crabs." They're nothing more or less than crabs which have recently shed their hard outer coverings.

You can see that the crayfish shown in Fig. 32-1 is a fairly complex animal. Note its jointed legs, and the large claws on the first pair of legs. They are used for capturing and holding their prey.

Like an earthworm, a crayfish has a *digestive canal.* This canal runs the length of the body. Below the digestive canal is a **nerve chain.** There is a **heart** near the back in about the middle of the body. From the heart, blood goes to all parts of the body. The system of blood vessels, however, isn't complete. Many blood vessels are open at their ends.

A crayfish gets oxygen from the water by means of gills. *Gills* are special organs through which oxygen from the water enters the blood.

What do crayfish eat? Just about any plant or animal material they find in the water. They even eat dead and decaying material.

A female crayfish lays about 100 eggs in early spring. These stay attached to her body and hatch in about two weeks. Young crayfish look like the adults but are smaller. They soon leave the mother and shift for themselves.

Crayfish, lobsters, crabs, and shrimp. Crayfish and their relatives are used as food in many parts of the world. The lobsters, crabs, and shrimp that you eat always come from the sea. They may come from shallow bays and inlets along the coast.

Early settlers along the Atlantic Coast learned to make traps for catching lobsters. The natural supply was good at the time and the lobsters were cheap. But as the years passed, lobsters became scarcer. Now you'll find they're luxury items.

Besides being shipped fresh, large quantities of lobsters are canned. The claws furnish the tenderest meat and sometimes are canned separately. When the lobster is cooked, its shell turns red.

Ever see a really big lobster? Well, some of them grow to weigh over 30 pounds! At the present there are laws which prevent anyone from selling under-size lobsters. Other laws keep fishermen from selling female lobsters with eggs. Hatcheries have been set up to raise young lobsters. The young are returned to the sea in great numbers. These measures should increase the natural supply to some extent.

Shrimps and crabs have also become scarce in some places. But crayfish are still common. Also, you can raise crayfish easily and in quite large numbers.

You may know, however, that crayfish aren't always useful. On some low-lying lands they destroy young crop plants. Also, the holes they bore in the ground often weaken dams and irrigation ditches.

In studying the crayfish and their relatives, don't overlook the little fellows. The sea, and many of our lakes and streams, contain many tiny, shrimp-like animals. Some of them are too small for you to see without a microscope. But they're important. They serve as food for fish and other animals that you use.

Spiders and their relatives. The joint-legged animals are also common on the land. Among the many land-dwelling types are the spiders and their relatives. Three of them are shown in Fig. 32-3 and 32-4.

Do you confuse spiders with in-

Fig. 32-3. A black-widow spider, a tarantula, and a scorpion. Each of these animals has eight walking legs. An insect has only six walking legs.

Fig. 32-4. A tick. Here again you see eight walking legs.

sects? Although both are joint-legged, you can easily tell them apart. A spider has eight walking legs, while an insect has six walking legs.

Many spiders catch insects in webs. You'd probably be glad enough to be rid of the insects. But at the same time, you'd hardly want your home cluttered up with cobwebs.

You've heard that black widow spiders and some tarantulas can bite viciously. They have a poison which causes pain and swellings. Black widows live in our own country. Most of the dangerous tarantulas are found in warmer parts of the world. Their bite is very painful.

Relatives of the spiders include ticks and scorpions. Ticks are blood-suckers. They're dangerous because they carry diseases. The diseases affect ourselves and also our stock animals.

Scorpions are most common in tropical countries although you may find them in California and Arizona.

They have a poisonous sting at the end of their body, which can cause a painful wound.

Have you been bitten by chiggers? They're tiny relatives of the spiders that burrow into your skin. They cause an unpleasant burning and itching feeling. They're found in various parts of our country and you may get them by sitting on the grass.

CHECK YOUR FACTS . . .

Number 1 to 6 on a sheet of paper. Answer the following items.

1. Black widow spiders are dangerous because they (<u>bite</u>, sting, carry diseases) . . .?. . .

2. A "soft-shell crab" is a crab that has recently shed its hard outer covering. *True* or *False*?

3. Ticks are dangerous because they (sting, carry diseases, bite) . . .?. . .

Fig. 32-5. A spider captures an insect.

4. You can recognize a spider because it has (four, six, eight) ...?... walking legs.

5. Chiggers are useful because they destroy insects. *True* or *False?*

6. One reason why crayfish are sometimes a nuisance is that they (eat dead materials, destroy crop plants, have gills) ...?...

CHAPTER 33

Most Insects Are Small

Before the dawn of history, our ancestors had their troubles. Among other things, they had to worry about many large and dangerous animals.

Today, we have no such worries. Most of our larger enemies are gone. But the small pests are another story. Among them are the insects — a big group of joint-legged animals which increase in spite of man.

Why is it so hard to get rid of the small pests? Largely because they're small. They can get in cracks and crevices. In addition, they're so numerous. This is partly because they reproduce rapidly.

A grasshopper. You've surely seen grasshoppers like the one shown in Fig. 33-1. When you walk through the fields in summer, grasshoppers jump out of the grass all around you. They have two pairs of wings and three pairs of walking legs. The third pair of legs is large, and is used for jumping.

Notice the large *compound eye.* A grasshopper has one of these eyes on each side of its head. Each compound eye is made up of many parts. The body has a hard outer covering. It's like the hard covering of a crayfish.

In fact, a grasshopper has many structures that are like those of a crayfish. But a grasshopper has no gills. Instead, it has a branching system of internal tubes. Air enters these tubes, and the cells of the body get oxygen from the air.

Probably you know that a grasshopper has chewing mouth parts. This insect eats all sorts of plant materials. Biologists think that grasshop-

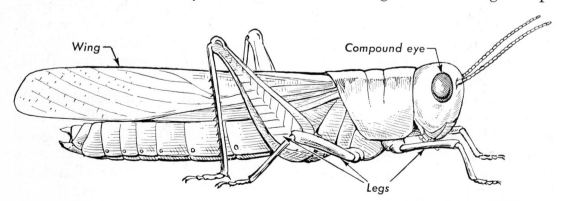

Wing

Compound eye

Legs

Fig. 33-1. Diagram of a grasshopper. Note the three pairs of jointed walking legs.

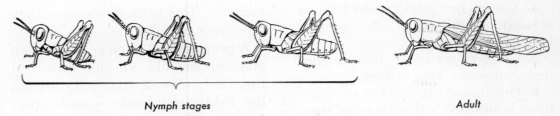

Nymph stages   *Adult*

Fig. 33-2. Stages in the development of a grasshopper.

pers destroy about 10% of all hay crops in our country each year.

A grasshopper's life cycle. A female grasshopper lays her eggs in the fall. She lays them in a little hole she makes in the soil. Here the eggs lie during the cold winter months. In the spring they hatch, and the young grasshoppers come out.

The young grasshoppers look very much like the adults, as you can see in Fig. 33-2. However, they're smaller. They don't have wings or sex organs at first. These young grasshoppers are called *nymphs.*

A nymph eats plant material and grows. It sheds its hard, outer covering several times. By late summer the nymph has become an adult. So you can see that the life cycle of a grasshopper includes: (*1*) an egg stage; (*2*) several nymph stages; and (*3*) an adult stage. The adult dies when cold weather comes.

Many other insects have this same type of life cycle. But there is another type of insect life cycle that you'll read about in Chapter 34.

The problem of grasshoppers. You can see that grasshoppers are pests because they eat plants. In some parts of the world, including our west-

ern states, they sometimes become very common. Then they move across the country destroying all the crops in their path. They cause what's called a grasshopper or "locust" plague.

If you ever go to Salt Lake City, Utah, you'll see a monument to the sea gulls. At one time grasshoppers were destroying the crops of early settlers in this area. Large flocks of sea gulls arrived, however, and ate the grasshoppers.

How to control insects. Have you ever seen the little bugs called "plant lice" or aphids? They are often a pest on flowers and vegetables.

An aphid feeds in a special way. Its mouth parts form a sort of tube. It shoves this tube into a leaf or stem. Then the aphid sucks up plant sap. One aphid couldn't do very much damage, but hundreds of aphids can damage a plant — and rather quickly too.

If you think about the aphid problem, you'll see that it's different from the grasshopper problem. A grasshopper eats whole leaves and stems. Therefore, dried poison on leaves and stems will kill grasshoppers.

Poisons on the outside of a plant

won't kill aphids because aphids don't eat outer plant parts. They merely puncture the plants and suck the sap inside.

As a matter of fact, we can protect plants against grasshoppers by dusting or spraying them with poisons. Substances containing *arsenic* (ar-sen-ick) are often used. As long as the poisons stay on the plants, they'll kill the insects which eat leaves and stems.

For insects with sucking mouth parts — like the aphids — a different spraying method is used. The spray must strike the insect itself. Sprays containing *nicotine* (*nih*-koh-teen), DDT, or soapsuds and kerosene are often used.

One problem of using poisons is to keep from killing useful plants. You can see that it does no good to kill insects if you kill the crop plants too. Some poisons are too strong for delicate plant tissues.

There are many special control measures. We also use poison baits and traps in our endless war against the insects. We destroy egg masses of some insect pests. We protect birds and other animals which eat insects. We even raise certain insects and bacteria because they will destroy insect pests. The measures which control one insect pest won't always work for another. Fall plowing of the soil will destroy many grasshopper eggs. But many insects don't lay their eggs in masses nor do they lay them in the soil.

Now you can begin to see that the

Fig. 33-3. A cotton boll weevil. This pest is noted as a destroyer of cotton crops.

insect problem isn't easily solved by any means. Many insects carry the germs of diseases of both man and animals. Insects attack our forest trees. They destroy or injure crop plants. They get in our gardens and our homes. They're among our most active competitors in the modern world.

CHECK YOUR FACTS . . .

Number 1 to 6 on a sheet of paper. Mark each of the following items True *or* False.

1. A garden plant whose outside is covered with dried poison is safe from attack by aphids. *TRUE.*

2. Sprays containing nicotine are sometimes used to kill aphids. *TRUE,*

3. A newly-hatched grasshopper has wings and sex organs. *FALSE.*

4. A grasshopper gets oxygen by means of a system of internal tubes. *FALSE,*

5. A grasshopper has the chewing type of mouth parts. *TRUE.*

6. An effective control measure for one insect pest is effective for all insect pests. *TRUE.*

CHAPTER 34

There Are Many Kinds of Insects

Are all insects pests? Not by a long shot! Probably you can think of many insects that are useful. What about honey bees and silkworm moths?

In addition, certain insects are necessary to the growth of some crop plants. They carry pollen from flower to flower, or from one plant to another. Also, some insects destroy other insects that are pests.

A moth's life cycle. Another thing you soon learn about insects is that they don't all have the same life cycle. In Chapter 33, you read about the life cycle of a grasshopper. How is it different from the life cycle of a moth?

Fig. 34-1 shows three stages in the development of a silkworm moth. The first stage is the *egg stage*. When the eggs hatch, they produce worm-like caterpillars called *larvae* (*lahr-vee*). These larvae look very different from the adults. They have chewing mouth parts and feed very actively. They eat mulberry leaves. As the larvae feed, they grow.

Silkworm larvae have silk glands in their bodies. When the larval stage is about over, they begin to spin *cocoons* (kuh-*koons*) as protective coverings. It's these silk cocoons that we unwind to get silk thread.

The larvae finish their cocoons and become *pupae* (*pew*-pee). Pupae stay inside the cocoons. They don't move around or take food. But changes are going on. When the pupae finally come out, they're adult moths.

When you compare the adult in Fig. 34-1 with the larva, you can see how great the change has been. The two stages don't look at all alike. You can see that the adult is a winged moth. Its main activity is to reproduce.

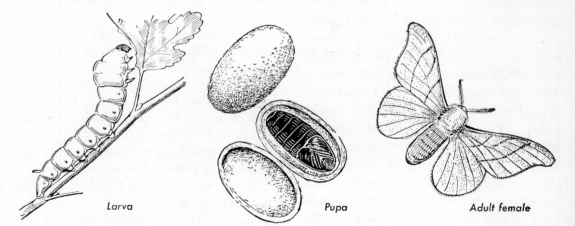

Larva   Pupa   Adult female

Fig. 34-1. Stages in the development of a silkworm moth. How does this kind of development differ from that of a grasshopper?

Mosquitoes are serious pests. The silkworm moth is a useful insect. But some of the insects which have similar life cycles aren't. For instance, there are the mosquitoes. Can you imagine worse pests?

A female mosquito lays her eggs in masses on the water. Such an egg mass is shown in Fig. 34-2. When the eggs hatch, the larvae are what people sometimes call " wrigglers." You often find these larvae in stagnant ponds. They breathe by taking air in through tubes at the end of their bodies.

Mosquito larvae swim around in the water and seek food. They grow and become pupae. Pupae can move about in their protective cases, but they don't eat. They usually just float at the top of the water.

When the pupal stage is over, the pupal cases break open. The winged adults come out. They rest on the floating pupal cases until their wings dry. Then they're ready to fly away and seek food.

This is a critical moment in a mosquito's life. If the water is moving, the new adult may fall in before its wings dry. In this case it will drown. You can see why few mosquitoes are likely to develop in running water.

The food of adult mosquitoes is blood. The adults have sucking mouth parts, and some get blood by piercing the skin of man and other animals.

Juices from a mosquito's mouth parts are irritating to most people. They cause swelling in the area of a bite. But the real danger is disease. Some types of mosquitoes bring us the germs of *malaria*. Other types carry the germs of *yellow fever*, and other diseases.

How can you control mosquitoes? Of course, malaria and yellow fever are most common in the tropics and subtropics. However, we've had many victims of these diseases in our own country.

You can see at once that one way to fight against mosquito-borne dis-

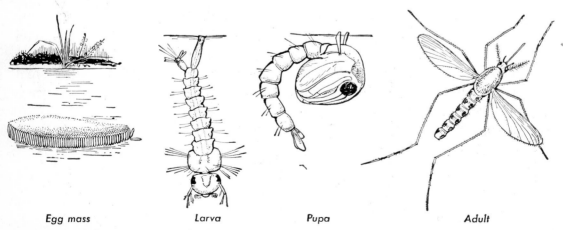

Egg mass   Larva   Pupa   Adult

Fig. 34-2. Stages in the development of a mosquito.

Fig. 34-3. Poison dust is spread over a swampy area. The old type of slow flying biplane is often used in this work.

eases is to get rid of the mosquitoes. And this we can do in various ways.

One way is to stock ponds and pools with certain small fish. The fish eat mosquito larvae and pupae. The fish won't get all pests, but every dead mosquito is one that can't bite you. Another way is to drain swamps. You should also get rid of empty barrels and all cans in which water can collect. Mosquitoes will breed even in a small can of water. This method works quite well. But draining ditches needs constant work. If they're not kept drained, water soon begins to collect again.

A third way to destroy mosquitoes is to poison the water of pools where they breed. In doing this, DDT is sometimes used. Airplanes can spread poison dust over swampy areas, as shown in Fig. 34-3. The poisoning method works fairly well. At least you can get rid of the mosquitoes. But you also kill a lot of small animals in the water. Often these other animals that get killed are parts of useful food chains.

CHECK YOUR FACTS . . .

Number 1 to 6 on a sheet of paper. Answer the following items.

1. Some types of mosquitoes spread the disease (cancer, <u>malaria</u>, measles) ...?...

2. The principal activity of a silkworm larva is to (<u>eat and grow</u>, fly, reproduce) ...?...

3. Some insects are useful to us because they destroy other insects which are pests in gardens, fields, and orchards. <u>*True*</u> or *False?*

Match Column A *with* Column B.

Column A

4. Mosquito larva
5. Mosquito pupa
6. Mosquito adult

Column B

a. Feeds actively in water
b. Floats in water but can't move
c. Feeds on blood
d. Can move but doesn't eat
e. Can't move or take food

The simplest animals are one-celled. Even one-celled animals are important. Some form useful skeletons whose products we use, or are parts of food chains. Some cause diseases.

Certain of the sponges are useful because their skeletons serve as bath sponges. Coral skeletons form reefs and sometimes islands.

For the most part, flatworms and roundworms are parasites. The flatworms have flattened bodies, often divided into segments. Roundworms don't have flattened bodies and aren't divided into segments. Members of both groups attack man and his domestic animals.

Earthworms and their relatives are segmented worms. Earthworms bore into the soil. They make the soil more porous and tend to cover rocks and other objects on the surface. Leeches are bloodsuckers. They make attacks on animals of ponds and streams.

Oysters and clams have food value and are sources of pearls and shell products. Their fleshy bodies are protected with hard shells that are lined with mother-of-pearl.

The joint-legged animals have hard outer skeletons. Crayfish, lobsters, crabs, and shrimp are important sources of food.

The joint-legged animals also include the insects. Their life cycles and habits vary. Some are useful and many are pests. We control insect pests by poison sprays, dusts, baits, traps, and other devices.

All the animals you read about in Topic 1 are without backbones.

WHAT DO THESE WORDS MEAN?

Body segment	Flatworms	Pupa
Body wall	Invertebrate	Roundworms
Bud	Larva	Segmented worms
Cilia	Life cycle	Spongin
Cocoon	Mantle layer	Stinging cells
Compound eye	Mollusk	Sucker
Digestive canal	Nymph	Tentacles
Eye spot	Protozoa	

ASK YOURSELF . . .

1. How have chalk and flint deposits been formed?
2. In what ways would you say that Paramecium differs from Amoeba?
3. From what part of a sponge colony do we get the bath sponge?
4. (a) In what ways is Hydra like a simple sponge? (b) How do the two animals differ?
5. (a) How are reefs formed? (b) What type of stone has come from some prehistoric coral reefs?
6. (a) Is a planarian a flatworm or roundworm? (b) Does a planarian lead a parasitic life?
7. (a) Where are the cysts of beef tapeworms found? (b) How do these tapeworms get into the human body?
8. How could you tell a roundworm from a flatworm?
9. (a) How do trichina worms get into the human body? (b) Why are they dangerous?
10. (a) How do hookworms get into the human body? (b) How can you prevent this?
11. How do earthworm activities improve soil fertility?
12. Why do we sometimes say leeches are pests?
13. (a) Where are soft-shell clams found? (b) Hard-shell clams? (c) Scallops? (d) Why are they of value?
14. (a) What is mother-of-pearl? (b) What useful products come from the shells of clams and oysters?
15. (a) How is a gem pearl formed? (b) A cultured pearl?
16. (a) Why have lobsters become less common today? (b) What efforts are made to increase the natural supply?

17. (a) To what extent are crayfish useful? (b) Why do they sometimes become pests?
18. What kind of skeleton do all the joint-legged animals have?
19. (a) Why are some spiders dangerous? (b) Scorpions? (c) Ticks?
20. How can you tell an insect from a spider or a tick?
21. (a) What are the stages in the development of a grasshopper? (b) A moth?
22. (a) What kind of foods are eaten by an insect that has chewing mouth parts? (b) Sucking mouth parts?
23. (a) Why are some insects useful? (b) Why are other insects pests?
24. What are some ways in which we can control insect pests?

GETTING THE FACTS . . .

1. With a microscope or projector, examine prepared slides bearing *foraminifera* (fo-ram-ih-*nif*-er-ah). They're among the one-celled animals which have skeletons. Note the holes in the skeletons through which strands of the living protoplasm can be extended. It's these tiny skeletons that form chalk deposits.

2. If you have a good pond culture, look for some Paramecium specimens. Try to locate the parts as shown in Fig. 27-1. Test the reaction of a Paramecium when you put a small amount of some stain in the culture (even ink will do). Note how the cilia act.

3. With a lens, examine some living or preserved specimens of Hydra. Locate the parts as shown in Fig. 28-1.

4. Examine some preserved or living specimens of planarians, tapeworms, and roundworms. Try to find out in what ways they are alike and in what ways they're different. For one thing, notice that only the roundworms have complete digestive canals.

5. *A Museum Trip.* Visit a museum if one is not too far away. Look at some of the commercially important animals discussed in Topic 1. You should see specimens of commercial sponges, corals, parasitic worms, leeches, starfish, clams, oysters, snails, squid, devil fish, spiders, scorpions, ticks, and various insects. Make notes that you think will be of interest to the class and report on your findings.

6. Collect about two dozen earthworms. Compare their external appearance carefully. Probably you'll have more than one species. Kill a specimen in 10% formalin solution or 70% alcohol. Your teacher will make these solutions for you. Cut your killed specimen open along the upper mid-line. See if you can find the structures shown in Fig. 30-2.

7. Examine shells of clams, oysters, and snails. Locate the mother-of-pearl layer, and study its relation to the rest of the shell. If possible, examine products from mollusks, such as cracked shell (bird food), pearl buttons, and pearl inlay work (mostly on furniture or ornamental boxes).

8. *A Field Trip.* Visit an area in the field where you can collect specimens from a pond, meadow, and woodland. See to what extent the animals without backbones are represented in the area.

9. Examine a living or preserved grasshopper. Locate the structures in Fig. 33-1. Remember that there are many different species of grasshoppers. So what you see may not look exactly like Fig. 33-1.

10. Study Riker mounts which show different stages in the life cycle of: (*a*) a grasshopper; and (*b*) a moth. Compare the two cases to see how they're alike and how they differ.

11. With a microscope, examine the mouth parts of a grasshopper. These are the chewing mouth parts, and you should see a pair of heavy jaws. Do the same in the case of an aphid or a mosquito. Now you see something different. The mouth parts are adapted for sucking fluids. In the case of the mosquito, you may see the sharp, slender structures that it uses to pierce the skin.

12. Put a little meat in a dish on a window shelf. In a day or two certain flies may lay eggs on the meat. Put the meat and eggs in a large jar. Cover the jar carefully with cheesecloth. Now you can watch the development of fly larvae, pupae, and adults.

13. After consulting an encyclopedia, and the references at the end of this unit, prepare a report which tells how coral reefs grow, and how coral islands are formed.

14. After consulting the references at the end of this unit, prepare a report on the food chains which exist in lakes and streams.

Topic 2

GETTING ACQUAINTED WITH THE LARGER ANIMALS

Here you see a couple of early men. They lived long before the dawn of history.

Then how do we know about these ancient people?

The story comes to us bit by bit. We learn some things from studying their skeletons which have been dug up. The stone tools these people used give us other facts about them. These men made crude drawings on the walls of their caves.

We have found out that they wore clothing made from animal skins. They hunted and they did a lot of fishing. So, you see how the use of animals goes way back to early man.

AMONG THE NEW WORDS FOR THIS TOPIC

- **AMPHIBIAN** (am-*fib*-ee-un). Cold-blooded animals with backbones but without scales and plates, such as frogs and toads.
- **CARNIVORE** (*kahr*-niv-or). A group of flesh-eating mammals which includes wolves, dogs, cats, leopards, lions, seals, bears, mink, foxes, and skunks.
- **MAMMALS** (*mam*-m'ls). Warm-blooded, air-breathing animals with backbones and a body covering of hair.
- **REPTILES** (*rep*-tils). Cold-blooded, air-breathing animals with backbones, scales, and plates such as lizards, snakes, and turtles.
- **RODENT** (*roh*-d'nt). A group of gnawing mammals which includes rats, mice, squirrels, and woodchucks.
- **VITAMIN** (*vy*-tuh-min). A substance present in foods in small quantities but necessary to good health.

CHAPTER 35

All Fish Have Backbones

Early man hunted and fished for a living. There are still some tribes of uncivilized men who live this way. But most people have learned to raise the animals they use.

Fish are an exception to this. We raise some fish today. But for the most part, we continue to depend on the natural supply. We get our fish mainly from the sea and our larger lakes and rivers. Some of them we use as food. We also get many other useful materials from fish.

Fish are animals with backbones. You've probably found this out if you've ever tried to clean a fish. The backbone runs clear down the back of the animal.

People often call some animals "fish" that aren't real fish at all. You shouldn't confuse a crayfish or a starfish or a silverfish (an insect!) with real fish. Crayfish and starfish are *invertebrates* — they don't have a backbone. The real fish all have backbones. Biologists call animals with a backbone *vertebrates* (*vert*-uh-brates).

One of our common fish is the perch. You see it in Fig. 35-1. You can catch it in streams, lakes, and ponds. It gets its oxygen by *gills*, which are special organs for taking oxygen from water. It uses its fins and tail to swim.

Like other animals of its type, a perch has a bony skeleton including the backbone. It has well-developed body systems, such as a digestive system and a nervous system. It eats small plants and animals in the water.

We get many fish from the sea. East Coast fishing dates back to Co-

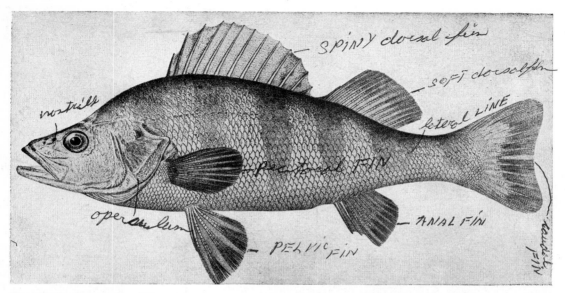

Fig. 35-1. A perch. This is a common type of fish in lakes and streams.

lonial days. It's still important, but more fish are now caught off the Pacific Coast and Alaska. Another large fishing center is the Gulf of Mexico. We also get many fish from the Great Lakes and from our large rivers.

Most of our market fish, as you see, come from the oceans. Modern fishing vessels are very different from those of the past. For one thing, they're likely to be driven by Diesel engines. For another, they're equipped to freeze the fish. Thus, fresh fish are brought to market all the time.

Some market fish are still taken on hand or set lines. Fishermen catch larger numbers, however, in nets. Look at Fig. 35-2. It shows a net full of fish being hauled on board a fishing vessel. Drag nets are also used in the shallow water of bays. Fishing is an important industry in many countries.

Fish are a good addition to your diet. For one thing, fish aren't hard to digest. For another, they contain large amounts of necessary vitamins (*vy*-tuh-mins). *Vitamins* are certain substances found in foods. They're only present in small amounts, but they're necessary to your good health. And fish are also unusually rich in proteins, minerals, as well as other elements.

Some of the more important food fish are shown in Fig. 35-3. You can find all of them in the markets today. However, some are less common than they once were. The codfish, for example, is no longer the Number 1 fish of the North Atlantic. Its place has been taken by a related fish, the haddock.

Some medical oils come from fish. Ever take cod-liver oil? It contains useful vitamins. Cod-liver oil comes

Fig. 35-2. Fishermen often catch fish for the market in large nets or seines.

from the livers of codfish. In the same way, haliver oil comes from the livers of halibut. Vitamin oil is also extracted from the livers of sharks. As a matter of fact, a number of fish livers are rich in vitamins, but aren't widely used today.

Fish provide other oils and fertilizers. You've learned that some oils come from plants. Others are from the fat of domesticated animals. But lots of commercial oil comes from fish. Both oils and fish meal are fishery products of importance to industry and agriculture.

The fish we use for oils are types that aren't very good for food. Most of them are small members of the her-

ring tribe. They are caught in nets in both the Atlantic and Pacific Oceans. Some young herrings are called sardines and are packed in tins for the table.

Fish used for oil are taken to factories on shore. They're steam-cooked in large vats until they fall apart. The oil is lighter than water, so it rises to the top of the vats. This oil is used for tanning leather, and for oiling machinery. It's also used in making soaps, paints, and varnishes.

The solid mass of the cooked fish is then pressed and dried. It's used to make fertilizers, and special food mixtures for domestic animals that we raise.

Fig. 35-3. Some important types of fish. On the left, top to bottom, a pike, two catfish, and a mackerel. Right, top to bottom, a salmon, a halibut, and a trout.

CHECK YOUR FACTS . . .

Number 1 to 6 on a sheet of paper. Select the best answer for each of the following items.

1. The animal in the following list which has a backbone is a (starfish, crayfish, perch) . . .?. . .

2. The part of a codfish from which we get vitamin oils is the (liver, heart, skin) . . .?. . .

3. Most of our market supply of fish comes from (lakes, rivers, oceans) . . .?. . .

4. Animals with backbones are called (invertebrates, vertebrates, nonvertebrates) . . .?. . .

5. Some sardines are the young of (mackerel, tunas, herring) . . .?. . .

6. A perch gets its oxygen through the action of (lungs, breathing tubes, gills) . . .?. . .

CHAPTER 36

Why Are Frogs and Some Snakes Useful?

Ed and Jim had found a small salamander (*sal*-uh-man-der). It was like the one in Fig. 36-1 which you'll see on page 156.

" That thing is like a lizard," said Ed.

"No, I think it's more like a frog," replied Jim as he looked at it more carefully.

Which one of the boys was right, Ed or Jim?

Amphibians and reptiles. Before you try to answer, consider these facts. Toads, frogs, and salaman-

155

Fig. 36-1. A salamander. These scale-less little animals are related to the frogs and the toads.

ders are **amphibians** (am-*fib*-ee-uns). Their skins don't have scales or other covering. If they have toes, they don't have nails or claws.

Lizards, snakes, turtles, and alligators are **reptiles** (*rep*-tils). Their skins have scales and bony plates. If they have toes, claws are present.

Many people confuse amphibians and reptiles. But now you know that Jim was right. A salamander looks something like a lizard, but it's more closely related to a frog.

A life in and out of water. Ever find any frog eggs in early spring? Female frogs lay them in shallow, quiet waters. You can keep a few eggs in a school aquarium. Before many days pass, the eggs will hatch.

As you know, tadpoles come from the frog eggs. These tadpoles live in the water. They get oxygen through their gills. The tadpoles feed on plant and animal matter. Soon they begin to develop limbs and their tails grow shorter. Lungs begin to form about this time. **Lungs** are the breathing organs of land vertebrates. Blood gets a supply of oxygen as it passes through the lungs.

Now the tadpoles have become young frogs. They can breathe air and can live in or out of the water. They feed largely on insects and other small animals. The different stages of this life cycle are shown in Fig. 36-3. Toads develop in much the same way.

Fig. 36-2. A frog (left) and a toad. Both of these animals are amphibians.

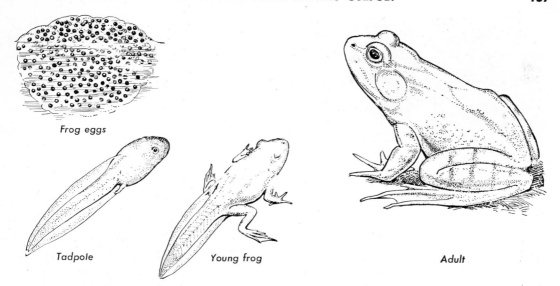

Frog eggs

Tadpole   Young frog   Adult

Fig. 36-3. Diagram to show stages in the development of a frog.

Amphibians are useful. Tadpoles and frogs are eaten by fish, birds, and some other animals. They're important parts of food chains in and about ponds. You know, of course, that man uses the legs of the larger frogs as food. Bullfrogs are the best type to use because of their large size. They once were common in eastern North America. But they've been hunted so much that now they're hard to find.

Since the big frogs have become scarcer, you might think that raising them would be a good idea. The fact is, there are such things as " frog farms " already. But raising frogs isn't too easy a job. The trouble is to provide enough insects and other small animals to feed the frogs.

You probably know that many tadpoles and frogs are used in laboratories. Scientists study them to see how body structures develop and work. They've learned many of the things they know about biology by studying frogs.

Toads and salamanders also eat insects and other small forms of life. Toads are very useful because they eat many insect pests in gardens.

Some snakes are useful. Snakes, as you know, are slender reptiles that are covered with scales. Some snakes bear their young alive, and others lay eggs. Some are tiny little things. On the other hand, regal pythons of the

Fig. 36-4. A python. Skins of these snakes are used as ornamental leather.

Fig. 36-5. A rattlesnake. Rattlesnakes are members of the dangerous pit viper group.

East Indies are big enough to eat deer and goats.

Some snakes feed largely on rats, mice, and other pests. So these snakes are useful. Among snakes of this type are bull snakes, black snakes, blue racers, and king snakes. On the other hand, some of our harmless snakes are of doubtful value. This is because they feed on fish, frogs, and bird eggs.

Poisonous snakes. Poisonous snakes are another story. We're glad enough to be rid of them. The largest group of poisonous snakes in North America is the *pit viper group*. It includes about a dozen species of rattlesnakes, the copperhead, and the water moccasin.

Could you recognize one of these dangerous snakes? Look at Fig. 36-5. All pit vipers have wedge-shaped heads. They have oval pupils in their eyes. They have a *pit* in addition to a *nostril* on each side of their head.

Pit vipers have two of their upper front teeth developed as fangs. These fangs are hollow. They connect with a pair of poison glands in the neck region. When the snake strikes, the fangs are moved so they point forward. The snake then injects venom from the poison glands into the wound.

You may know that the coral snakes of our Southeast and Southwest are also poisonous. They're small snakes, related to the cobras rather than the pit vipers.

In places where poisonous snakes are found, you should wear high rubber or leather boots. It's also wise to carry a modern " snake bite " kit. Know how to use it, too. Such a kit includes a suction cup for removing venom from wounds. It also includes anti-venom serum and a hypodermic needle to inject it into the body. Of course, a person who has been bitten should have a doctor treat him *as soon as possible*.

Lizards, turtles, and alligators. Ever hear of eating snake meat? Well, it's done in many parts of the world. Even rattlesnake meat is canned for the market. Eating lizards is a fairly common practice, too, in warm countries. Some of the tropical lizards are big fellows, and supply a good deal of food.

The lizards are the closest living relatives of snakes. Some lizards look almost like snakes. Other large ones look much like crocodiles.

Turtles, of course, are also used as food by man. One of the important types is the green turtle, an ocean species. The green turtle grows to a weight of 500 pounds. Another famous turtle is the little *diamondbacked terrapin*, once common along

Fig. 36-6. A Gila monster (left) and a box turtle. Both of these animals are reptiles. The Gila monster is a poisonous type.

the Atlantic Coast. It's the turtle from which terrapin soup is made. In its native haunts, the diamond-backed terrapin has become rare. It's now raised for the market on " turtle farms."

Alligators were once common in the swamp areas of the South. They grew to lengths of over 20 feet. Man has hunted them for sport and for their hides for many years. Now the larger specimens have become scarce except in the deeper swamps and on alligator farms. One bad effect has been an increase of cane rats and other pests which alligators destroy. Thus, the hunting of alligators is forbidden in some parts of Florida.

CHECK YOUR FACTS . . .

Number 1 to 6 on a sheet of paper. For each item in Column A, *select the best answer in* Column B.

Column A	Column B
1. Bullfrog	a. A type of turtle used in making soup
2. Regal python	
3. Copperhead	
4. Terrapin	b. A poisonous type of lizard
5. Salamander	c. A useful type of American snake
6. Blue racer	d. A warm-blooded animal
	e. Member of the pit viper group of poisonous snakes
	f. Closely related to the cobras
	g. Large snake found in the East Indies
	h. An amphibian that is not a frog
	i. Spends early part of its life in a tadpole stage

CHAPTER 37

Birds Are Adapted for Flying

When you think about flying, you're likely to think of birds. Are birds the only animals that fly? Can all birds fly?

Fig. 37-1. Most species of birds can fly, but a few types are flightless.

Of course, the answer to both questions is no. But at least most birds fly. Their wings are modified front limbs bearing feathers. The muscles which move the wings are very strong. They have to be, or birds like those shown in Fig. 37-1 couldn't keep their bodies in the air.

Birds have special structures for flying. Having eaten chicken many times, you know that birds have backbones. They're vertebrates. You may not know, however, that some of their bones are hollow. Try breaking the leg bone of a chicken, and see what you find. Many of the smaller bones are solidly joined to other bones. The result is a skeleton that is light in weight but strong. Such a skeleton is useful to any animal that flies.

You can easily see that birds use a lot of energy. So you won't be surprised to know that birds eat more than many other animals their size. Their food is soon digested, and absorbed. Their blood is warm, and is pumped by a four-chambered heart. The blood passes through a surprisingly complete system of blood vessels. Digested food materials and oxygen are quickly carried to the cells in the bird's body.

Bird feathers are outgrowths of the skin. Although they don't look like it, feathers are similar to the scales of reptiles. No doubt you've read that female birds are seldom as brightly colored as males. Feathers, and especially those of the wings and tail, form the flying surface of a bird.

Many birds migrate. Some birds stay more or less in the same place the year round. Other species migrate (*my*-grate). *Migrate* means spending part of the year in one place and part in another. Some birds travel long distances. Some migrate only short distances.

The champion traveler among birds is probably the *Arctic tern*, which you'll see in Fig. 37-3. This bird flies from the Arctic Circle to the Antarctic Circle and back again each year. The round trip totals 22,000 miles!

You usually think of birds flying south in the fall and coming north in the spring. Not so — at least not in all cases. Some birds travel from east to west. For instance, certain birds migrate between the Hawaiian Islands and our West Coast.

Bird bills and food habits. Everyone knows that birds have bills or beaks. But did you know that you can just about tell what a bird eats? Well, you can, and by looking at its bill.

What do you see in Fig. 37-4? Four types of bird bills. The songbird has a bill suited to catching insects. The woodpecker has a chisel-like bill which it uses to drill holes in trees. Woodpeckers find the insects on which they feed in or under the bark. The eagle uses its sharp, curved bill to tear flesh. The spear-like bill of a heron serves to seize fish and frogs in shallow water.

Most birds are useful. Only a few kinds of birds eat grain or attack other birds. When you study birds, you soon find that most of them are useful. Many destroy insects. Others eat huge amounts of weed seeds each year. Many hawks and owls do useful work in killing rats and mice. Here you have good reasons why the law protects most birds.

Birds also add to the food supply. Most of the birds that you eat, however, are birds that are raised on farms. To these are added a smaller number of wild ducks, pheasants, and other game birds taken by hunters.

The birds that farmers raise include chickens, turkeys, ducks, geese, guinea hens, and ostriches. Their ancestors came from different parts of the world. Chickens, for example, possibly came from a jungle fowl of Asia. Turkeys came from wild turkeys of North and South America.

Fig. 37-2. Some birds that do not fly. From top to bottom, an Australian kiwi, an ostrich, and a flock of penguins.

Fig. 37-3. An Arctic tern. This bird is famous for the long migration it makes each year.

Guinea hens were bred from a wild African guinea hen.

"But," you say, "what about the ostriches? Why raise them?"

For the feathers, of course, although people eat the eggs sometimes. For centuries people have used bird feathers as ornaments. This practice caused almost complete destruction of some wild birds. Now, there are laws which ban the sale of many kinds of feathers. To be sure, we still use feathers, and many of them, but most of these feathers come from birds that farmers raise.

Why protect birds? You probably are willing to grant that most birds are useful. But you may still have one question. Do birds need any special protection?

Before trying to answer this question, let's hear the story of the passenger pigeon. A passenger pigeon is shown in Fig. 37-5.

Years ago the passenger pigeon was one of the most common birds in North America. Vast flocks migrated across the United States in the spring and fall. Many hunters sought them eagerly. Thousands of birds were killed and shipped to the city markets for food. Passenger pigeons became scarcer. Today, *not a single one* of these birds is known to survive.

Much the same sort of thing has happened to other species of birds. Man has hunted them. He has destroyed their nesting places. Wild fruits on which they feed have become scarcer as lands are cleared.

So, attempts have been made to save birds by giving them special protection. The federal government and the states have made laws to protect various birds. Bird sanctuaries have been set up in many parts of the country. All this makes good sense. It's foolish to destroy useful animals.

Downy woodpecker

Song-bird (Blackpoll Warbler)

Bald eagle

Great blue heron

Fig. 37-4. The bills of birds are adapted for eating various kinds of foods.

CHECK YOUR FACTS . . .

Number 1 to 6 on a sheet of paper. Mark each of the following items True *or* False.

1. The bill of an eagle is adapted for tearing flesh. *true*

2. All birds that migrate travel in a north and south direction. *false*

3. Birds are cold-blooded animals without backbones. *false*

4. Some birds are useful because they eat weed seeds. *TRUE*

5. The passenger pigeon is one of the common species of North American birds today. *TRUE*

6. Our market turkeys came from wild African ancestors. *FALSE*

CHAPTER 38

What Are Mammals?

Fig. 37-5. A passenger pigeon. Once one of the most common birds of North America, now not a single one is known to survive.

The *mammals* (*mam*-m'ls) are vertebrates. They include most of our larger animals. Cows, horses, dogs, cats, sheep, and goats are in this group. So is man, which makes the mammals especially interesting to you. You can see some of the many types of mammals in Fig. 38-1.

The structures of mammals. All mammals, of course, have backbones. They're all air-breathers, and most of them live on the land. However, whales, seals, and some others live in the water.

Mammals, like birds, are warm-blooded. They all have four-chambered hearts. They have more or less hair as an outer covering, and have teeth in bony sockets. Most mammals bear their young, but two types lay eggs. The egg layers live in Australia and New Guinea. One of them, the duckbill, is shown in Fig. 38-1 on page 165.

The importance of mammals. Some mammals are useful to man. In fact, they're so useful that man raises them as domestic animals. You'll read about these in Chapter 39. On the other hand, some mammals are pests, such as the mice and rats. Still others have no real importance one way or the other.

Gnawing mammals. One interesting group of gnawing mammals is called the *rodents* (*roh*-d'nts). How

Armadillo

Squirrel

Mountain lion

Walrus

Whale

Deer

Fig. 38-1. A group of mammals. All of these animals have backbones, are warm-

these animals can gnaw things! Some of their front teeth keep right on growing through life. Members of this group include rats, mice, chipmunks, gophers, ground squirrels, flying squirrels, muskrats, beavers, and

guinea pigs. Some are useful animals and some are pests.

You know, of course, that beavers, muskrats, and squirrels have useful fur. You'll learn more about them in Chapter 41. Muskrats and squirrels

Duckbill

Kangaroo

Mole

Ape

Bat

blooded, and have at least some hair.

are used, to some extent at least, as human food.

On the other hand, consider the case of the house rat. This pest seems to have come from Asia. It reached this country back in colonial days.

The house rat eats all kinds of food, and destroys a lot of things it merely gnaws. It chews holes in the wooden parts of buildings and weakens foundations. It kills young chickens and other small animals. It eats the eggs

Fig. 38-2. The house mouse — one of our worst pests. Other species of native mice are also pests.

of wild and domestic birds. It carries the germs of several diseases which affect men.

The house mouse is also a pest. It's another foreign species that has been brought to our shores. In addition, we have many native types of mice which do great damage to field and garden crops.

Maybe at this point you'll ask: "Why not get rid of rats and mice?"

It's a good idea, but like so many good things, it's easier said than done. Rats and mice hide in out-of-the-way places and in burrows. They can find food almost anywhere. They reproduce rapidly. Rats, in particular, are clever about poisons. They won't eat some poison baits that other animals will.

The control of rodent pests. Just the same, poison baits of the right type are used on both rats and mice. Poison gases can be used in warehouses or storage places, or in outdoor burrows. But there's always a danger in using either poison baits or poison gases. Children or domestic animals

might eat the baits. Some poison gases are deadly to any animal that inhales them.

Traps of various sorts are used to catch rats and mice. In farming areas, hawks, owls, and certain snakes kill a good many rodent pests. Then too, rats and mice won't become common where they can't find food and shelter easily. If food containers are rodent-proof, at least half of the battle is won.

The flesh-eating mammals. When anyone talks of flesh-eating mammals, or *carnivores* (*kahr*-niv-ors), you may think of tigers and lions. But the carnivores also include dogs, wolves, coyotes, cats, leopards, seals, walruses, bears, minks, raccoons, weasels, foxes, and skunks.

Most of these animals eat flesh. Some of them even become a nuisance in parts of the West because

Fig. 38-3. A house rat. This common pest destroys foods and other materials. It is also a disease carrier.

they prey on livestock. However, others serve to control rats, mice, and similar pests.

In some areas people still eat bear, seal, and walrus meat. But as a group, the carnivores aren't of great value as food. Furs, however, are another matter. We get useful furs from many carnivores. We even raise minks, foxes, and skunks for their furs.

Whales and whale products. Before we leave the mammals, let's consider one group that lives in the sea. This is the whale group. It includes some species less than 10 feet long and some species nearly 100 feet long.

From whales we get some unusual articles of commerce. A hundred years ago people used whale oil in lamps. Today it goes into paints, face creams, butter substitutes, varnishes, and leather dressings. From whale oil we get glycerin, and from glycerin explosives are made.

A special oil from certain whales is used to make candles. Whalebone, from the mouths of some whales, goes into brush handles and dress stays.

Only certain whales have whalebone in their mouths. The whalebone forms a sort of sieve. This is what the whale uses to strain food out of the water.

Of course whales aren't as common as they once were. Like other useful animals, man has hunted them for many years. The result in such cases is a reduced natural supply. It may even be the complete destruction of a species or a group of species.

CHECK YOUR FACTS . . .

Number 1 to 6 on a sheet of paper. Select the best answers to complete the following statements.

1. (All, most, few) mammals bear their young.

2. A seal is a member of the (rodent, carnivore, whale) group.

3. Native species of mice are generally (useful, pests, of no consequence).

4. The least desirable animal in the following group is a (mink, fox, house rat).

5. The rodent in the following group is a (fox, coyote, beaver).

6. A valuable oil comes from (whales, muskrats, foxes).

CHAPTER 39

Many Mammals Have Been Tamed

" Why do you suppose ancient man tamed wild animals? " Ed asked.

" Probably for the same reason he raised plants," Jim told him.

Jim was right. Man has always tried to have a good supply of food. And he's always wanted other things like clothing and shelter.

Old and new animals. Man has raised some animals for centuries. The dog was probably one of the first he tamed. Dogs were followed by pigeons, chickens, cattle, sheep, pigs, camels, goats, and horses. The chart on page 169 will give you some facts about various animals that man raises.

Today, there are over 200 breeds of

Fig. 39-1. Men have raised pigs and cattle for centuries. By comparison, the guinea hen is a "new" domestic animal. It first came from Africa and is a member of the pheasant group. It can be bred like poultry, but it is harder to raise.

dogs! Their ancestors were species of wolves and coyotes from different parts of the world. Of course, you know that we raise dogs largely as pets and companions. However, savages have eaten their flesh. And in cold countries, the people use dogs to pull sleds.

You soon learn several things about animals that man has raised for a long time. For one thing, there usually are many breeds of such an animal. It's not apt to be wild, and it isn't hard to raise. It probably is attacked by various parasites but has good resistance against them.

On the other hand, what about animals that we have tamed more recently? Such a group would include guinea hens, pheasants, minks, foxes, ostriches, and reindeer. There are only a few special breeds of such animals. They're wilder and more apt to roam. They're attacked by fewer parasites, but they haven't much resistance to these attacks.

"Are we still trying to tame animals?" you ask.

Yes, indeed. And we're still developing new and special breeds. Some of the animals tamed long ago are only useful in certain places, such as desert or mountain countries. Others can live only in certain parts of the world. Then, too, remember we always try to improve what we have.

What makes a good domestic animal? You can probably guess that some of our domestic animals are better than others. What, then, is really needed in a good domestic animal?

SOME COMMON DOMESTIC ANIMALS

Animal	Source	Present Distribution	Uses
Camel	Asia and Africa	Desert areas of the Old World	Draft animals; food, and other materials
Cattle	Europe and Asia	Worldwide	Food, leather, and other materials
Chicken	Asia	Worldwide	Food, feathers, eggs
Goat	Europe and Asia	Barren areas of Old and New World	Food and other materials
Guinea hen	Africa	Scattered areas of Old and New World	Food, feathers
Horse	Europe and Asia	Worldwide	Draft animals; food, and other materials
Ostrich	Asia and Africa	Africa, Australia, and United States	Plumes
Pig	Europe and Asia	Worldwide	Food, leather, and other materials
Pigeon	Europe and Asia	Worldwide	Food, feathers
Reindeer	Northern Europe and Asia	Northern lands in Old and New World	Draft animals; food and other materials
Sheep	Europe and Asia	Worldwide	Food, clothing, leather, and other materials
Turkey	North and Central America	Scattered areas throughout world	Food, feathers

Well, for one thing, such an animal shouldn't compete directly with man for food. You can see that if a domestic animal eats things that man can't or doesn't eat, it isn't a competitor. It actually adds to the food supply.

In the second place, a good domestic animal is useful. Let's consider the pig. From its hair we get material to make mattresses, brushes, and upholstered furniture. The hide gives us leather for gloves, baseball gloves, footballs, traveling bags, wallets, handbags, and lots of other articles. From the flesh come pork, ham, bacon, lard, and several kinds of greases and oils. We also use the fleshy parts in making sausage containers, and some of the glands for medicines. The bones yield bone meal, bone

Fig. 39-2. Ostrich farms exist in various parts of the world. We raise these birds mainly for their feathers.

charcoal, glue, and even more oils and greases.

In the third place, a good domestic animal must live well in captivity. It must be able to reproduce in captivity. It must resist the attacks of parasites. And it must be able to live where man lives. Many of our domestic animals fail on one or more of these counts. Llamas, for instance, are animals of the high mountain areas of South America. They don't do well in captivity, or when forced to live in low countries.

Some domestic animals have special uses. "Well, if we can't raise one

thing," you say, " why not raise something else? "

That's just about what we do. Which is better as a source of milk and meat, a cow or a goat? No doubt you say " a cow." But some people have an allergy for cow's milk. However, they can drink goat milk safely.

Remember too that in some places cattle have a hard time finding food. The grass is too short, or there isn't enough of it. But goats are famous for their ability to survive in barren areas.

Better domestic animals. We try to improve our domestic animals in much the same way that we try to improve our plants. We use our scientific knowledge to develop new breeds. Today there are breeds of cattle which are famous for milk production. Other cattle produce good yields of beef. Still others are good for both purposes.

We also improve the quality of our animals by giving them proper foods. We try to keep them free from disease. Such efforts mean better products in the long run.

Fig. 39-3. One type of camel. Notice that it has two humps on its back. The other modern type of camel has only one hump.

CHECK YOUR FACTS . . .

Number 1 to 6 on a sheet of paper. Match the items in Column A *with the best answers in* Column B.

Column A	Column B
1. Llama	*a.* Probably the first animal that man has tamed
2. Camel	
3. Dog	*b.* Animal of far northern countries which has been recently tamed
4. Turkey	
5. Reindeer	*c.* Animal of desert regions used for carrying people and supplies
6. Sheep	
	d. Animal of high mountain areas of South America and not adapted to live elsewhere
	e. Fur from this animal is the common source of wool
	f. A large bird native to North and Central America and used for food

g. Animal not known to be attacked by parasites

h. This animal is used only by people of Australia

CHAPTER 40

Some Animals Are Sources of Leather

If you've ever read about life in the Indian days, you surely have heard of buckskin. It's a kind of leather made from the hides of deer. In other parts of the world early man learned to make leather, too. The habit of wearing fur and leather is as old as man himself.

The sources of leather. Today, most of our leather comes from cattle that we raise. But large amounts also come from horses, pigs, sheep, goats, and kangaroos. Snakes, lizards, and

Fig. 40-1. A female kangaroo and her offspring. During early life, the young kangaroo is carried about in a pouch.

even sharks yield special leathers. We use some leathers because they wear well. Other leathers are used mostly because they are attractive.

How leather is made. Ever try to make a piece of leather from a raw hide? Many young people have done so, and sometimes with good success. The first thing you learn about leather-making is that there are several ways to do the job.

Raw hides of animals usually are salted or dried to keep them in good condition until they reach the tannery. At the tannery the hides are washed to clean and soften them. Any excess flesh is removed from their inner sides. Then the hides are soaked in a chemical solution for several days. Now the hairs can be scraped away easily. Finally, the hides are washed again and are ready to be tanned.

The process of tanning varies, depending on the kind of leather you want to produce. If you want leather for shoe soles, you may put the hides in tannin solution. Tannin comes from the bark of trees such as hemlocks, chestnuts, and oaks. You may leave the hides in the tannin solution for as much as four months. Then the new leather is ready to be finished.

Finishing is done by smoothing out

Fig. 40-2. An alligator. People sometimes eat the flesh and eggs of these animals.

the leather and treating it with other chemicals. Then the leather is oiled, scraped, and waxed. Finally, it's flattened and allowed to dry.

Of course if you want a soft leather, you must do a different kind of job. Cleaning and tanning the hide are about the same. But the leather must be scraped and rubbed as it dries. Otherwise, it gets hard.

Leather from mammals. As you've read, most of our leather comes from mammals. Also, most of it now comes from mammals that we raise. But we still get some leather supplies from wild animals.

For instance, you surely have heard of kangaroos. You know that they live in Australia. What you may not know is that there are about two dozen different kinds of kangaroos or kangaroo-like animals. They range in size from types no bigger than a rabbit to the large gray kangaroo.

The gray kangaroo is a big fellow. Fully-grown males often weigh over 200 pounds. This kangaroo lives on the plains, and feeds on plant materials. It's something of a nuisance because it eats the grass that sheep might use. On the other hand, it's used to some extent as human food. Kangaroo-tail soup is a quite favored dish in Australia.

But the main value of kangaroos is their fur and leather. More than a million hides are sold each year. Many of these hides finally come to the United States. We use kangaroo leather for a number of things, mostly for making gloves and shoes.

Fig. 40-3. A large tropical lizard. Hides from such lizards yield special types of leathers.

Leather from reptiles. We also get some leathers from reptiles. You read in Chapter 36 how alligators in the South have been hunted for their hides. A hundred years ago these animals were common in swamps from Florida to Texas. Many of them were over 15 feet long.

But the hunting of alligators has greatly reduced their numbers. Also, large specimens are hard to find. This isn't surprising, since alligators grow slowly.

We use alligator leathers for making many small articles. Among them are handbags, shoes, and luggage.

Fig. 40-4. Such snakes as this small boa are a source of skins used to make shoes, belts, handbags, and other things.

In the same way, there's been demand for snake and lizard skins in some years. We bring in most of the skins from other countries. The demand has been so great at times that we have made substitutes from other leathers. The use of these substitutes is desirable. Actually, many of the snakes and lizards killed for skins are useful destroyers of insects and rodents.

CHECK YOUR FACTS . . .

Number 1 to 6 on a sheet of paper. Mark each of the following items True *or* False.

1. Alligators are more common today in the swamps of our South than they were a hundred years ago.

2. Some types of leather are made from the skins of sharks.

3. Kangaroo leather is often used to make shoes.

4. We can get tannin from the bark of hemlock trees.

5. Most of the leather that we use today comes from domestic animals.

6. Buckskin is a type of leather made from the hides of cattle.

CHAPTER 41

Some Animals Are Sources of Fur

Why did many early American settlers move away from the seacoast and push back into Indian country?

"Looking for gold," you say? Perhaps some of them. Usually the men of the frontier were hunters and trappers. They traded with the Indians. Most of them were after furs.

Furs from wild animals. Of course, the days of the frontier are gone. Most of the beavers that lured the trappers westward have disappeared, too. We now produce only about half the furs we use in this country.

But we still get some furs from wild animals. If you look at the chart on page 175, you'll find some facts about furs we use today.

Fur farming. The steady demand for certain furs has given rise to fur farms. Fur farming isn't new. Cen-

Fig. 41-1. Beavers were once common along many streams of North America. They now survive only where they are protected.

SOME FUR—BEARING ANIMALS

Name of Animal	Comments
Beaver	Sheared beaver popular
Chinchilla	Rare and costly type from South America
Ermine	Rare and costly type, used for special occasions
Fox	Preferred types are silver, black, platina, and cross fox raised on farms
Lamb	Breeds having special types of furs now raised on farms
Leopard	From jungles of various countries
Lynx	Trimming for collars and cuffs of cloth coats
Marten	Rare and costly type
Mink	Best grades now raised on farms
Muskrat	Sometimes used to imitate mink and sable
Nutria	South American type which has recently become popular
Opossum	Sometimes used to imitate Russian sable
Otter	Rare and costly type which has recently become popular
Rabbit	Commonly used to imitate more costly furs
Raccoon	Sheared raccoon popular
Sable	Rare and costly type from northern Asia
Seal	Fur seal the preferred type
Skunk	Very durable type of fur
Squirrel	Commonly used to imitate various furs

turies ago the Chinese raised a special type of sheep. They used the robes made from the hides of these sheep in religious ceremonies.

It's true, however, that fur farming wasn't common before 1900. About this time a Canadian farm began to produce some fox furs. These foxes were bred from the common red fox, but they had special color patterns.

People knew them as silver fox, cross fox, and black fox. Later on, another special type called platina (*plah*-teen-ah) fox was developed on a farm in Norway.

Fox farming soon became popular. These animals are now raised in Canada, northern Europe, and the northern part of the United States. The blue fox is raised in Alaska. It's a

Fig. 41-2. Many of the furs that reach the market today come from fur farms.

bluish-black color phase of the Arctic fox.

As you probably know, minks are also raised on many fur farms. Other fur-bearers such as muskrats, beavers, skunks, and raccoons have been raised, but not always at a profit.

Fur-farming is no hit-and-miss business. Fur raisers must choose breeding stock with care. They must feed the animals the right foods. They must protect them against parasites and diseases. Their fur must be taken during cold weather when the pelts are at their best. When all this is done, the product is good. In fact, the furs may be even better than those of wild animals.

Why do fur coats cost so much? A fur coat may cost several hundred dollars or it may cost several thousand dollars. It depends on how rare the skins are and how much work goes into making the coat.

Let's take a medium-priced fur like muskrat. Here's what happens before you buy it made up into a coat.

First, good raw hides must be bought for the job. The raw hides are then stretched, cleaned, and dried. Then they're carefully tanned. This turns the skins into leather and helps preserve the hair.

When the tanning is over, a worker scrapes and rubs the hides as they dry. You see, they mustn't ever get stiff and hard as they dry. Then, they're shaved down so the thickness is the same. Next, a skilled workman cuts them into strips about an inch wide. After the fur is cut, another workman matches and sews the strips together. He has to do this carefully so the seams won't show. Then, the skins are tailored according to a pattern. Finally, a lining is sewed in. Now the coat is ready to be sold.

See what a lot of work goes into making a fur coat? The raw hides are really only the beginning. More than half of the cost is due to the manufacturing.

You'll pay more for a mink coat than for a muskrat. It takes from 50 to 80 mink skins to make one coat, depending on the length. The matching process here is even more careful, because both color and size of the skins are important.

Fig. 41-3. Hides are cleaned, tanned, softened, and trimmed before they are made into garments.

CHECK YOUR FACTS . . .

Number 1 to 6 on a sheet of paper, For each item in Column A *select the best answer in* Column B.

Column A	Column B
1. Cross fox	a. Used largely to imitate more costly furs
2. Chinchilla	b. Rare and costly type from South America
3. Blue fox	c. Found only in Australia
4. Sable	d. From jungles of various tropical countries
5. Squirrel	e. Rare type of fur-bearer from Asia
6. Beaver	f. Color phase of Arctic fox
	g. Color phase of red fox
	h. Once common along many streams of North America

IN A NUTSHELL

Men have used animals for centuries. At first, they merely hunted and fished. Now we raise animals so that we may have a greater supply.

We still take many fish from the oceans, lakes, and rivers. They're a good addition to the diet, and a source of vitamin oils.

Toads, frogs, and salamanders are amphibians. Lizards, snakes, turtles, and alligators are reptiles. The amphibians are generally useful, and so are some reptiles — even certain snakes.

Birds are a group of animals which have special structures for flying.

Most birds are useful. This is because they eat weed seeds, and insect and rodent pests.

The mammals include most of our large land animals. Like birds, mammals are warm-blooded and have four-chambered hearts. One mammal group is made up of rodents. Some rodents are useful as fur-bearers. But other rodents, such as rats and mice, are among our worst pests. Another mammal group is made up of the flesh eaters or carnivores. Several members of the carnivore group are valuable sources of furs.

Man began to domesticate animals very early. The idea was to have more supplies of foods and other materials. Most of our domestic animals are birds and mammals.

WHAT DO THESE WORDS MEAN?

Amphibian	Reptile	Tannin
Carnivore	Rodent	Vitamin
Mammal	Salamander	Vertebrate
Pit viper	Tadpole	Whalebone

ASK YOURSELF . . .

1. Why are fish and shellfish a desirable addition to your diet?
2. Why are we better able to market fresh fish today than half a century ago?
3. What kinds of oils do we get from fish?
4. How does stream pollution affect the fish supply?
5. Why are most amphibians useful?
6. What poisonous snakes do we find in the United States?
7. What special structures do birds use for flying?
8. Why are most birds useful?
9. (a) Why are house rats and house mice pests? (b) How can you control them?
10. (a) What gnawing mammals and what flesh-eating mammals are useful? (b) Why?
11. Why did man begin to domesticate animals at an early date?
12. In what ways does a newly domesticated animal differ from one that has been domesticated for a long time?

13. What measures do we use to improve our stocks of domestic animals?

14. Why is it desirable that a domestic animal eat foods that man doesn't eat?

15. (a) Where do we get most of our leathers used today? (b) How are these leathers made?

16. What fur-bearers are commonly raised on farms?

17. Why do fur garments cost as much as they do?

GETTING THE FACTS . . .

1. Visit your local fish market or markets. Find out what kinds of commercial fish they sell. Find out where these fish come from.

2. Visit a fish hatchery if one is nearby. Learn how eggs are hatched and how the young fish are raised. Find out when and how lakes or streams are stocked.

3. With the aid of your teacher, examine a fresh fish. Locate the fins, gills, and the larger internal organs.

4. Wrap a small goldfish in moist cotton and attach it to a microscope slide with a rubber band. Use a projector or a microscope to watch the flow of blood cells in blood vessels of the fish tail.

5. In the spring of the year collect a few frog eggs. Allow them to hatch in your school aquarium. Watch the development of the tadpoles from day to day.

6. With the aid of your teacher, dissect a preserved frog. Locate the more important internal organs.

7. With the aid of your teacher, examine an anti-venom (snake-bite) kit. Learn the uses of all of the items in this kit.

8. Save some wing and leg bones of a chicken. Cut them in two with a saw. Study their hollow structure. If you have a bird skeleton at hand, study the way in which bones are joined together. The result is strength and light weight.

9. Observe the skeleton of any mammal. Note especially the structure of the backbone, and the bones which are in the front and hind limbs.

10. Make a list of the mammals which live or have lived in your locality. Which have become scarcer? Which have become more common? Which can you no longer find? What new types has man brought in?

11. Using pictures from advertisements, prepare a poster which shows the various ways in which leathers are used today. You may also be able to get samples of different kinds of leathers.

12. Visit a tannery if you can arrange such a trip. Observe the various steps in the making of leathers. It may also be possible to visit a factory where furs are being processed or fur garments are being made.

13. If a fur farm is nearby, try to arrange a visit. Study the ways in which the animals are housed, fed, and protected against disease.

14. Find as much as you can about the fish and game laws of your state and write a report about them.

Books You May Like . . .

Brown, A. W. A. *INSECT CONTROL BY CHEM—ICALS.* John Wiley and Sons, New York. 1951. A book for the experts, but a valuable source of facts concerning the effects of various poisons on insects and plants.

Burt, W. H. and Grossenheider, R. P. *A FIELD GUIDE TO THE MAMMALS.* Houghton Mifflin Co., Boston. 1952. A book with color to help the user identify the mammals found in the United States.

Ditmars, Raymond L. *REPTILES OF THE WORLD.* The Macmillan Co., New York. 1946. A standard reference work dealing with the structures, habits, and importance of reptiles.

Hamilton, W. J. *AMERICAN MAMMALS.* The McGraw-Hill Book Co., New York. 1939. A good book on the mammals which gives special attention to hibernation, migration, population, and their economic importance.

Harpster, Hilda T. *THE INSECT WORLD.* The Viking Press, New York. 1947. Interesting reading for the beginner on the structure and behavior of various types.

Hylander, Clarence J. *SEA AND SHORE.* The Macmillan Co., New York. 1950. A useful reference on marine plant life, and such animals as corals, sea anemones, clams, oysters, snails, starfishes, sea urchins, crabs, shrimps, and lobters.

Miner, Roy W. *FIELD BOOK OF SEASHORE LIFE.* G. P. Putnam's Sons, New York. 1950. A useful reference on animals of the shore and shallow sea.

Robertson, Gladys Vondy, and Graham, Vera. *STRANGE SEA LIFE.* Henry Holt and Co., New York. 1950. In this fascinating and revealing book, the reader is introduced to various and unusual kind of fish and other sea life.

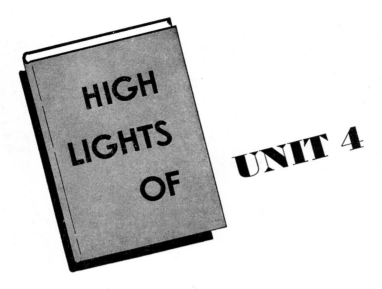

HIGH LIGHTS OF UNIT 4

There are many animals in your environment. Some are useful. Others are pests, or are of little importance. Man's problem is to make the best use of useful animals, and to control the pests.

Many of the invertebrate animals are useful because they're parts of food chains. But some of the small animals cause diseases. The worm parasites are important because they affect the welfare of man, other animals, and plants. From oysters and clams we get food, pearls, and shell products. Crayfish, lobsters, crabs, and shrimp are also important sources of food. Some types of insects are useful, but many species are pests.

The animals with backbones (vertebrates) include the fish, amphibians, reptiles, birds, and mammals. Fish taken from oceans, lakes, and rivers are still a valuable factor in our food supply. They're also a source of oils and fertilizers. Most amphibians are useful, and so are many reptiles. But a few reptiles are pests.

Most birds are useful because they eat either weed seeds, insect pests, or rodent pests. Such mammals as house rats and house mice are pests, but many other mammals are useful fur-bearers, or sources of food, leather, and other products.

Unit 5

Your Body

and

How It Works

Ed was broken-hearted when the coach told him he was too light to make the football team. Jim, who had already made the team, tried to cheer him up.

"You drink lots of milk, fella," Jim told him, " and get to bed earlier and eat more of the right food. You'll soon gain enough to make the second team, anyway."

"Easy enough for you to talk," grumbled Ed, " you made the first string. What have you got that I haven't? Aren't we twins?"

"For one thing, I've got more muscle. And I've got steadier nerves. Now, do you see what smoking does?" Jim asked him. " I told you when you started you'd be sorry. But no, you were the wise guy!"

"O.K.," Ed assured him, " I've just smoked my last cigarette. And I mean that! From now on, I'm drinking a quart of milk a day. I'm going to be in bed by ten o'clock and get over nine hours of sleep."

"Good guy," Jim patted him on the back. " Come on home, and let's ask Mom if we can have an early dinner."

Topic 1

HOW YOUR BODY IS PUT TOGETHER

Like to play tennis, baseball, or golf? What about running and other track events? You enjoy some of these sports, but how well do you do them?

Whether or not you're good at sports depends partly on your body form. It also depends on how well your muscles work and how well they control your body actions.

Another aid to success in sports is knowing how your body is put together. Knowing this, you can learn how to avoid injuring it and what to do if something happens you couldn't avoid. It's yours, and your duty is to take the best possible care of it.

AMONG THE NEW WORDS FOR THIS TOPIC

- **ABDOMEN** (ab-*doh*-men). Cavity in the trunk of the body below the diaphragm.
- **CARTILAGE** (*kahr*-ti-lij). An elastic tissue which makes up most of the skeleton of the very young animal. Becomes largely changed to bone in the adult.
- **CHEST CAVITY.** Cavity in the trunk of the body above the diaphragm.
- **DIAPHRAGM** (*dye*-uh-fram). A muscular wall dividing the chest cavity from the abdomen.
- **SPECIAL SENSES.** The senses of sight, hearing, taste, smell, and touch.
- **VERTEBRA** (*ver*-tuh-bruh). One of the small bones of which the backbone is made.

CHAPTER 42

What Are the Regions of Your Body?

Why is man now the dominant form of life in the world? Think carefully before you try to answer this question. There's more than one reason why man has been able to get along so well.

For instance, what about man's food habits? He likes certain things and he doesn't like others. The human body can use many different kinds of food. In fact, man likes a variety of plant and animal materials. Does that give him an advantage? Decidedly, yes! It means that he finds food where lots of animals would starve.

What about the human brain? No need to tell you it's better than the brains of animals. Man profits from his past experiences. He invents tools and machines. He's learned to control many of the things and forces around him.

Don't forget his hands. Because of the thumb, man can use his hands to do all sorts of things. They're the tools of his brain.

Man's body has a lot to do with his habits. It also has a lot to do with his success.

The general regions of your body. Look at Fig. 42-1. It shows the general body regions. They are, of course, much like those of animals which have backbones. Biologists call these general regions of the body the *head, neck, trunk, arms,* and *legs.*

Now look at Fig. 42-2. It shows the *body cavity.* In the trunk region, a muscular **diaphragm** (*dye*-uh-fram) divides this cavity into two parts. The part of the cavity in the upper trunk is the chest. The part of the cavity in the lower trunk is the **abdomen** (ab-*doh*-men).

The neck and the head. Now look at Fig. 42-3. There you see the human **brain.** This controls your **nervous system.** From the brain, a **spinal cord** runs down through the trunk.

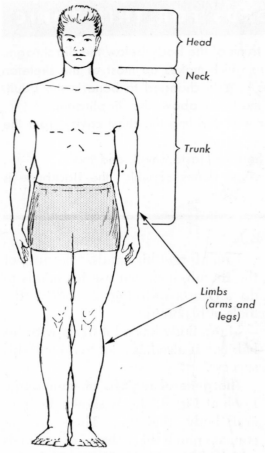

Fig. 42-1. Diagram to show the general regions of the human body.

The backbone protects the spinal cord. The spinal cord is also a control center for many body actions.

Most of your special senses are represented in the head region. These five special senses are: (**1**) *sight;* (**2**) *hearing;* (**3**) *smell;* (**4**) *taste;* and (**5**) *touch*. Of course, touch is represented in all parts of your body; for instance, in the fingers. The other four special senses, however, are in the head region.

Note that the *eyes* (organs for see-

ing) are in deep sockets. They're protected by the eyebrows, eyelids, and eyelashes. The *ears* (organs for hearing) catch sound waves and send them inward to cells in the brain. The *nose openings* are right above the mouth. You can smell food as you put it in your mouth. Smell and taste often warn you when food is spoiled. The *tongue* is the center for tasting.

Now look at the *neck region* in Fig. 42-3. Muscles in your neck let you turn your head so you can see or hear better. Part of your backbone and part of your spinal cord are in this region. Important blood vessels and nerves also pass through your neck. So do passageways, or tubes, leading to your lungs and stomach. The neck region also contains some glands. These *glands* secrete substances that are used in various parts of your body.

The trunk region. Look again at Fig. 42-2. Remember, the chest cavity is part of the body cavity above the diaphragm. It's more or less enclosed by the ribs and the backbone. The ribs are attached to the backbone.

" Yes, but what are the main organs of the chest cavity? " you'll ask.

There are two main groups in the chest cavity: (**1**) the heart; and (**2**) the lungs. The *heart* pumps blood through blood vessels to all the tissues of the body. In the *lungs,* the blood gets new supplies of oxygen and gets rid of carbon dioxide waste.

The abdomen, on the other hand, contains quite a few organs. The *stomach* and the *intestines* are here.

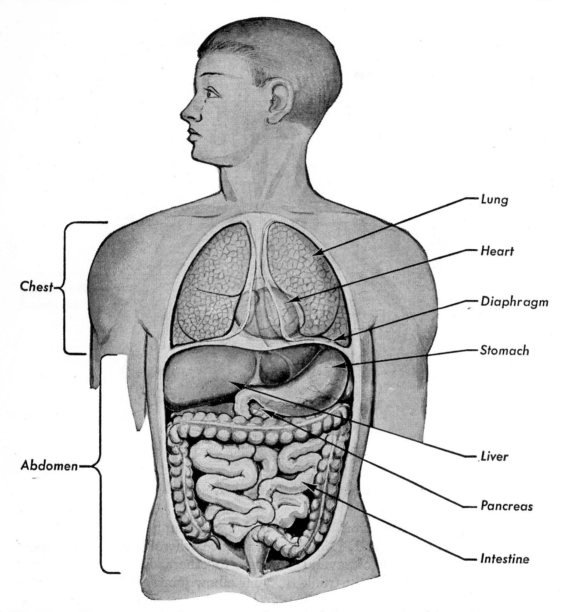

Lung

Heart

Diaphragm

Stomach

Chest

Liver

Pancreas

Abdomen

Intestine

Fig. 42-2. The human body cavity, and some of the organs in this cavity.

So are the *liver* and the *pancreas* (*pan*-kree-us). All four of these organs have to do with digestion and the uses of foods.

The *kidneys* lie outside the body cavity, next to the muscles of the back. They remove wastes from the blood. Tubes from the kidneys enter the abdomen and carry liquid wastes to the *bladder.* From the bladder, these liquid wastes are passed outside of the body.

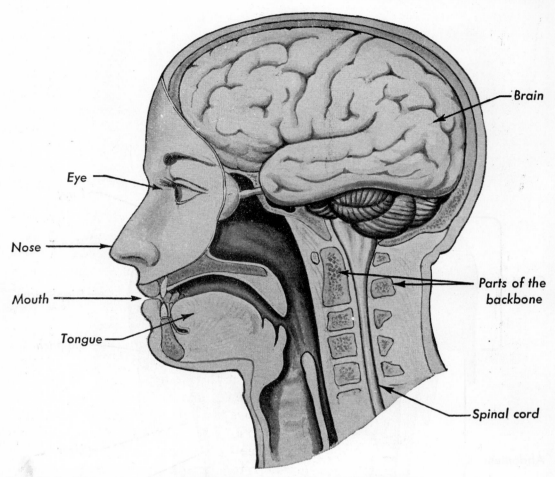

Fig. 42-3. Diagram to show structures of the human head region.

The limbs include the arms and legs. Look again at Fig. 42-1. Note that the arm is made up of several parts. That part attached to the trunk is the *upper arm*. Then comes the *forearm*, the *wrist*, and the *hand*. The hand includes a *thumb* and four *fingers*.

What about the legs? Their regions are: *thigh, shin, ankle,* and *foot.* The foot normally has five *toes.*

Sprains and dislocations. These can be bad, and very painful. Your body has a number of joints. A *joint* is a place where two or more bones come together. For instance, there's your elbow joint. It has a hinge that raises or lowers your forearm.

Ever sprained a thumb, a knee, or an ankle? Probably so, because sprains are common. A *sprain* occurs when the muscles at a joint are stretched too much. Blood vessels may be injured, too. There's usually swelling and pain. A bad sprain often needs a long period of rest to heal.

A *dislocation* occurs when the bones at a joint are pulled out of place. Their ends don't come together in a normal way. So, the doctor has to bring the ends of the bones to their right positions. Usually muscles and other tissues are injured, too. Then you use a sling or cast to support the joint until the tissues have healed.

CHECK YOUR FACTS . . .

Number 1 to 6 on a sheet of paper. For each group of items in Column A, *select the best answer in* Column B.

Column A	Column B
1. Kidneys	a. Separates the chest cavity from the abdomen
2. Lungs	
3. Diaphragm	
	b. Part of the digestive system where food is absorbed
	c. Not in either chest cavity or abdomen
	d. In the head region but not a part of digestive system
	e. In the chest cavity

Column A	Column B
4. Lungs	a. Located in the head and a part of digestive system
5. Spinal cord	
6. Kidneys	
	b. Remove liquid waste from the blood
	c. A control center for certain actions of nerves and muscles
	d. Pumps blood to the tissues of the body
	e. Where the blood receives new supplies of oxygen

CHAPTER 43

Your Body Has Over 200 Bones

Jim and Ed were in one of the workrooms of the museum. They were watching Mr. Thomas, who was sorting out some bones.

"What are those bones?" asked Jim.

"Why," answered Mr. Thomas, "they're part of a human skeleton. They probably belonged to a man who died before the first settlers came to America."

"How can you tell all that from just a few bones?" asked Ed.

"Well, the bones don't give us the whole story," replied Mr. Thomas, "but they do tell us some things. Notice this skull. The general shape, the jaws, and the teeth show that it belonged to a human. Now count the teeth. There are 32 of them. A young person would only have 28."

"Yes, I see that," said Ed, "but how do you know it wasn't a woman?"

"Various ways," responded Mr. Thomas. "For instance, look at these hip bones. The space between them would be larger in a woman. These bones belonged to a man who had narrow hips."

Your body framework. Mr. Thomas didn't have time to tell the boys the whole story. But from his remarks you get some idea about bones. The skeleton of one species is different from the skeleton of another species. Sometimes the skeleton of a

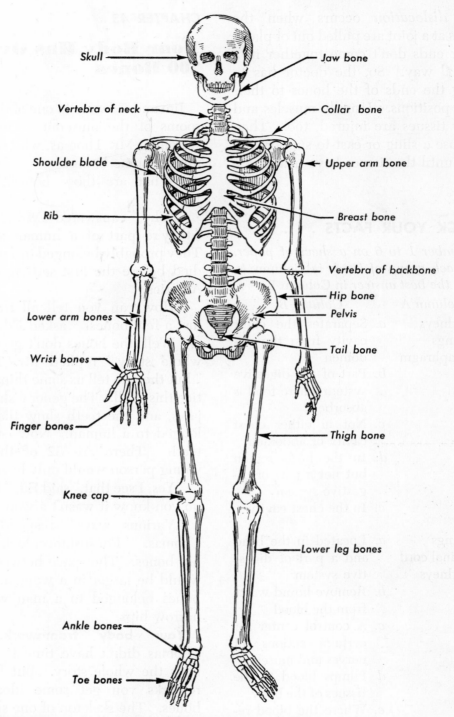

Skull

Vertebra of neck

Shoulder blade

Rib

Lower arm bones

Wrist bones

Finger bones

Knee cap

Ankle bones

Toe bones

Jaw bone

Collar bone

Upper arm bone

Breast bone

Vertebra of backbone

Hip bone

Pelvis

Tail bone

Thigh bone

Lower leg bones

Fig. 43-1. Diagram to show bones of the human skeleton.

male is different from the skeleton of a female. The skeleton of an adult is different from the skeleton of the young, too. Often you can tell quite a lot about an animal just by examining its skeleton.

The adult human skeleton is made up of about 200 bony parts. You see them in Fig. 43-1. This skeleton serves several purposes: (*1*) it gives shape and support to the body; (*2*) it more or less surrounds and protects important internal organs; (*3*) it forms a necessary place of attachment for muscles that move the body parts.

The ends of the long bones are covered with *cartilage* (*kahr*-ti-lij). Cartilage isn't nearly as hard as bone. Fig. 43-2 shows a diagram of cartilage. You see that it contains a few cells, and a lot of solid materials that cells have secreted.

As you grow older, some of the parts that were once cartilage become changed into bone. In a child, for instance, there's more cartilage at the ends of bones than in an adult. Bone is harder because it contains deposits of mineral materials, especially lime. You probably know that young bones, being softer, can be bent somewhat. Older bones are generally more brittle, however. That's why older people can break a bone more readily.

The human skull. Now look at Fig. 43-1 again. The *skull* is made up of the bones in the head region. It rests on the upper end of the backbone. Notice that the bones of the skull completely surround the brain. This protection is important because the brain

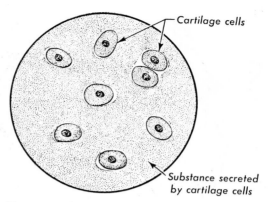

Fig. 43-2. Diagram to show the nature of cartilage. The solid material has been formed by the cartilage cells.

is a delicate structure. When any of these bones around the brain cavity is cracked or broken, the skull is fractured.

The bones which form the upper jaw are firmly attached to the skull. But as you know, the lower jaw is movable. Both upper and lower jaws have bony sockets where the teeth are.

What's your backbone? Your *backbone* is made up of small bones called *vertebrae* (*ver*-tuh-bree). One vertebra appears in Fig. 43-3. You can see it consists of a solid, central mass of bone. Above this are bony processes which surround a cavity. The spinal cord passes through this cavity.

There are seven vertebrae in the neck region, and twelve in the region of the chest. These twelve vertebrae in the chest are attached to the *ribs.* There are five vertebrae without ribs in the small of the back. Then come five more vertebrae, more or less grown together, and attached to the *hip bones.* Finally, there are four

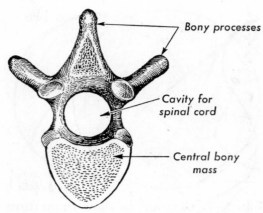

Bony processes

Cavity for
spinal cord

Central bony
mass

**Fig. 43-3. A backbone is made up of
parts like this. Each part is a vertebra.**

small bones, also more or less grown
together, which form the *tail bone.*

The ribs and breast bone. Now
look again at Fig. 43-1. The twelve
pairs of ribs are all attached to the
backbone. They curve around the
cavity of the chest. The first ten pairs
of ribs are also attached to the *breast
bone.* The eleventh and twelfth pairs
of ribs don't reach the breast bone.
They're what people call "floating
ribs."

The breast bone is a flat bone in
front of the chest region. It's really
made up of several bones that are
more or less joined together. You can
see that the backbone, ribs, and breast
bone form a sort of framework around
the cavity of the chest.

The shoulder and arm. Now look
at the shoulder in Fig. 43-1. There
are two bones in each shoulder. One
is the *collar bone.* This is attached
to the breast bone and extends out to
the point of the shoulder. The other
is the *shoulder blade,* which is attached at the point of the shoulder

only. Otherwise, the shoulder blade
is just supported by muscles in the
back.

You can see at once that the collar
bone is the main support of the shoulder. A broken collar bone makes the
shoulder and arm quite useless things,
for the time being.

As you can see by looking again at
Fig. 43-1, there's only one bone in the
upper arm. But what about the forearm? You'll see two there. And in
the wrist you'll find eight small bones.
Next come the five main bones of the
hand, extending from the wrist to the
knuckles. Finally, there are two
bones in the thumb and three in each
of the four fingers.

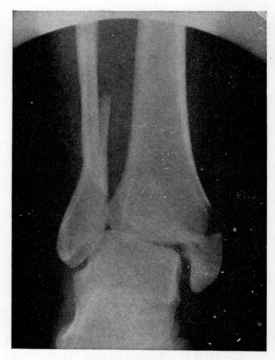

**Fig. 43-4. An X-ray photograph show-
ing a fracture of one of the bones in a
leg before setting.**

What holds you up? The bones of the hips and legs, of course! Those in the hip region are joined together forming the *pelvis* (*pel*-vis). The pelvis acts as a cup-like support for the organs in the abdomen. The leg bones are also attached to the pelvis.

You can see in Fig. 43-1 that there's just one long bone in the thigh. Between this and the two lower leg bones is the *knee cap.* Doesn't look like much, does it? But this small, flat bone is useful in all activities where you use your legs. The ankle contains seven small bones and the instep region of the foot has five.

Broken bones aren't fun. Any break in a bone is a *fracture.* You can get a fracture from a hard blow or a fall. In many cases the break isn't complete and what you have then is called a *simple fracture.* If a fracture of this kind is properly supported and protected, it usually heals up quickly.

But in some cases, it's a *displaced fracture* like the one you see in Fig. 43-4. Here, the broken ends of the bones are out of position. The doctor has a harder job here. He has to get the bone ends back where they belong. Then, he wraps the bone in a cast until it heals. This helps to protect and support the broken ends.

Maybe you've heard of *compound fractures.* At least, if you've ever had one, you know they can be serious. In a compound fracture, the ends of the broken bone have pushed out through the skin. This makes an open wound. There's danger then that germs will get in.

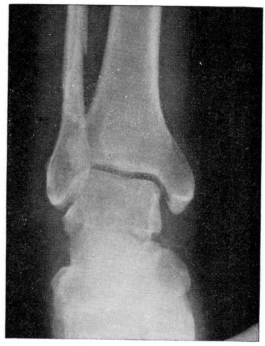

Fig. 43-5. This shows the same leg as in Fig. 43-4 after setting of the bone.

CHECK YOUR FACTS . . .

Number 1 to 6 on a sheet of paper. Select the best answer for each item.

1. The knee cap is a bone of the (arm, leg, skull) . . . ? . . .

2. In each shoulder, the shoulder bone attached to the breast bone is the (collar bone, shoulder blade, pelvis) . . . ? . . .

3. When a bone is broken and the broken ends push out through the skin, the injury is a (simple fracture, dislocation, compound fracture) . . . ? . . .

4. The bones of a child are (harder, softer, heavier) . . . ? . . . than an adult's.

5. The ends of long bones are covered with (vertebrae, cartilage, fractures) . . . ? . . .

6. The twelve pairs of ribs are all attached to the (backbone, breast bone, shoulder blade) . . . ? . . .

CHAPTER 44

How Do Your Muscles Work?

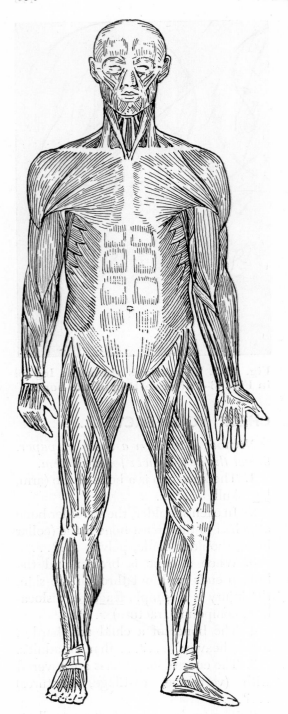

In Chapter 5 you read about Amoeba. And in Chapter 27 you learned some things about Paramecium. Both of them are one-celled animals. Yet they're able to move about. Their motion results from the movement of the protoplasm in the cells.

Your own body contains a lot of cells. Some of them have special work to do. Nerve cells, for instance, carry nerve messages. They do this job well, but they have very limited power to contract (shorten). On the other hand, muscle cells have good ability to contract. We say that in complex bodies like your own there's *division of labor* among cells.

When you talk, play a game, or walk, your muscle cells do work. They do work which moves parts of your body such as your arm when you throw a ball. They also do the work which moves your whole body from place to place, as when you walk or run. At the same time, other cells in your body also do work. For example, nerve cells from your brain and spinal cord carry messages to the muscles.

What is a muscle? Can you answer this question? Of course, you know in a general way, but do you know the whole story?

You see several muscles in Fig. 44-1. They're the muscles which lie just under the skin. By this time you can

Fig. 44-1. Diagram to show muscles of the human body.

probably guess that many cells make up each muscle. Most of these cells are *muscle cells.* The leg of lamb, roast beef, or steak you buy at the butcher's are mostly muscle cells.

But some other kinds of cells are also present in a muscle. For instance, there are blood vessels. The blood brings food and oxygen to the muscle cells. It carries away the wastes and heat which are given off when muscle cells do work. Then too, there must be nerves. Nerves control the action of muscle cells. As a result, many muscle cells work or act together.

Your body has three kinds of muscles: (*1*) *voluntary;* (*2*) *involuntary;* and (*3*) *heart.*

Voluntary muscles. The muscles you see in Fig. 44-1 are *voluntary muscles.* This means that you can make them work when you wish. Suppose you decide to walk across the room. A group of your voluntary muscles does the job.

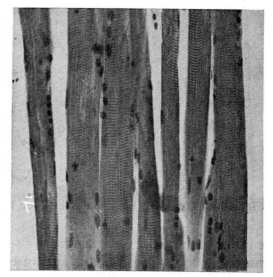

Fig. 44-2. Greatly enlarged photograph of voluntary muscle cells.

A voluntary muscle is made up of cells like those in Fig. 44-2. Notice the heavy stripes. Notice also that each cell has several nuclei.

Each muscle cell is surrounded by a covering of tough *connective tissue.* This connective tissue is joined together throughout the muscle. At the

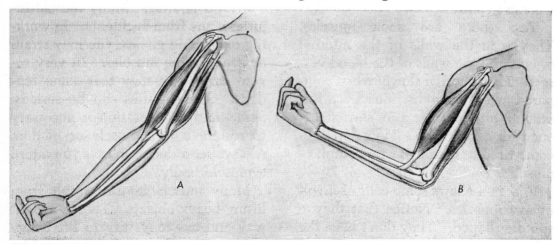

Fig. 44-3. One set of muscles straightens the arm as in A. Another set of muscles bends the arm as in B.

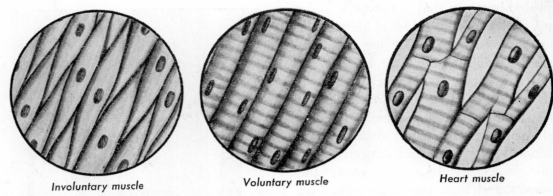

Involuntary muscle   *Voluntary muscle*   *Heart muscle*

Fig. 44-4. Diagram to show the three types of muscle cells from the human body.

ends of the muscle, the connective tissue forms **tendons.** These tendons are attached to bones of the skeleton, or to other muscles.

So when a muscle shortens, it pulls on another muscle or on a bone. Usually there's another muscle which pulls in the other direction. Thus, one set of muscles bends your elbow, and another set straightens the arm out again. This is shown in Fig. 44-3.

Involuntary muscles. Now you may ask: "Are there muscles which we can't control?"

Yes, there are such muscles. They're in the walls of the internal organs and the walls of the blood vessels. They shorten slowly when compared with voluntary muscles. But *involuntary muscles* can stay shortened for a long time. They don't become tired as quickly as do voluntary muscles.

Fig. 44-4 shows some cells of involuntary muscles. Notice that they're spindle-shaped. They don't have the heavy stripes of voluntary muscle cells.

Your first guess might be that involuntary muscles aren't important. You'd be wrong. Proper function of many internal organs depends on the slow but steady work of these muscles.

Heart muscle. Finally, there's a third kind of muscle tissue. It's found in the wall of the heart. The cells of this muscle are striped. But the muscle is *not* voluntary. Its action goes on all the time. But it is influenced or affected by your nerves.

Muscle injuries. Many muscle injuries come from accidents. In working or playing games, you may strain or bruise some muscles. In very severe cases, you may tear some tendons. Such injuries can be serious. Sometimes an operation is necessary to restore a torn muscle or tendon. Always see a doctor in case you injure a muscle badly.

Many muscle injuries result from lifting heavy objects. There's a right way and a wrong way to lift heavy things. These ways are shown in Fig. 44-5.

RIGHT   WRONG

Fig. 44-5. The right way and the wrong way to pick up a heavy object.   The wrong way can result in serious muscle injury.

" Charley horse " is the name athletes give to an overstrained muscle in the thigh or arm.   To a football player, it usually means that he has strained a thigh muscle.   To a baseball player, it may also mean that he has strained an arm muscle.   The result is stiffness and soreness.   Sometimes a " charley horse " is made worse by a bruise.   Tiny blood vessels in the strained area have been broken. Blood seeps out of them and forms a black-and-blue spot.   A " charley horse " may be mild or severe.   Usually rest, heat, and massage are used to relieve the stiffness and soreness.

CHECK YOUR FACTS . . .

Number 1 to 6 on a sheet of paper. Mark each of the following items True *or* False.

1. A cell or fiber of voluntary muscle contains more than one nucleus. T

2. The cells of heart muscle have no stripes, and are under voluntary control. F

3. The actual work which a muscle cell does is to shorten. T

4. Muscle cells receive supplies of food and oxygen from the blood. T

5. Involuntary muscle shortens more rapidly than does voluntary muscle. T

6. In case you injure a muscle badly you should see a doctor. T

Man has an advantage over other living things because he's intelligent.   His diet is mixed, and thus he can eat foods many other living things can't.   His body is divided into a head, trunk, and limbs.   His special sense organs and his brain are located in the head region.

The trunk is divided into a chest and an abdomen. The lungs and heart are in the chest.   The main digestive organs are in the abdomen.

The human limbs are jointed. A joint is a place where two or more bones come together. You can injure them by sprains or dislocations.

There are about 200 bones in the human skeleton. This skeleton is made up of bones and cartilage. It supports the body, forms a place of attachment for the muscles, and protects the vital organs. The skeleton includes the skull, backbone, ribs, bones of the shoulders and hips, and bones of the arms and legs.

All movement of your body is the work of muscles. A muscle is made up of muscle cells, together with connective tissue and cells of nerves and blood vessels. You control the action of voluntary muscles. But you can't control the action of involuntary muscle or of heart muscle.

WHAT DO THESE WORDS MEAN?

Abdomen	Dislocation	Skeleton
Body cavity	Fracture	Skull
Bone	Heart muscle	Special senses
Breast bone	Involuntary muscle	Spinal cord
Cartilage	Joint	Sprain
"Charley horse"	Muscle	Tendon
Chest	Pelvis	Vertebra
Diaphragm	Shoulder blade	Voluntary muscle

ASK YOURSELF . . .

1. Give some reasons why man is now the dominant form of life in this world.
2. (a) Name those organs that are located in your chest region. (b) What organs are located in your abdomen? (c) What separates your chest cavity from your abdomen?
3. Where are your brain and spinal cord located?
4. What are the functions of your brain and spinal cord?
5. List the five special senses which man has.
6. Where are the organs of each of these five special senses located?
7. How would you know whether you had a sprain or a dislocation?
8. Describe three general functions of the human skeleton.

9. (a) In what ways are bone and cartilage related?   (b) Why are you more apt to break a bone the older you are?

10. (a) What bones make up your backbone?   (b) How is your backbone related to your spinal cord?

11. What structures make up one of your muscles?

12. (a) What substances do your muscles get from your blood vessels?   (b) What substances do your blood vessels carry away from your muscles?

13. (a) What's the difference between a simple fracture and a compound fracture?   (b) Why is a compound fracture more dangerous?

14. (a) Why should you see a doctor if you have a muscle injury?   (b) What can cause you to have a muscle injury?   (c) What is a " charley horse "?

GETTING THE FACTS . . .

1. Examine a chart of the human body. Find and study the regions and structures described in Chapter 42.

2. Examine the skeletons of a bird and a mammal. Compare them as to: (a) size of bones; (b) number of bones that are joined together; (c) the way in which the forelimbs are supported; and (d) their weight.

3. Get several beef, pork, or chicken bones. Let them dry out, and then weigh them. Now soak them for three days in 10% hydrochloric acid. Dry the bones and weigh them again. Have the bones become softer or harder? How much weight is lost? What has been removed from the bones?

4. After reading directions in the *Red Cross First Aid Textbook* practice: (a) splinting and bandaging a " broken arm "; and (b) bandaging a " sprained ankle."

5. Get an animal joint from your butcher. Examine it to see how the bones are held together. Do you find any cartilage? Any tendons? What is bone marrow?

6. Get a complete voluntary muscle from your butcher, or remove one from the leg of a preserved frog. Note the presence of blood vessels and nerves. Observe the continuous sheath of connective tissue, and the tendons at the ends of the muscle.

7. If you have microscope slides and a microscope, examine cells of: (a) voluntary muscle; (b) involuntary muscle; and (c) heart muscle. Note how they differ as to shape, stripes, and number of nuclei.

8. Do various " setting up " exercises. Feel the contraction of your own arm and leg muscles as you do these exercises.

Topic 2

HOW YOUR BODY USES FOODS

Here are the "basic seven" groups of foods. The one at the top left includes the green and yellow vegetables. Just below it is the Vitamin C group, which includes citrus fruits. Then you see a group containing potatoes, and other vegetables and fruits. Follow on and note the milk and milk products group; the meat, poultry, fish, and egg group; the bread and cereal group; and lastly the butter and butter substitute group.

If you eat certain foods from each group every day, you'll be eating a *balanced diet*. It's a diet that includes all the foods your body needs to keep you in the best of health.

AMONG THE NEW WORDS FOR THIS TOPIC

- **ALLERGY** (*al*-er-jee). A reaction to certain proteins in foods, dusts, and other things.
- **CALORIE** (*kal*-or-ee). A unit of energy. Often used to describe the amount of energy in different foods.
- **DIGESTION** (duh-*jes*-chun). The process of changing foods so they become soluble in water, and can be used by the body.
- **HORMONE** (*hor*-moan). A gland secretion which is carried by the blood stream.
- **NARCOTIC** (nar-*kot*-ick). A drug which dulls pain and brings on sleep. Some narcotics are habit-forming.
- **VITAMIN** (*vy*-tuh-min). One of several substances needed for a good diet. Present in certain foods.

CHAPTER 45

What Is Digestion?

Ever hear someone say that " one man's food is another man's poison "?

Well, there's something in this old saying, as you'll see shortly.

All of us differ from each other in certain ways. One way in which we differ is in digestion, and the use of energy.

On the other hand, we're all more or less alike. As far as digestion is concerned, all of us have three things in common: (*1*) a digestive system which includes the same organs or parts; (*2*) a need for foods to provide energy and the materials used in growth and repair; and (*3*) a need for certain minerals and vitamins in our diets.

Your digestive organs. Look at Fig. 45-1. It shows the organs of the digestive system and some glands re-lated to digestion. You can see that food passes from the mouth through the *esophagus* (uh-*sof*-uh-gus) to reach the stomach. Then the food goes through the **small intestine** and the **large intestine.** Solid wastes are passed outside.

While you're about it, look at the liver and pancreas in Fig. 45-1. Both of these glands have ducts which empty into the small intestine. Also note that the *appendix* is at about the point where the small intestine joins the large intestine.

Digestion starts in your mouth. The main structures in your mouth are your **teeth** and your **tongue.** As you can see in Fig. 45-2, you have 32 teeth in your adult set. In each jaw (upper and lower) the teeth are as follows: (*1*) four *incisors* (in-*sy*-zers) across the front of the mouth; these teeth are like chisels and are used in biting and cutting; (2) two *canines* (*kay*-nines) which tend to be pointed.

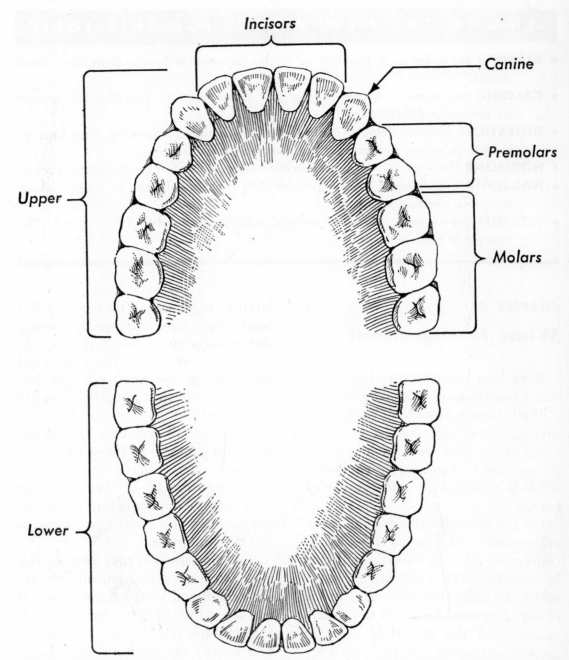

Fig. 45-1. Teeth of a human adult. Incisors and canines are used mostly for biting. The premolars and molars are used to chew the food.

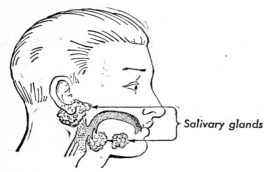

Fig. 45-2. Three pairs of salivary glands discharge saliva into the mouth cavity.

They're used mostly in biting and cutting; (**3**) four *premolars* (two on each side of the jaw). They're used for chewing; and (**4**) six *molars* (three on each side of the jaw). These are used to crush and grind food. The last molar on each side usually comes in later than the others. It's called a "wisdom tooth," but of course it's a third molar.

Your tongue is a muscular structure. You use it in chewing, swallowing, and speaking. On your tongue are the nerve endings of taste. So you also use your tongue to taste foods. You learn to know different tastes like sweet, sour, bitter, and salty.

In your neck region there are three pairs of glands. These secrete *saliva* (sal-*eye*-vah). You can see them in Fig. 45-3. Ducts from these glands carry the saliva to your mouth. This liquid saliva contains an agent (called an *enzyme* [*en*-zyme]) which begins the digestion of starches.

"What's digestion?" you say.

It's the process of changing foods so they become soluble in water. *Soluble* means that they'll dissolve in water. In this soluble form, your blood can absorb the foods. They are carried to cells of the body.

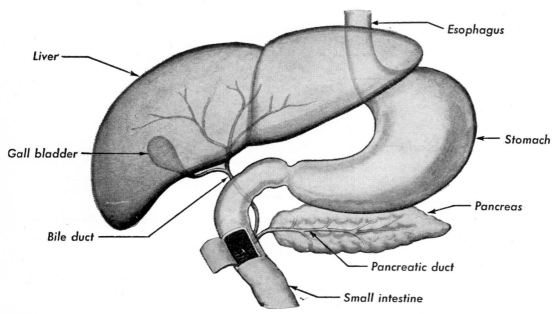

Fig. 45-3. Diagram to show relations of the stomach, intestine, liver, and pancreas.

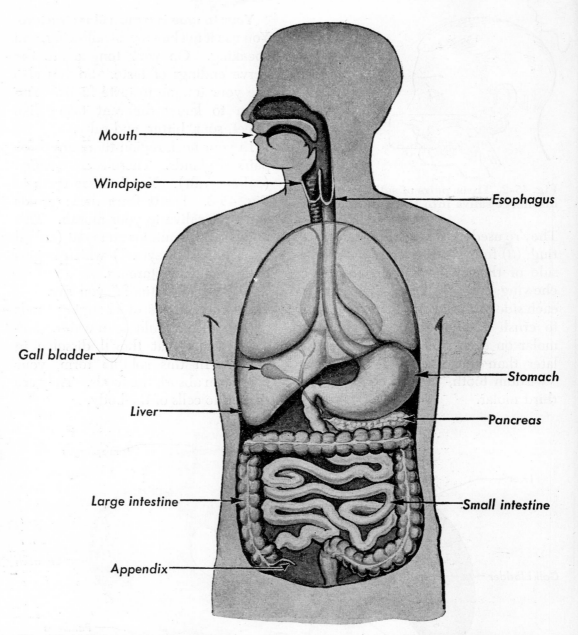

Mouth

Windpipe

Esophagus

Gall bladder

Stomach

Liver

Pancreas

Large intestine

Small intestine

Appendix

Fig. 45-4. Diagram to show the human digestive system and related structures.

Digestion in your stomach. As you've learned, your esophagus passes food on to your stomach. Your stomach is a pear-shaped, hollow organ. Its walls contain glands which secrete digestive fluid. This fluid also contains agents (or enzymes).

Your stomach holds the food you've eaten. Meanwhile, digestion of the food goes on. There's some digestion of starch by the agent in saliva, which comes down from the mouth with the food. But mainly there is digestion by agents in the stomach fluid. As you can see from the chart below, there are three of these stomach agents. These act on three different kinds of foods.

The stomach has two valves. They're just rings of muscle tissue. One of them is at the point where the esophagus enters the stomach. When this valve contracts, the opening is closed. Then food can't back up into the esophagus.

The other stomach valve is at the end where the stomach joins the small intestine. After you've eaten a meal, muscles in your stomach wall contract. The food mass is forced toward the small intestine. The valve stays closed most of the time. But it opens every now and then to let some food pass into the intestine. So in time, the stomach is emptied again.

Digestion continues in the small intestine. Here the food is acted on by two groups of enzymes. This is shown in the chart on this page. One group of three enzymes comes from the pancreas. Another group of enzymes comes from glands in the wall of the

THE STORY OF YOUR DIGESTIVE FLUIDS

Gland	Fluid	Agent (enzyme) in Fluid	Acting on
Salivary glands	Saliva	Ptyalin (*ty*-uh-lin)	Starch (carbohydrates)
Stomach glands	Gastric juice	Rennin Pepsin Gastric lipase (*ly*-pace)	Casein (protein) Proteins Fats
Pancreas	Pancreatic juice	Trypsin (*trip*-sin) Amylopsin (am-ih-*lop*-sin) Lipase (*ly*-pace)	Proteins Carbohydrates Fats
Glands of the small intestine	Intestinal fluid	Erepsin (ee-*rep*-sin) Inverting enzymes	Proteins Carbohydrates
Liver	Bile	None	Fats

intestine. Also coming into the small intestine is the *bile*, from the liver.

The story of the different digestive fluids is shown in the chart on page 205. You can see at a glance just what gland secretes a special fluid. You can see, too, what agents this fluid contains. And you can see what kinds of food the agent acts on. If you study this chart, you'll know more about how digestion works in your own body.

After these agents have done their work, digestion is completed. Of course, not everything that you eat can be digested. Most foods contain some materials that your body can't use. Such materials become a part of solid wastes.

CHECK YOUR FACTS . . .

Number 1 to 6 on a sheet of paper. Select the best item to complete each of the following statements.

1. To be absorbed by the blood, foods must be soluble in (agents, acids, water) . . .?. . .

2. The last molar to come in on each side of your jaw is known as a (premolar, canine, wisdom tooth) . . .?. . .

3. A full set of adult teeth contains (28, 32, 16) . . .?. . . teeth.

4. Agents secreted by the pancreas act on (one, two, three) . . .?. . . different kinds of foods.

5. Saliva is first mixed with food in the (stomach, small intestine, mouth) . . .?. . .

6. After each meal, food in the stomach is kept from passing quickly into the intestines by a (gland, agent, valve) . . .?. . .

CHAPTER 46

How Do You Use Food?

Remember from Chapter 11 that there are three general classes of foods? These are: (*1*) carbohydrates; (*2*) proteins; and (*3*) fats. These materials are also parts of protoplasm. Most foods are mixtures of the three classes but with more of one than another. Lean meat and eggs are largely protein. Bread, cake, waffles, or pancakes are largely carbohydrate. Other foods are shown in Fig. 46-1.

How are foods absorbed? In Chapter 45 you learned that digestion makes foods soluble. Then the blood can absorb (which means to take in) the food. The blood carries the absorbed food to the cells of the body.

What actually happens to the foods? Carbohydrates are broken down to simple sugar. Animal fats and plant oils become fatty acids and glycerin (*glih*-sir-in). Proteins are broken up into the different **amino** (ah-*mee*-no) **acids** of which they're made. Simple sugar, fatty acids, glycerin, and amino acids are absorbed and enter the blood. Then they are carried to the body cells.

Where are foods absorbed? Almost all of them are absorbed in the small intestine. Look at Fig. 46-2. It shows finger-like structures called *villi* (*vill*-eye). Millions of these villi line the inside of the small intestine. Notice that each villus contains a set of blood and lymph vessels. These vessels absorb the digested foods.

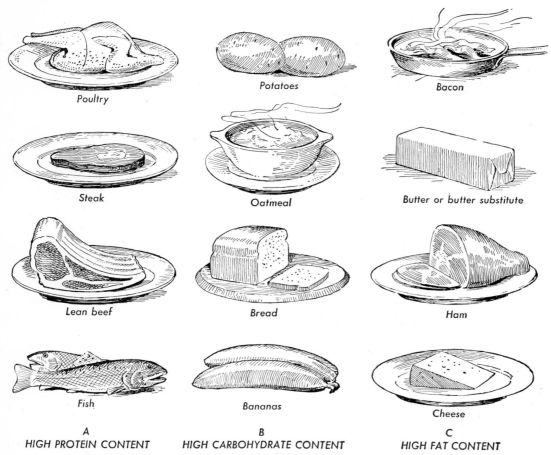

Poultry

Potatoes

Bacon

Steak

Oatmeal

Butter or butter substitute

Lean beef

Bread

Ham

Fish

Bananas

Cheese

A
HIGH PROTEIN CONTENT

B
HIGH CARBOHYDRATE CONTENT

C
HIGH FAT CONTENT

Fig. 46-1. Some foods contain a lot of proteins, some a lot of carbohydrates, and some a lot of fats.

The absorbed food substances are carried to the cells of the body. Here some of them are taken into the cells. They're changed into the proteins, carbohydrates, and fats in these cells.

But suppose the cells of the body don't need all the absorbed foods? Well, as you know, some of them may be stored. Fat is one form in which food is stored. Too much stored fat means you're overweight. In addition, the liver changes sugar into a special substance which it stores.

This substance can be changed back into sugar and used by the cells when needed.

What happens in the large intestine? Now at this point you'll want to ask: "What about absorption in the large intestine?"

Absorption does take place in the large intestine. But it's mostly just absorption of water into the blood stream. As a result, the wastes become more solid. They follow the large intestine to the outside.

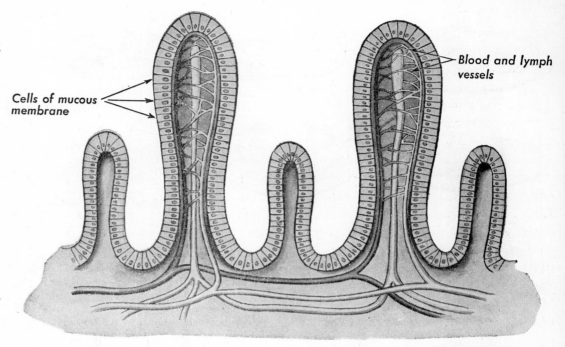

Fig. 46-2. Diagram to show lining of the intestine. The finger-like structures are the villi.

Millions of bacteria live in both the small and large intestine. This is true whether you're sick or well. In fact, some of the bacteria in the intestines may favor digestion. But not all of them. If typhoid fever germs reach the intestines, they can multiply and cause serious illness. You've also learned that many worm parasites may live in the intestines. Do you see now why it's important to dispose safely of human wastes?

Bacteria and your appendix. Look at Fig. 46-3. You see that the *appendix* is attached to a small pouch of the large intestine. This pouch is at the point where the small intestine joins the large intestine. The appendix itself is like a small tube with a closed

end. It's about the size of your little finger.

What's *appendicitis?* It's an infection of the appendix. This means that germs are present, and that they're multiplying. Usually these germs are

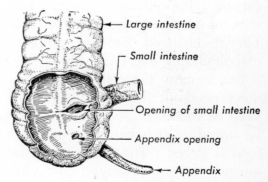

Fig. 46-3. Diagram to show the nature and location of the appendix.

some of the bacteria that are found in the intestines. Naturally, the appendix becomes sore and swollen. Unless a doctor removes it by an operation, there's danger that it will burst. If it does, the infection gets out into the body cavity. Then the chances of getting well safely are much less.

Warning signs of appendicitis include vomiting. There's also soreness and pain in the region of the abdomen. Muscles of the abdomen may contract and get rigid. Better call your doctor immediately when such signs appear. He can decide if an operation is necessary. Never take any laxative or other medicine unless he tells you to. Remember, too, that early treatment may be very necessary.

CHECK YOUR FACTS . . .

Number 1 to 6 on a sheet of paper. Mark each of the following items True *or* False.

1. If there is pain and stiffness in the region of your appendix, do not take any medicine unless your doctor tells you to.

2. In digestion, a carbohydrate is broken down to form amino acids.

3. In your body, most digested foods are absorbed by blood and lymph vessels in the wall of the small intestine.

4. In your body, most of the digested food is absorbed while it is in your stomach.

5. Absorption takes place while the food is in the large intestine, but it's mostly absorption of water.

6. There are likely to be many bacteria in your small and large intestines.

CHAPTER 47

How Does Food Supply Energy?

" John's getting fat," remarked Jim. " Yes," replied Ed, " he eats all the time, and he doesn't move around much."

How often have you heard this said? Is there any truth in Ed's idea?

Yes, when you get the facts, you find that Ed wasn't far from the mark. A certain person needs a certain amount of food for growth. He needs a certain amount for repair. He needs a certain amount for energy. All this adds up to a total amount of food that he needs. If one person gets more food than this total, what happens? Why, some of the food is stored. The result is he gets fat.

What's the energy value of foods? Now you're going to ask right away: " How much food does a person need? "

Before we can answer, we have to have some way to express the food value of different things. You don't get as much energy from a pound of lettuce as you do from a pound of meat.

When we speak of food values we speak of calories (*kal*-or-ees). A *calorie* is a unit of energy just as a pound is a unit of weight. You soon find that equal amounts of different foods aren't equal as sources of energy. Some foods contain more calories than others. Look at the chart on page 210. It shows the number of calories in

Fig. 47-1. A man who does this kind of work may need no more than 3,000 calories (food) per day.

need a day?" Sometimes this is answered by saying that a young, active person needs 20 calories for each pound of body weight. So, if you weigh 120 pounds, you need 20 × 120 or 2,400 calories. But this is only the general rule. How much you work or play makes a big difference. So does age. Look at the chart on page 211. It will show you how food needs vary.

Your age and the amount of work you do aren't the only things that affect your food needs. As you might expect, you find differences among people. Some use up energy faster than the average person. Others use up energy slower than the average person.

Why is this? For one thing, there's

different foods. A food having 1,000 calories per pound will yield twice as much energy as one having 500.

People's food needs vary. Now we're ready to come back to your question. Only this time you can ask: "How many calories does a person

IS THE ENERGY VALUE OF YOUR FAVORITE FOOD HERE?

Food	Calories per Pound	Food	Calories per Pound
Butter	3,491	Veal	700
Bacon	2,940	Eggs	594
Chocolate	2,625	Baked beans	565
Nuts	2,250 to 3,000	Boiled rice	500
Pork	1,900 to 2,950	Potatoes	400 to 475
Cream cheese	1,885	Bananas	400
Crackers	1,850	Whole milk	314
Mutton	900 to 1,650	Codfish	300
Beef	900 to 1,500	Apples	250
Bread	1,000 to 1,400	Tomatoes	100
Chicken	400 to 1,050	Lettuce	83

the effect of the *thyroid* (*thy*-royd) *gland.* You can see where this gland is located by looking at Fig. 47-3. It's in the neck region and it secretes a substance known as a *hormone* (*hor*-moan). A hormone is a gland secretion which can regulate body activities. Hormones are carried in the blood. Thyroid hormone regulates the speed at which the body cells use energy.

If your thyroid gland secretes too much thyroid hormone, you use energy faster than the average person. If your thyroid gland secretes too little hormone, you use less energy than the average person. This use of energy varies from the average as much as 40%. So you can see right away that the food needs in the chart on this page aren't right for everybody.

Fig. 47-2. These men are doing hard manual labor. They may need as much as 5,000 calories (food) per day.

They're only right for people who use energy at an *average rate*.

Why do you need roughage and water in your diet? When you look at the figures in the chart on page 213, you may ask: "What makes up the rest of the food?"

Take spinach, for instance. Only about 7% to 8% spinach is usable

WHAT'S YOUR AVERAGE DAILY FOOD NEED?	
Type of Person	*Calories per Day*
Child under 2 years	1,000
Child 2 to 5 years	1,300
Child 6 to 9 years	1,700
Child 10 to 12, or woman not working	2,000
Girl 12 to 14, or woman doing light work	2,200
Boy 12 to 14, girl 15 to 16, or man not working	2,600
Boy 15 to 20, or man doing light work	3,000
Moderately active man	3,200
Farmer in busy season	3,500–4,500
Man at hard labor	4,000–5,000

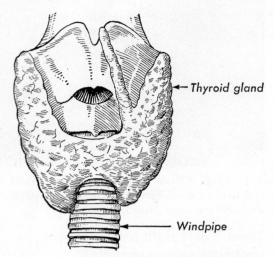

Fig. 47-3. The human thyroid gland. A hormone of this gland affects the speed at which energy is used by the body.

food material. What about the rest? Well, a lot of it is water which is needed in the diet. Some of it is solid materials that your body doesn't digest. This is *roughage.*

You get roughage mainly from vegetables and fruits. You need some of this material. It adds bulk to the solid wastes. This makes them pass along the intestine at a regular rate. If the wastes lack normal bulk, *constipation* may result. But too much roughage in your diet can also irritate your intestines. In this case, the result is sometimes *diarrhea* (dy-uh-*ree*-ah).

A good diet must contain the right foods. It must include proper amounts of water and roughage. But this isn't the whole story.

For instance, *iodine* (*eye*-uh-dyne) is a mineral the thyroid gland needs. *Iron* is a mineral the red blood cells

need. You also need *calcium* (*kal*-see-um) and *phosphorus* (*fos*-for-us) for your bones. And you probably know that your body also needs table salt. All these are **minerals.**

If you eat a variety of foods, you'll get these minerals. But you may not get enough of some of them. The minerals you're most likely to need in the largest amounts are: (*1*) calcium; (*2*) iodine; and (*3*) iron.

You also have to think about your protein needs. An average meal contains some proteins, some carbohydrates, and some fats. All three of these kinds of food give energy. And all your cells use all three of these kinds of foods for growth and repair. But the vital parts of cells are largely protein. Some people don't get enough protein in their foods.

The average person needs about two ounces of protein a day. These must be proteins that the cells can use. A good deal of the protein in some foods isn't used. Look at the chart on page 213. Your cells can use most of the proteins in lean beef. Would two ounces of this beef supply your daily proteins? No. You see right away that the beef is only about one-fifth protein. So you'd need ten ounces, not two. This is a little more than half a pound.

Now look at the other figures in this chart on page 213. You see that fish, veal, ham, and eggs also contain more than 10% of proteins. They're good sources. White bread is a fairly good source. But you'd have to eat about three loaves a day to get enough pro-

HERE'S WHAT THESE FOODS CONTAIN

Food	Per Cent of Protein	Per Cent of Carbohydrates	Per Cent of Fat
Apples	.3%	12.8%	.5%
Bacon	9.6%	—	64.0%
Bananas	1.0%	20.0%	.5%
Beans (baked)	4.8%	19.6%	2.3%
Beans (lima)	5.3%	21.6%	.6%
Beef (lean)	19.1%	—	12.1%
Bread (corn)	6.5%	45.2%	4.2%
Bread (white)	9.6%	57.3%	2.0%
Cabbage	1.2%	5.5%	.3%
Eggs	11.9%	—	9.3%
Fish (salmon)	21.1%	—	11.5%
Ham	15.8%	—	36.9%
Lettuce	.9%	2.9%	.3%
Peas	5.2%	16.7%	.5%
Potatoes	1.9%	20.0%	.1%
Rice	2.3%	23.8%	.1%
Spinach	1.6%	3.2%	.3%
Veal	19.7%	—	7.3%

tein. Among the vegetables, you can see that peas and beans are fairly good sources, also.

A balanced diet is necessary for good health. What then is a *balanced diet?* *First* of all, it's a diet that gives needed energy. *Second,* it's a diet that includes the proteins, carbohydrates, and fats for growth and repair. *Third,* it's a diet that includes all the minerals a healthy body needs. *Fourth,* it's a diet that includes the right amount of roughage and water. And *fifth,* it's a diet which includes the vitamins (*vy*-tuh-mins). **Vitamins** are substances, usually present in foods, which are necessary for good health.

The basic seven groups of foods contain everything you need for a balanced diet. If you eat some foods from each group every day, you are probably fairly safe. Is your present daily diet balanced? If not, how about trying to make it so?

CHECK YOUR FACTS . . .

Number 1 to 6 on a sheet of paper. Answer each of the following items.

1. You get the largest number of calories from a pound of (bread, butter, lettuce) ...?...

2. You get the largest amount of protein from a pound of (apples, beef, potatoes) ...?...

3. Two kinds of foods which contain a large amount of roughage are fruits and vegetables. *True* or *False?*

4. All people of the same age and doing the same kind of work need the same amount of food. *True* or *False?*

5. More thyroid hormone causes (no change, an increase, a decrease) ...?... in the rate of energy use by the body.

6. Peas and beans are better sources of proteins than are apples and bananas. *True* or *False?*

CHAPTER 48

What Are Vitamins?

Ever read stories about the old sailing ships? Sometimes they made long voyages. They didn't touch land for weeks at a time. Supplies of fresh foods ran out. Then the crews got a disease called *scurvy*. Their gums bled easily. Their teeth decayed, got loose, and even fell out. Sores appeared on their skins.

Then about 200 years ago someone found that drinking fruit juices kept people from getting scurvy. Before long the British Navy began to give lime juice to sailors. To this day British sailors are known as "limies."

You have to have vitamins. Years later, scientists learned that vitamins were part of this story. A *vitamin* is a substance, usually present in foods, which is necessary for good health. In the case of the sailors, a lack of Vitamin C caused scurvy. Whenever a person lacks this vitamin, the signs of scurvy begin to appear.

Fortunately, a good many fruits and vegetables contain Vitamin C. If you look at the chart on page 217, you'll find some of the better sources. Just the same, a good many people lack Vitamin C. They show the signs of scurvy in a mild form.

Vitamin A and "night blindness." Have you heard of "night blindness"? It's a bad thing to have if you drive a car after dark. Some people see well enough in daylight, but see badly at night.

Well, "night blindness" may be due to lack of Vitamin A. This vitamin is found in a number of common foods, as you can see in the chart. Oddly enough, it seems that the human body can change the yellow-coloring material of plants into Vitamin A. So yellow-colored vegetables like carrots, and fruits like canta-

Fig. 48-1. The rat on the left shows a typical eye condition produced by lack of Vitamin A in the diet. The one on the right shows the eyes restored to normal by feeding Vitamin A.

loupes are usually good sources. Thus, a yellow sweet potato is a much better source of Vitamin A than a white potato.

The B vitamins are a large group. The "B complex," as it's sometimes called, is really a group of vitamins. A glance at the vitamin chart will show you that these vitamins occur in many different foods.

You might well ask: "How could anyone seriously lack B vitamins?" It does happen. Some people eat only a few different foods. Or, they eat foods that they don't choose wisely. The result is a good many lack one or another B vitamins, to some extent.

A partial lack of one B vitamin has a bad effect on your digestion. Loss of weight and constipation are common results. There also is a bad effect on your nervous system. If you lack this vitamin, you're apt to get a disease called *beriberi* (ber-ee-ber-ee). It's common in China and Japan where the people live mostly on rice.

Another B vitamin prevents the disease *pellagra* (peh-*lay*-gruh). This disease is all too common in our own country. The digestive system doesn't work properly. Muscular weakness develops. The tongue is red and sore and areas of the skin become inflamed.

Pellagra appears among people who live largely on corn meal. There's nothing wrong with corn meal, of course, except that it doesn't have the needed vitamin. Here again, you see what happens when you don't eat a variety of foods.

Vitamin D is called the "sunshine vitamin." As you may know, some rays of sunlight are ultraviolet rays. When these rays fall on your skin, certain substances in the skin are changed into Vitamin D.

215

Fig. 48-2. Vegetables and fruits are sources of roughage and vitamins.

A serious lack of Vitamin D is rare among adults. But in young children this lack sometimes brings about the disease *rickets*. In rickets the developing bones of the skeleton don't harden properly. The chest and skull may be deformed. Knock-kneed or bowlegged conditions are common. Many adults show that they had rickets when they were children. Sometimes these effects are slight, but in other cases they're obvious.

When you look at the vitamin chart, you see that Vitamin D is well represented in only a few foods. This is why cod-liver oil and halibut-liver oil are sometimes added to the diets of children. It's also why doctors advise youngsters to play out-of-doors in the sunlight.

There are other vitamins. The vitamins we've told you about here aren't the only ones. But they're the ones you'll commonly get in your well-balanced diet. Vitamins A, C, D, E, and the B complex are necessary parts of the diet. You're fine when you have them, but when you lack them your

Fig. 48-3. When the sun's rays fall upon the body, substances in the skin are changed into Vitamin D.

QUICK SUMMARY OF THE VITAMINS

Vitamin	Good Sources	Conditions Related to Lack of Vitamin
A (The human body can change yellow substance of plants into this vitamin)	Apricots, beef liver, butter, cantaloupes, carrots, celery, egg yolk, fish liver oils, greens, peaches, pineapples, oysters, sweet potatoes, tomatoes, yellow squash	Night blindness; effect on eyes, skin of the face, and hair
B complex (several different vitamins in this group)	Beans, beef, butter, cabbage, carrots, corn meal, eggs, fish liver oils, lettuce, liver, mutton, pork, potatoes, tomatoes, unpolished rice, whole wheat	1. Effect on nervous and digestive systems in mild cases; the disease beriberi in severe cases. 2. Effect on the skin and membranes in mild cases; the disease pellagra in severe cases
C	Apples, beef liver, cabbage, carrots, celery, grapefruit, lemons, lettuce, oranges, limes, potatoes, peaches, pineapples, strawberries, tomatoes	The disease scurvy, which may appear in mild or severe form
D (Substances in human skin, when exposed to ultraviolet light, are changed into Vitamin D)	Butter, egg yolks, fish liver oils, irradiated foods, oysters	Failure of bones to harden during their development; causes the condition known as rickets
E	Beef, butter, egg yolks, lard, lettuce, oranges, tomatoes, whole grains or cereals	Failure of reproductive organs to function properly

growth and vigor are affected. When the lack is serious, various diseases or conditions may develop.

You can usually get all the vitamins you need from ordinary food — if you eat the right things. The main exceptions are youngsters who are growing rapidly. They may need some extra supplies of vitamins, and some adults may need them, too. But don't take extra vitamins unless your doctor tells you to. Let him decide. He'll tell you which ones you need and how much.

CHECK YOUR FACTS . . .

Number 1 to 6 on a sheet of paper. For each item in Column A *select the best item in* Column B.

Column A	*Column B*
1. Vitamin C	a. Lack of Vitamin D can cause it
2. "Night blindness"	b. When it's lacking, typhoid fever may result
3. Vitamin E	c. A group of several vitamins
4. Sunlight	d. Scurvy may result when it's not in the regular diet
5. Vitamin B complex	e. Too much causes beriberi
6. Rickets	f. When it's lacking, reproductive organs may fail to function
	g. Changes skin substances into Vitamin D
	h. Lack of Vitamin A can cause it

CHAPTER 49

What Are Allergies?

"Don't touch that plant," said Jim to Ed.

The plant looked like a green vine growing on the fence. Its leaves were in groups of three, like those in Fig. 49-1. Jim knew about such plants. He'd spent three summers on a farm.

"What's wrong with the plant?" Ed asked.

"Why, that's poison ivy," replied Jim, "it gives you an awful rash."

Many people are sensitive to proteins. Jim was quite right. *Poison ivy* plants have a wax-like coating on their leaves and stems. This coating contains a protein to which many people are sensitive. Also, they may be more sensitive at some times than at others. Reaction to such a protein means that the person has an *allergy* (*al*-er-jee).

If you think you've come in contact with poison ivy, wash your skin thoroughly with strong yellow soap and water. It isn't easy to get the wax-like coating off. It clings to the skin, and you can't see it. You can get the ivy poisoning by handling shoes, clothing, or other things that have been in it. And beware of smoke from a fire that contains any parts of poison ivy plants. Don't breathe such smoke.

A small outbreak of ivy rash isn't dangerous. But it itches, and you shouldn't scratch it. Scratching may

Fig. 49-1. Leaves of poison ivy plant.

give a little relief, but it spreads the poison over more of the skin. There are various ivy lotions that will relieve the itching. In bad cases, you should see your doctor.

Closely related to poison ivy, and just as bad, is *poison oak*. It isn't an oak, of course, and doesn't even look like an oak. It looks like what it is — an ivy plant. *Poison sumac* is another pest in the form of a bush or small tree. It looks something like other sumacs, except that its berries are white.

Hay fever is due to an allergy. Another common type of allergy results in *hay fever*. This is a reaction to proteins in the pollen of ragweeds. One of the three common North American ragweeds is shown in Fig. 49-2. These ragweeds begin to produce pollen at the end of summer. Then people begin to sneeze and suffer other discomforts of hay fever.

In fact, some people get hay fever very badly. One way out is to go places where there are few, if any, ragweeds. But remember that winds carry ragweed pollen long distances. A community can help matters by cutting down ragweeds before they form pollen. These plants are most common in vacant lots, along the sides of roads, and along fences in fields. Some of the new chemical weed killers are good in getting rid of the ragweeds.

Another reaction to plant pollen is called *rose cold*. Rose colds have nothing to do with roses and they aren't "colds." Actually, they're

Fig. 49-2. One of the common ragweeds. The pollen of these ragweeds causes hay fever.

caused by the pollen of grass plants. These plants form their pollens in late spring and early summer.

Other kinds of allergies. Some people are sensitive to the pollens of other plants. They may also have allergies for a lot of different things. They may react to dust on the fur or feathers of animals. They may react to certain kinds of clothing, like wool, or even to some kinds of soap. Of course, many people have allergies for certain kinds of foods, too.

Food allergies. Some foods are more likely to cause reactions than others. These include strawberries, oysters, clams, lobsters, milk, onions, eggs, oatmeal, and various fruits. Often a rash appears, and the victim has an upset stomach.

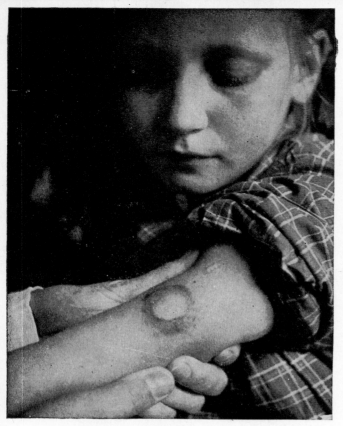

Fig. 49-3. Skin tests can be used to detect proteins which cause trouble.

So you see, " One man's food is another man's poison." Here's at least one old saying that has some truth in it. You could add: "A food today may be a poison tomorrow." For food allergies, like other allergies, change from time to time.

Fortunately, it's often possible to find out just what your allergies are. Look at Fig. 49-3. Your doctor can give you skin tests with different kinds of proteins. A red spot develops where your skin comes in contact with any protein to which you're sensitive.

Food poisoning. You know, of course, that reactions to foods aren't all caused by allergies. For instance, people are killed every year because they eat poisonous mushrooms.

Bacteria cause many other kinds of food poisoning. Bacteria may get into cans of preserved food. They may also get into fresh foods that have spoiled. In general, it's not wise to eat foods which don't smell or taste right. Even after they've been cooked thoroughly such foods may cause trouble.

Meanwhile, remember that some bacteria which get in foods are deadly. Take a good look at any can of food you're going to use. If the ends are bulged out, throw it away. Cans with bulged ends usually contain dangerous bacteria. The bulging is due to gases caused by the activity of these bacteria.

It's also a good rule to cook home-canned foods before eating them. Cooking won't get rid of *all* the poisons which are present, but will destroy many bacteria and poisons.

CHECK YOUR FACTS . . .

Number 1 to 6 on a sheet of paper. Select the best item to complete each of the following statements.

1. A rash developed by using a certain kind of soap is best described as: (*a*) common thing; (*b*) case of poisoning; (*c*) allergic reaction; (*d*) rare happening.

2. If the preserved food in a can you open smells sour, the safe thing to do is to: (*a*) boil the food before eating it; (*b*) throw the food away; (*c*) add a chemical preservative to the food; (*d*) freeze the food overnight before eating it.

3. In the following list, a plant whose pollen causes hay fever is: (*a*) poison ivy; (*b*) poison oak; (*c*) goldenrod; (*d*) ragweed.

4. Rose colds are caused by the pollens of: (*a*) grasses; (*b*) ivy plants; (*c*) goldenrods; (*d*) ragweeds.

5. Allergies are: (*a*) caused by fats in various foods; (*b*) caused by fur and feathers but not by food; (*c*) likely to change during a person's lifetime; (*d*) always the same for a given person.

6. It's possible to have an allergy for: (*a*) dog hair; (*b*) strawberries; (*c*) oysters; (*d*) all of the above.

CHAPTER 50

Why Are Alcohol, Tobacco, and Some Drugs Harmful?

"Ann, you're going to be a nurse. Is tobacco a medicine?" Ed asked.

"Well hardly," she told him. "Back in the days when men first brought tobacco to Europe from the Americas, people thought it was a medicine. But they soon found it wouldn't cure them."

"Gee, thanks," Ed said. "I've got to go write a paper on tobacco and one of the boys told me he'd read somewhere it was a medicine."

"Well, it certainly isn't. And don't let anyone tell you smoking won't hurt you, either. It will. I'm no prude, but I'm not going to smoke. And if I ever catch you and Jim smoking, I'm sure going to do something about it."

The tobacco habit. Maybe you don't know it, but tobacco contains a poisonous substance called *nicotine* (*nik*-uh-teen). Farmers use it a lot in plant sprays to kill insects. And it does the job! The smoke from cigars, pipes, and cigarettes also contains other chemicals which may hurt you.

There's no doubt that smoking harms your body. As you know, many people have upset stomachs the first few times they smoke. Most athletic coaches forbid their teams to smoke during training. And for good reason.

But more important are facts like those in Fig. 50-1. Records of smokers and non-smokers have been kept for years. They tend to show that non-smokers live longer.

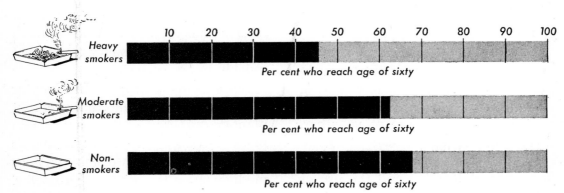

Fig. 50-1. **Records indicate that non-smokers live much longer than heavy smokers.**

Fig. 50-2. This is the sort of thing that happens when reaction time is slowed down.

The alcohol habit. Anyone who drinks constantly is likely to become an alcoholic. Then he usually can't work. In his weakened state, he may be a victim of diseases.

One of the worst dangers from the alcohol habit relates to driving cars. Even a small amount of alcohol cuts down reaction time. And this is what causes the trouble.

"Yes, but what's reaction time?" you ask.

Well, it's the time between a stimulus and a response. Here's a way to explain it. Let's say you're driving along a street. A dog (*the stimulus*) suddenly darts in front of your car. You slam on the brakes (*the response*). The time between your first sight of the dog and the use of your brakes is your reaction time.

Reaction time takes longer when the body contains alcohol.

Here's another thing. The speed of the car makes a difference. If the car is moving slowly, the driver has more time to use his brakes. But you probably know that people who've been drinking are apt to drive fast. Their judgment of speed and distance is poor. Their reaction time is slowed down. Here you have all you need for a serious accident. A person with slow reaction time isn't likely to act quickly in an emergency.

Habit-forming drugs. In Chapter 26 you learned some things about plant drugs. Among them are certain habit-forming types. You should take these habit-forming drugs only as medicines, on the advice of a doctor.

You may remember that one habit-forming drug is *opium*. It comes from the poppy plant. Two other habit-forming drugs come from opium. They are *morphine* (*mor*-feen) and *heroin* (*hair*-oh-in). *Cocaine* (koh-*kayn*), you remember, comes from the coca plant.

These drugs have proper uses in medicine. They're **narcotic** (nahr-*kot*-ik) **drugs.** This means that they dull pain and bring on sleep. But these drugs are habit-forming and people who become slaves to them ruin their health. To get money for illegal drugs, these people often turn to crime. Many drug users have police records.

Marijuana (mair-uh-*wah*-nuh) is another dangerous drug. It's found in the leaves of hemp plants. Victims of this drug smoke it in cigarettes called "reefers." The use of marijuana also ruins the health. It dulls the senses and makes users unable to think clearly. Worse yet, marijuana users often "graduate" to the use of heroin. They are easily led to do things they wouldn't normally do.

CHECK YOUR FACTS . . .

Number 1 to 6 on a sheet of paper. Mark each of the following items True *or* False.

1. Heroin is a habit-forming drug obtained from opium.

2. Carefully kept records tend to show that tobacco users live longer than people who don't use tobacco.

3. Marijuana is a harmful drug, but there's no evidence that it's habit-forming.

4. Nicotine is used in some poison sprays to kill insects.

5. Even small doses of alcohol tend to slow down a person's reaction time.

6. Alcoholics often become victims of various other diseases.

IN A NUTSHELL

Foods give you energy, and the materials cells use in growth and repair. But all people don't have the same food needs. These vary with age, size, and the rate of energy use.

The human digestive system consists of the mouth, esophagus, stomach, small intestine, and large intestine. There are also related glands, including the liver and the pancreas.

Digestion is the process of making foods soluble, so they can be absorbed and used. Foods are acted on by enzymes in saliva, stomach fluids, intestinal fluids, and fluids from the pancreas. Carbohydrates are broken down into simple sugar, proteins into amino acids, and fats into fatty acids and glycerin. Lymph and blood vessels absorb these products of digestion in the walls of the small intestine.

The calorie is the unit used to express the energy value of fo

Among other things, the amount of energy you use depends on the activity of your thyroid gland. A good diet must include the right energy values, water, roughage, minerals, and vitamins.

You need Vitamins A, B (complex), C, D, and E for normal growth and proper nutrition. Various diseases or conditions come from lack of these vitamins.

Some people have allergies to various proteins. These proteins may be in plant pollens, dust, foods, and other things.

Tobacco contains a poisonous substance called nicotine. Records indicate that non-smokers live longer than people who smoke. Too much alcohol injures health. In any quantity, alcohol slows down reaction time, and is a dangerous hazard to drivers. Opium, morphine, heroin, cocaine, and marijuana are dangerous habit-forming drugs.

WHAT DO THESE WORDS MEAN?

Allergy	Enzyme	Molar teeth
Amino acid	Esophagus	Nicotine
Appendix	Fat	Premolar teeth
Calorie	Hay fever	Protein
Canine teeth	Heroin	Thyroid gland
Carbohydrates	Hormone	Villi
Digestion	Incisor teeth	Vitamin

ASK YOURSELF . . .

1. What is the possible advantage in using a " basic seven " chart to select your foods?
2. Defend the saying: " One man's food is another man's poison."
3. What needs of the human body are met by a well-balanced diet?
4. What enzymes act on food in: (a) the mouth; (b) the stomach; and (c) the small intestine?
5. In what form are food substances absorbed?
6. (a) What germs may be present in the intestines? (b) What causes appendicitis? (c) Typhoid fever?
7. (a) When do you gain weight? (b) Lose weight? (c) What does the thyroid gland have to do with such gains or losses?

8. What kinds of foods should you eat to supply needed roughage?

9. What mineral substances are apt to be deficient in your diet?

10. (a) What are the protein needs of the human body?   (b) Are all proteins equally useful?

11. (a) What conditions are related to lack of Vitamin A?   (b) The Vitamin B complex?   (c) Vitamin C?   (d) Vitamin D?

12. If you eat a variety of different foods, is your body likely to be seriously lacking in vitamins?

13. (a) What is an allergy?   (b) To what kinds of substances are people allergic?   (c) How can you find out if you have an allergy?

14. (a) What are some ways you might be warned that foods are spoiled? (b) Will cooking the foods protect you?

15. Why are the use of tobacco and alcohol dangerous?

16. (a) What are narcotic drugs?   (b) Why is their use dangerous?

GETTING THE FACTS . . .

1. Examine a chart of the human teeth. Locate the incisors, canines, premolars, and molars. Try to get a chart which shows the effects of tooth decay. Show by means of a chart or diagram how a dentist removes decay and fills a tooth.

2. Prepare three small dishes of: (a) sugar solution; (b) salt solution; and (c) vinegar. Dip the end of a toothpick in the sugar solution, and touch your tongue with the sugar solution in several different places. Do you taste the sugar on all parts of your tongue? Repeat with salt solution and vinegar. What do you learn from the results?

3. Examine a chart of the human digestive system, and locate the main structures, including related glands. If you have a microscope and prepared slides, examine sections of: (a) the stomach wall; and (b) the intestinal wall. Locate glands and blood vessels.

4. Put pieces of several foods in test tubes one-fourth full of water. Use cooked egg white, meat, bacon, cheese, bread, potatoes, crackers, or any other foods you have at hand. Add three or four drops of iodine solution to each test tube. Shake the contents. If starch (a carbohydrate commonly found in foods) is present, a bluish-black color appears. Which foods contain a large amount of starch?

5. Put pieces of several foods in test tubes one-fourth full of water. Use the same kinds of foods as in No. 4. Add a pipette full of Fehling's solution A to each tube and heat to boiling. Add a pipette full of Fehling's solution B and heat again. If the food tested contains sugar, a coppery brown color will appear. Which foods contain large amounts of sugar?

6. Put a piece of bread or cracker in a test tube one-fourth full of water and another piece in a test tube one-fourth full of saliva. Allow each to stand a

half-hour. Test each for sugar as in No. 5. Is sugar present in both tubes? What did the saliva do?

7. If you have some pancreatin (*pan-cree-at-in*), mix up a digestive fluid. You can do this by dissolving some of the pancreatin in water. Place pieces of crackers, bread, and potato in test tubes, and cover them with the digestive fluid. Warm the test tubes gently and allow them to stand for 30 minutes. The foods you're using contain large amounts of starch. After they've been standing for 30 minutes, test them for sugar as in

No. 5. What has happened to some of the starch? Try the same thing on pure starch as an added check.

8. Plan a balanced diet for a week, which will provide you with: (*a*) 2,400 calories per day; (*b*) Vitamins A, B, C, and D; and (*c*) a reasonable amount of roughage. In selecting foods use the various charts on pages 210, 213 and 217.

9. Examine specimens of poison ivy and ragweed (preserved specimens or live plants in the field). Learn to recognize these plants. Write a report on what to do if you're allergic to them.

Topic 3

HOW YOUR BODY USES ENERGY

These runners are just finishing a race. Are their bodies doing work?

Yes, indeed. Some people may call it sport, but it's work just the same. Energy is being used.

Where does the energy come from? Actually, from the protoplasm in the body cells. Oxygen is necessary to set this energy free. When the energy is set free, wastes are formed.

Body cells must have food materials to restore their protoplasm. They must also have oxygen to release the energy needed to do work. Wastes must be removed from the cells. The story of energy is the story of life.

AMONG THE NEW WORDS FOR THIS TOPIC

- **ARTERY** (*art*-er-ee). A blood vessel which carries blood from the heart toward the tissues.
- **BLOOD.** A basic fluid in which there are red and white blood cells.
- **CAPILLARY** (*kap*-il-air-ee). Very small blood vessel. Normally connects a branch artery with a branch vein.
- **CIRCULATION** (serk-you-*lay*-shun). The normal flow of blood through a system of blood vessels, to and from various parts of the body.
- **PLASMA** (*plaz*-mah). The liquid part of blood.
- **URINE** (*yoo*-rin). A body waste, removed from the blood by the kidneys.
- **VEIN.** A blood vessel which carries blood from the tissues toward the heart.

CHAPTER 51

How Does Your Blood Flow?

Ever cut your finger? Who hasn't! Sooner or later nearly everyone does. Sometimes just a little blood oozes out. In other cases the blood flows freely.

What makes the difference? The size of the cut? How deep it is? These are important factors, but they're not the whole story. The kind of blood vessel you cut has a lot to do with how much blood you lose.

If you cut a fairly large blood vessel, the blood may flow freely. It may flow for some time unless you take measures to stop it. This is because of circulation (serk-yoo-*lay*-shun). *Circulation* is the normal flow of blood through a system of blood vessels. This carries the blood to all parts of your body.

What is blood? Of course, you know blood flows like a liquid. It's more or less red-colored. It usually forms a *clot* (solid mass) when you get a small cut or scratch.

What does blood look like when you see it under a microscope? You'll see that it's a basic fluid, in which there are many cells. This basic fluid is the *plasma* (*plaz*-mah). It makes up over half of the blood, and is just about colorless. Plasma is very important. It carries absorbed foods to cells of the body. It also carries waste products away from the cells.

More than a third of the blood is made up of *red blood cells.* You see them in Fig. 51-1. They're like tiny, round discs. Your blood contains billions of these red cells. The red-colored matter in them gives the blood its color. [If you want to know its real name, doctors call it *hemoglobin* (*hee*-moh-globe-in).] Oxygen in the lungs combines with this red-colored material. In this way, oxygen is carried from the lungs to all cells of your body.

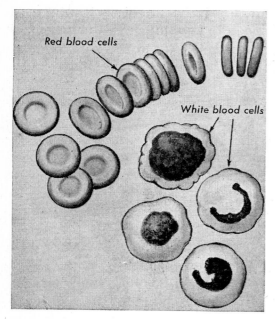

Fig. 51-1. Cells of human blood. There are several different types of white blood cells. The red blood cells don't appear to have nuclei.

You also see *white blood cells* in Fig. 51-1. There are several different kinds of white cells and there are fewer of them than red cells. The white cells have nuclei. They're gray in color and move like an Amoeba. Some of them destroy disease germs and other foreign materials that get in the body.

How much blood is in your body? If you weigh 140 pounds, you have about 12 pounds of blood. This is roughly 12 pints, or 6 quarts.

Sometimes you're asked to give blood, a painless act. It's usually taken from a vein in your arm. Then it's put in a blood bank or given immediately to someone who needs it. Doctors give the stored blood from

the blood bank to patients who are very sick or who have been seriously wounded. Just any blood type won't do. There are several types of human blood. A doctor must find out what type of whole blood his patient needs before giving it. When only blood plasma is used, the type is of no importance.

Blood is pumped by the heart. In Fig. 51-2 you see a drawing of the human heart. Note that it has four main regions. The two upper regions are the *auricles* (*aw*-rih-k'ls). The left auricle gets blood coming from the lungs. The right auricle gets blood coming from all other parts of the body.

The two lower regions of the heart are the *ventricles* (*ven*-trih-k'ls). These have heavy, muscular walls. The ventricles pump blood away from

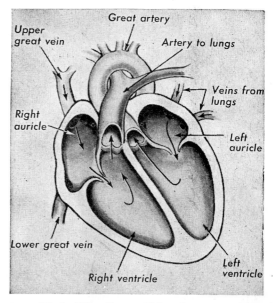

Fig. 51-2. The flow of blood to and from the human heart.

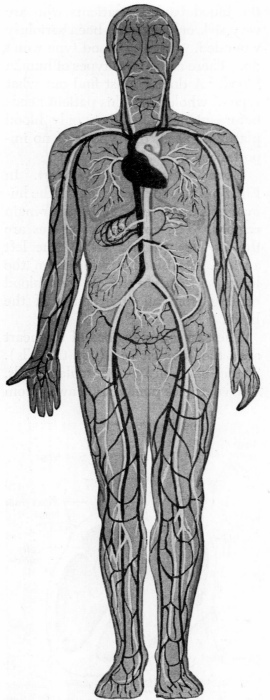

Fig. 51-3. The main arteries and veins of the human body. In this diagram the arteries are white. The veins are black.

the heart. The right ventricle pumps blood to the lungs. In the lungs this blood gets new supplies of oxygen. Then the left ventricle pumps blood to the rest of the body.

The heart also contains a number of valves. Normally, these valves prevent the blood from flowing back. In some types of heart disease, the valve openings are too small. Not enough blood is pumped through them. In other types of heart disease, the valves don't close properly. As a result, a back-flow of blood takes place. In either case, circulation isn't normal.

The arteries and the veins. *Arteries* (*art*-er-ees) and *veins* are two kinds of blood vessels. If you look at Fig. 51-3, you'll see the system of arteries and veins in the human body.

The arteries have elastic, muscular walls. They carry blood away from the heart. The blood goes through the arteries and their branches to the tissues. Then it passes into even smaller blood vessels called *capillaries* (*kap*-il-air-ees). Foods and oxygen pass from the capillaries to the cells of the body. The blood in the capillaries gets waste materials from the cells, too.

Capillaries that have passed through tissues come together again to form *branch veins.* In these branch veins, the blood now flows back toward the heart. Branch veins join to form larger veins. The largest veins carry the blood back to the heart.

Have you ever tried taking your pulse? Use the first finger of your left hand to find your pulse on the inside

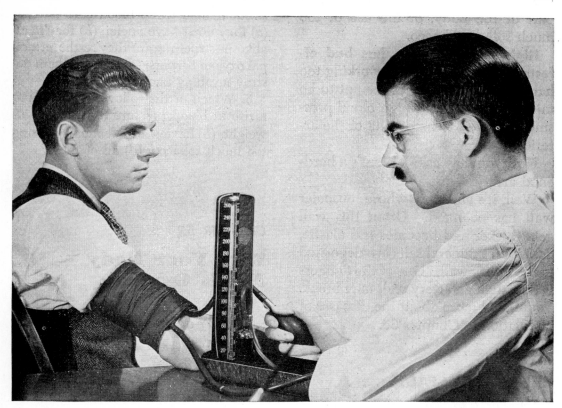

Fig. 51-4. This is one way in which a reading of blood pressure can be made.

of the right wrist. What you feel is the swelling of an artery as the blood gushes through it each time your heart beats. You can count the number of beats for one minute. The pulse rate varies in different people. Usually it's higher in young people than in adults. It's also generally higher for women than for men. When you exercise, your pulse will rise quickly, but the rise is only temporary. After exercising, it gradually goes back to normal.

Blood pressure. The pressure of your blood is highest in the arteries. When the blood reaches the capillaries, its pressure drops to the lowest point. This is because the capillaries

are the "widest part of the road." Each capillary is small, but there are a lot of them. In the veins, blood pressure is higher than in the capillaries. But it's less than in the arteries.

Look at Fig. 51-4. It shows how a doctor reads blood pressure. Actually, he makes two readings. One is the highest pressure — when the heart is contracting. The other is the lowest pressure — when the heart is relaxed. Normal range of the higher reading is from 110 to about 150. If the reading is higher or lower, something is wrong. For instance, a high reading may be due to a poor diet, being overweight, an infection in any part of the body, or the use of too much salt or tobacco.

High blood pressure has bad effects. Often the heart is working too hard. Also, the arteries are apt to be injured. Permanent high blood pressure is related to hardening of the arteries.

Now you may ask: "What's a hardened artery?"

Well, it's an artery whose muscular wall has changed. Often this wall gets thicker and becomes less elastic. Sometimes mineral salts are deposited in the artery wall. One of the dangers is that such an artery wall may break. You'll read more about the diseases of circulation in Chapter 66.

CHECK YOUR FACTS . . .

Number 1 to 6 on a sheet of paper. Select the best answer for each of the following items.

1. Blood returning to the heart from the lungs enters the: (*a*) right auricle; (*b*) right ventricle; (*c*) left auricle; (*d*) left ventricle.

2. Permanently high blood pressure is apt to cause: (*a*) an infection in some tissue; (*b*) loss of weight; (*c*) hardening of arteries; (*d*) all of these.

3. If you weigh about 140 pounds, your body contains, roughly, the following amount of blood: (*a*) one quart; (*b*) three quarts; (*c*) four quarts; (*d*) six quarts.

4. Which of the following makes up the largest part of the human blood: (*a*) red cells; (*b*) absorbed foods; (*c*) plasma; (*d*) white cells?

5. Which of the following statements about human white blood cells is true: (*a*) they don't have nuclei; (*b*) they're all alike in structure; (*c*) they're the principal oxygen carriers; (*d*) some of them destroy invading bacteria?

6. Which of the following may cause a rise in blood pressure (*a*) being overweight; (*b*) having an infection; (*c*) using too much tobacco; (*d*) all of these?

CHAPTER 52

Why Your Body Needs Oxygen

"Why do people drown?" Jim asked Ed.

"Because they run out of air when they're under water," Ed replied.

Do you think this is a good answer? Of course you see that it's not complete. Could you give a better answer?

Why does your body need oxygen? In Chapter 5 you learned that all cells need oxygen. They use it to oxidize (burn) their contents. When cell contents are oxidized, the process is like slow burning. In this process energy is set free. This is the energy your muscle cells use to move the body and do other work.

How the lungs work. You know, of course, that all living things use oxygen in much the same way. But only the higher animals have lungs.

Let's look at Fig. 52-1. It will help you to understand just how you breathe. Air, containing oxygen, can

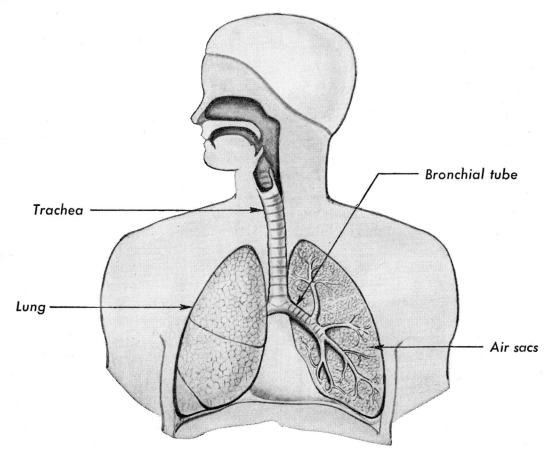

Fig. 52-1. This diagram shows the human breathing structures.

enter your body either through the nose or the mouth. In either case it gets into the back of the mouth cavity. Then it passes down the windpipe or *trachea* (*tray*-kee-uh) to the two *bronchial* (*bronk*-ee-ul) *tubes.* You see that one bronchial tube goes to each lung. In the lung a bronchial tube branches to form smaller tubes. These small tubes go to the many *air sacs* of the lung.

The tissues which form the walls of these air sacs contain a great many tiny blood vessels. It's here that oxygen from the air in the air sacs passes into the blood. At the same time the blood discharges carbon dioxide waste into the air sacs. This carbon dioxide leaves the body when air is forced out of the lungs.

What happens when you breathe? You *inhale* (take air into your lungs) and you *exhale* (force air out of your lungs). You're not conscious of these movements, of course. They're controlled by your nervous system. When you run, you breathe quicker without even thinking about it. And when you're resting, your breathing rate slows down. But you can control your breathing to some extent. You can deliberately slow down your breathing movements, or speed them up for a short while.

When you inhale, muscles of the chest wall contract. Your ribs are moved upward and outward. Your diaphragm is lowered at the same time. When this happens, your chest cavity gets larger and your lungs expand. Air then rushes into the lungs to fill the larger space.

When you exhale, your ribs and diaphragm return to their resting positions. Your chest cavity gets smaller and your lung tissues contract. Air is then forced out of your lungs.

Probably you've heard of *artificial respiration.* It's used to revive people whose breathing movements have slowed down or stopped. This can happen when people are under water for too long. Or, it can happen when they've been badly hurt, or when they've breathed poison gases. You can see how to use artificial respiration in Fig. 52-2. Better learn how it's done. No telling when you may want to use it on someone whose life will depend on it.

The blood and the body cells. Blood, carrying oxygen, goes to all tissues of the body. In these tissues an exchange takes place between the blood and the cells. The cells take in oxygen from the blood. And the cells give up carbon dioxide and other wastes to the blood.

Now you see how cells get rid of waste. You also see how they get new supplies of oxygen which they can use to release energy.

What makes a room stuffy? Ever felt uncomfortable in a closed, crowded room? Here's why you may have had that feeling. Water vapor leaves your body when you exhale. This adds to the water vapor in the room. When many people are in the room, quite a lot of water vapor is present. Heat also leaves your body. With many people in the room, it can get quite warm. Thus, the room seems stuffy and you begin to feel uncomfortable. It's not a lack of oxygen, but merely because the room contains more water vapor and heat.

Of course, the greatest danger of being in a crowded room has nothing to do with your comfort at the time. It's the fact that you may get germs from other people. One of the ways to get a cold is to be in a crowded room which isn't properly ventilated.

Viruses are the cause of colds. Doctors call these "common colds." They're surely common enough, and you know how miserable they can make you. They affect your breathing, your nose, and your throat. Doctors believe they're caused by a virus, or probably by several viruses.

Signs of a cold often begin with a watery discharge from the nose. The membranes inside your nose get inflamed. Then the cold often spreads down your air passages to your lungs. Most of the things you can do for a cold won't cure it. They may, however, make you feel better until you

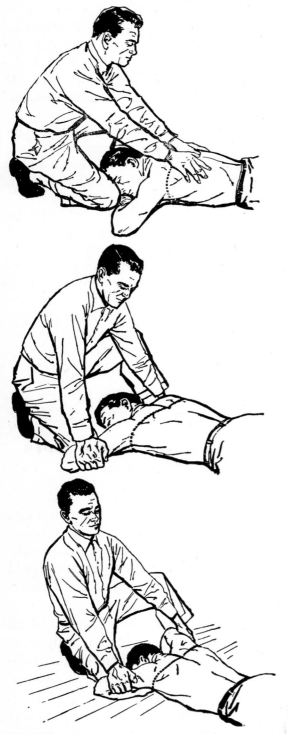

The victim lies on his stomach with his elbows bent and one hand on the other. The operator kneels, as shown here. He presses on the victim's back.

The operator then rocks backward, and slides hands up on the victim's arms, as this diagram shows.

The operator raises the victim's arms as shown, and then drops them to complete the cycle. The cycle is repeated 12 times per minute.

Fig. 52-2. The new back pressure-arm lift method of artificial respiration.

get well. Usually, the cold runs its course in from three or four days to a week.

Ever noticed that one cold affects you one way and another cold affects you another way? Well, there may be several cold viruses that cause different effects. Different parts of your breathing apparatus may be affected. But there's another reason why your colds aren't all the same. When you get a cold, various germs in and around your air passages may become active. Their activities add to your discomfort. What they add depends on the kind of germs that become active. This is likely to vary from time to time and from person to person.

Some diseases of the lungs. You've heard of *pneumonia* (noo-*moh*-nee-uh). It's a dangerous disease of the lungs and over 30 different kinds of germs cause it. There are even virus types of pneumonia.

Pneumonia often strikes people who have first been weakened by other illnesses. Until recent years it was a common cause of death. But science has added a number of new drugs, such as penicillin, to our defenses. The death rate from pneumonia has gone way down in recent years. But it is still a common cause of death.

Another serious disease that may center in lung tissues is *tuberculosis* (too-ber-kyoo-*loh*-siss). It's also a germ disease. The search for drugs that will kill the tuberculosis germ has been a long one. Only recently some drugs have been found which may give promising results.

CHECK YOUR FACTS . . .

Number 1 to 6 on a sheet of paper. Select the best answer for each of the following items.

1. Doctors believe that common colds are caused by (lack of vitamins, bacteria, viruses) . . . ? . . .

2. When you inhale, your diaphragm is (lowered, raised, unchanged) . . . ? . . .

3. Human blood receives new supplies of oxygen as it passes through the (heart, lungs, kidneys) . . . ? . . .

4. Air passes from the trachea to the lungs through the (nasal passages, windpipe, bronchial tubes) . . . ? . . .

5. When materials of a cell are oxidized (food, energy, oxygen) . . . ? . . . is made available to do work.

6. In recent years the death rate due to pneumonia has (increased, remained about the same, decreased) . . . ? . . .

CHAPTER 53

How Your Body Gets Rid of Wastes

Imagine a city without chimneys, sewers, or garbage removal! Such a city would be a mess. Waste substances would pile up. People would soon have to move out and find homes somewhere else.

Waste disposal is a function of all living things. The human body must get rid of wastes. Even the most simple plants and animals dispose of wastes.

Where do these wastes come from? They result from the normal activities of cells. When the living substance is oxidized, wastes are formed. Two common forms of wastes are carbon dioxide and water. You know already that carbon dioxide is set free in breathing. So is some water. So is some excess heat, which is one form of energy.

Wastes and the lungs. You can easily test the part breathing plays in waste disposal. First, breathe through a soda straw into some limewater. At first, the limewater is clear and colorless. But when your breath passes through it, the clear limewater turns milky. The milky color shows that carbon dioxide has entered the limewater.

Now blow your breath on a piece of cold glass. What happens? You can see tiny drops of moisture on the glass. In breathing, your body loses about a pint of water every day. This is why the amount of moisture in the air rises in a room full of people.

What do the kidneys do? There are other ways for excess water to leave the body. Various waste substances go out with the water.

In Fig. 53-1 you see a diagram of the human kidneys. Blood passes through the kidneys all the time. The kidney cells remove *urine* (*yoo*-rin) from the blood. Urine passes through two ducts to the bladder, and then through another duct to the outside.

Urine is mostly water. But in the water there are several different waste substances. They include wastes from your liver and other tissues of your body. For instance, extra sup-

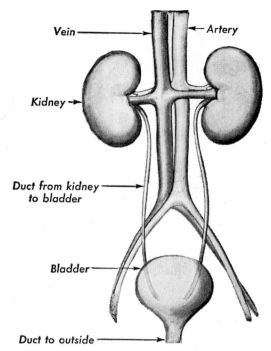

Fig. 53-1. Waste is removed as blood passes through the kidneys. It passes through two ducts to the bladder and then outside the body.

plies of common salt appear in urine. But most of the wastes come from proteins. The urine also may contain various poisons. These may be poisons resulting from disease.

The quantity and color of the urine will vary, even when your body is perfectly healthy. In fact, quantity and color are related. If the quantity is small, the color is likely to be dark. On the other hand, if the kidneys are getting rid of a lot of water, the urine may be nearly colorless.

The work load of the kidneys is greatest when they have to remove a lot of waste and there isn't much excess water. So when your kidneys

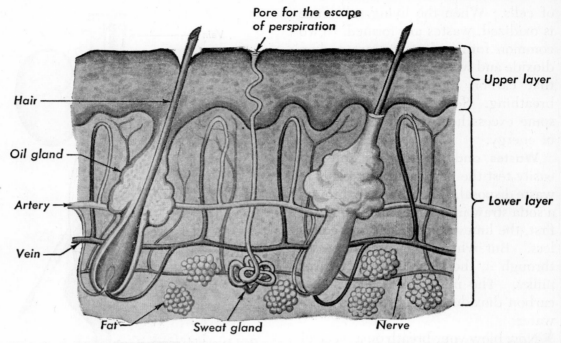

Fig. 53-2. This diagram shows the relations of a sweat gland to other structures in the skin.

need a rest, you drink plenty of water. You don't eat things that contain a lot of protein or salt.

Your skin gets rid of extra heat. It also gets rid of surplus body water. Fig. 53-2 shows a *sweat gland.* These glands occur in the skin and in tissues just below the skin. Their ducts run through the skin to the surface.

Of course you know that you perspire when it's warm. Water is given off by the sweat glands. Excess body heat goes off with the water. Substances from oil glands contain oil which lubricates the skin.

Some people have the idea that sweat contains a lot of body wastes. Actually, this isn't true. About 98% of sweat is plain water. Only a small amount of salts, carbon dioxide, and other wastes are present when your body is healthy. If the kidneys are diseased, however, the amount of these wastes in perspiration increases.

Solid wastes. These pass out of the body through the large intestine. Actually, these wastes aren't as solid as you might think. To be sure, the blood absorbs excess water as food passes through the large intestine. Just the same, solid wastes contain a lot of water.

What, then, is the solid waste material? It includes parts of foods that haven't been digested or absorbed. Some material in the walls of plant cells, for instance, can't be digested. To this mass are added dead bacteria that once lived in the intestine. *Bile,* secreted by the liver, also passes from the body with the solid wastes. For the most part bile seems to be a waste product, too.

Diseases of the kidneys. As you might expect, the general health of your body depends in part on the kidneys. Wastes must be disposed of.

Sometimes the kidneys fail to do a normal amount of work. Severe exposure to cold can cause this. It may also be due to poisons that have gotten into your body, or to poisons which injure the kidneys. Luckily, the kidneys may go back to work if you remove the cause of the trouble. But any failure of the kidneys causes wastes to pile up in your body. And this is bound to be serious if it goes on for too long a time.

CHECK YOUR FACTS . . .

Number 1 to 6 on a sheet of paper. Mark each of the following items True *or* False.

1. A part of solid waste normally consists of dead bacteria.

2. In normal health, the main work of the sweat glands is to dispose of excess salts.

3. Some water normally leaves the human body in the process of breathing.

4. One important function of the sweat glands is to get rid of excess heat.

5. Eating large amounts of proteins and salt increases the work load of the kidneys.

6. If your body is badly chilled, your kidneys may fail to do a normal amount of work.

CHAPTER 54

Do You Always Look Your Best?

Jim, Ed, and Ann were sitting in the living room talking about their uncle who had just left. He was a TV actor and had been visiting the family for a few days.

"Nice guy," Ed remarked, "I'd say he was a real smoothie. He sure has nice clothes."

"Clothes don't make a man," Ann observed. "He has that well-scrubbed look. That's what has made him so popular on TV."

"It was interesting to hear him tell about all the TV actors and actresses," Ed added. "How they couldn't be overdressed or use too much makeup."

"Well," Ann said, "just look at the pictures in the magazines. Those people don't use much makeup. They have to keep healthy and look their best. I guess Uncle Bob is right — we're not all born beautiful but we can try to look our best."

Ann was right. Few of us are born beautiful, but there's no excuse for any of us not trying to look our best.

You can't see yourself (except when you look in a mirror), but your friends see you. They notice how you look, but they won't tell you when you're unattractive. If your mirror tells you you're not looking your best, it's time you did something about it.

People notice your hair. It's one of the first things people look at when they meet a stranger. Haven't you

Fig. 54-1. Brushing your hair every morning will keep it looking at its best.

ever done that? Everyone should brush or comb his hair at the beginning of each day. It may need a little touching up sometime during the day, too.

Ever wonder why some hair is naturally curly and some is straight? Look back at Fig. 53-2. It shows hairs growing out of the skin layer. Note that each hair grows out of a long, slender opening in the skin layer. If this opening is straight, and the hair is round in cross section, the hair is straight. But if this opening is curved and the hair is flattened in cross section, the hair is curly.

How often should you wash your hair? Depends on your hair and the weather. Most people wash it once a week, but some do it more often, and some do it less. When you wash your hair, use a good shampoo and lather

it thoroughly. Then rinse several times in clear, warm water. Dry it immediately with a towel so you won't run the risk of getting chilled.

Some people use oils, grease, or tonics to hold their hair in place. Too much of these may do harm, in some cases.

The important thing is to watch your hair and see that it's always neat. Nothing is more objectionable than hair which is dirty and uncombed.

People notice your nails. No matter how well dressed you are, if your nails are untidy you've got one strike against you. Nicely manicured nails are just as desirable as nice looking hair.

Use a nailbrush once a day and oftener, if necessary. A nailfile or scissors will keep your nails neatly trimmed. Some people use an orange

Fig. 54-2. In brushing your teeth use a brisk, circular motion. This will aid in removing any food particles that may have lodged between the teeth.

stick to keep the cuticle pushed back.

It's a matter of personal taste whether you use nail polish or not. If you do use it, keep it in good repair. Polish that is cracked or has begun to wear off looks messy.

Beauty is more than skin deep. You've seen girls whose faces were coated with powder. You've probably thought: "She'd look better if she used just plain soap and water."

You're quite right. The thing to remember is that no amount of powder will really cover up a dirty skin. Powder is fine, as we'll see in a moment, but too much is too much. Covering up surface dirt may push that dirt into the pores of the skin. This can result in pimples or blackheads. A clean skin isn't apt to get these blemishes.

Your skin needs regular care. A warm bath once a day is the best skin treatment there is. It doesn't matter whether you take a shower or a tub. They're equally good. Use a good soap and lather it quickly. Then rinse your body. Rub briskly with a hard towel and dress at once. Don't stand around where you're likely to get into drafts.

As far as your face is concerned, use a little powder sparingly. A little goes a long way. The point is to bring out your good qualities, not to cover them up. There's no harm in using facial creams at night, if you want to. But it isn't really necessary. Like nail polish, it's a matter of personal choice.

In the cooler months of the year your daily bath and a fresh change of

Fig. 54-3. That clean, wholesome look comes from proper care of the body and general good health.

clothes will protect you from body odor. During the warmer months, you may find that a bath in the morning and one at night is necessary. If you want to use a dash of cologne or your favorite deodorant, that's fine. But a clean skin is not apt to offend by excessive perspiration. The best way to prevent body odor is to scrub and scrub.

Clean teeth are a part of your appearance. Not all of us are blessed with even teeth like pearls! Those who aren't can make an effort to keep their teeth clean.

Brush your teeth at least twice a day. If possible, do it after each meal. Use a brisk, not a harsh, circular motion and give the back ones as much brushing as the front ones. Either a dental cream or powder is good. Rinse your mouth after you're through brushing with a mouthwash or with warm water. Rinsing will give your mouth that clean feeling and will help in preventing bad breath. This is just as objectionable as body odor. You'll want to be sure that you don't offend others.

See your dentist at least every six months. Let him give your mouth a thorough examination. He'll be able to check any decay and will also look at your gums. Remember that bad breath may be due to tooth decay.

The secret of looking well is feeling well. If you feel well you'll take care of your appearance. Then your friends will really admire you for what you are — a healthy person with that clean, wholesome, well-scrubbed look.

CHECK YOUR FACTS . . .

Number 1 to 6 on a sheet of paper. Mark each of the following items True *or* False.

1. A curly hair is round in cross section.

2. It's not necessary to use soap in taking a bath.

3. The secret of looking well is feeling well.

4. If you use a mouthwash every day, you'll never have to see your dentist.

5. Hairs grow out of the skin.

6. The best way to keep from having body odor is to scrub and scrub.

Human blood consists of plasma which contains red and white blood cells. The main work of plasma is to carry absorbed foods and waste products. Red blood cells serve largely to carry oxygen. Some white blood cells destroy invading germs.

Contractions of the heart cause the blood to circulate. It passes through a system of arteries, capillaries, and veins. Food materials and oxygen are brought to the cells. Wastes are removed from the cells.

Breathing includes inhaling and exhaling. In the lung tissues, blood gets new supplies of oxygen, and gets rid of carbon dioxide waste. Cells of the body get oxygen from the blood. The oxygen is used to oxidize living substances of the cells. Thus, energy is set free to do work.

Waste disposal is a function of all living things. In your body, carbon dioxide is given off in breathing. Excess heat leaves your body in perspiration. Various liquid wastes are removed in the urine. Solid wastes pass out through the large intestine.

The kidneys have their greatest work load when there's a maximum of liquid wastes and a minimum of water.

Good appearance comes from keeping your hair, nails, skin, and teeth looking their best.

WHAT DO THESE WORDS MEAN?

Artery	Blood pressure	Sweat gland
Auricle	Bronchial tube	Trachea
Bile	Capillary	Urine
Blood	Circulation	Ventricle
Blood clot	Red blood cells	White blood cells

ASK YOURSELF . . .

1. (a) What is the basic fluid of blood? (b) What work does this fluid do?
2. (a) What cells are found in human blood? (b) What work do these cells do?
3. Why is there an advantage in having various types of blood in a blood bank?
4. Suppose you looked at some blood in which the red cells were oval and had nuclei. Would it be human blood?
5. White blood cells often collect around a cut in the skin. What useful work may they do?
6. (a) What is the pulse? (b) How do you count the pulse rate?
7. (a) What is high blood pressure? (b) Hardening of the arteries? (c) Why are they important?
8. What is the relation of oxygen to the use of energy?
9. (a) Where does oxygen enter the body? (b) Where is it used?
10. What causes you to be uncomfortable in a closed, crowded room?
11. (a) How do you get common colds? (b) What causes them?
12. How does the human body get rid of: (a) excess water; (b) excess heat; (c) wastes in the blood?
13. Why should you drink more water on a warm day than on a cold day?
14. Suppose you had a disease that affected your kidneys for the time being. What things would you avoid eating?
15. Why should you take a bath at least once a day?
16. What is the correct way to brush your teeth?

GETTING THE FACTS . . .

1. After referring to the *Red-Cross First Aid Textbook,* show the class first-aid methods to stop bleeding.

2. Place a small drop of blood on a glass slide. Dilute it with a drop of salt water. Cover with a cover glass. Examine under a microscope. Study the red blood cells. Can you find any white blood cells?

3. Dissect a lamb or pork heart. Locate the two auricles and the two ventricles. Observe the location and form of the heart valves.

4. After you've been sitting down for about 20 minutes, find your pulse and take your pulse rate. Then stand up and sit down again a half dozen times. Take your pulse rate again. How do you account for the difference?

5. You may have microscope slides showing cross-sections of arteries and veins. Examine them through a microscope. How do they differ? How is the difference related to the work they do?

6. Using a microscope, examine a sample of frog or chicken blood. Dilute the blood as described in No. 2 above. You will find many red blood cells. However, they are not like the red cells of human blood. What is the difference?

7. You may have microscope slides showing sections of lung tissue. Examine a slide under a microscope. Find the air sacs. Locate blood vessels in the lung tissue.

8. After referring to the *Red-Cross First Aid Textbook,* show the class how to apply artificial respiration.

9. After you've been sitting down for 20 minutes, count the number of breaths you take per minute. Now get up and sit down again a half dozen times. What happens to your breathing rate? Is this what you would expect?

10. See how much air you exhale in a normal breath. You can do this by exhaling through a rubber tube into an inverted jar full of water. Compare a normal breath with a deep breath.

11. After consulting the books listed on page 261, write a short report on carbon monoxide gas. How do people happen to inhale this gas? Why is it dangerous? What first aid treatment can be given?

12. Examine and dissect a beef, pork, or sheep kidney. Locate the artery that brings blood to the kidney, and the vein that carries blood away. Find the duct that carries urine to the bladder.

Topic 4

WHY DO YOU ACT THE WAY YOU DO?

How well do you observe things? How well do you remember what you see?

Look at this picture for *just 30 seconds*. Take a good look at what's in it. Note as many of the different objects and activities as you can. Now, write down everything you saw. Include as many details as you can remember. Check with others in the class. You'll find they missed things you saw and you missed things, too.

What does this test tell you about careful observation? Do people sometimes fail to see things? Do they think they've seen something that isn't there?

AMONG THE NEW WORDS FOR THIS TOPIC

- **BEHAVIOR** (bee-*hay*-vyer). The sum total of your actions and responses.
- **CEREBRUM** (*seh*-ruh-brum). The part of the brain which is the center of memory and intelligence.
- **HABIT.** A response you make so often you don't need to think about it.
- **HORMONE** (*hor*-moan). A substance produced by a ductless gland and carried by the blood.
- **INTELLIGENCE** (in-*tel*-uh-jenss). Using past experience to solve problems.
- **MEMORY.** The ability to remember past events.
- **RESPONSE.** How you react to a stimulus.
- **STIMULUS** (*stim*-yoo-lus). Something which causes you to act in a definite way.

CHAPTER 55

How Your Special Senses Serve You

What happened at eight o'clock this morning? Can you remember where you were; what other people were there; what you saw and heard; and what you smelled, tasted, or touched?

Your memory of what happened depends on what came to you through your special senses. These *special senses* include: seeing, hearing, touching, tasting, and smelling.

How your eyes work. Fig. 55-1 shows the main parts of the human eye. You can see that the *optic nerve* (the large nerve which connects your eye and your brain) enters the eye. There it connects with the retina (*ret*-ih-nuh). The *retina* is an inner layer of the eyeball. Nerve cells in the retina are responsible for what you see. From the retina, nerve fibers run through the optic nerve to the brain.

Now look again at Fig. 55-1. You see that the *pupil* is really a hole in the iris. You recognize the *iris* as the colored part of your eye. Behind the pupil is the *lens.* Light rays pass through the pupil and the lens. They also pass through the colorless liquids which fill the cavities of the eyeball.

You focus a camera by moving the lens back and forth. But the lens of your eye doesn't work that way.

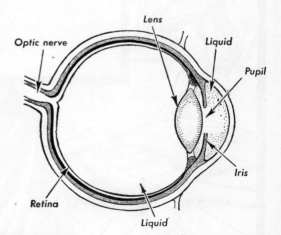

Fig. 55-1. Diagram showing the parts of the human eye.

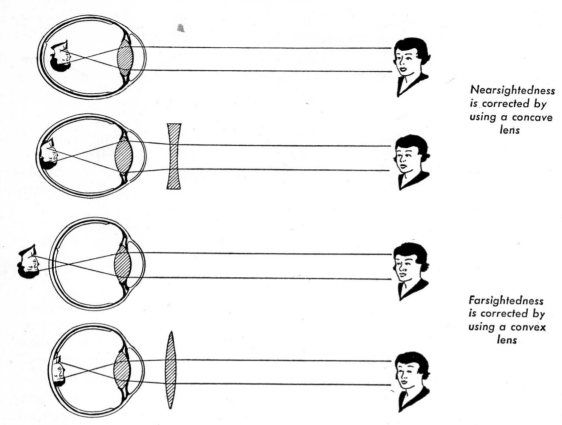

Nearsightedness is corrected by using a concave lens

Farsightedness is corrected by using a convex lens

Fig. 55-2. For sharp vision, the image must be focused on the retina.

You focus it when muscles contract and change its shape.

Nearsighted and farsighted eyes. Your eyes don't always focus properly, even when you're young. In such cases you should wear glasses which correct the defects. Eye strain can have a bad effect on your health. Headaches are a common symptom.

Fig. 55-2 shows two eye defects. In the normal eye, of course, the image is focused on the retina. But in the *nearsighted eye,* the image is focused *in front* of the retina. And in the *farsighted eye* the image is focused *behind* the retina.

These two eye defects can be corrected by wearing the proper type of glasses. The *concave lens* (see Fig. 55-2) corrects the nearsighted condition. The *convex lens* corrects the farsighted condition. They're not the only defects human eyes may have, however.

The right kind of light. Have you ever been told that reading in bed is bad for the eyes? Is this true? The fact is, it all depends on the light you have. In the first place, it should be free from glare.

People measure the brightness of light by using *light meters.* The unit

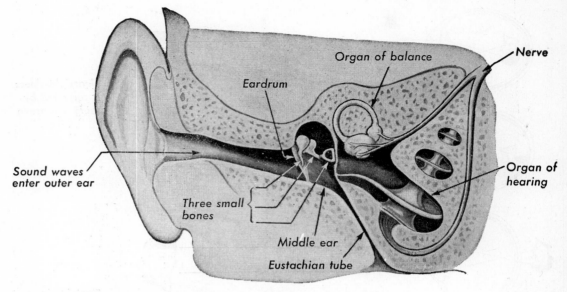

Fig. 55-3. Diagram showing the parts of the human ear.

on these meters is the *foot-candle*. You should have from 20 to 50 foot-candles for ordinary reading. At two feet a 100 watt electric bulb gives you about 30 foot-candles.

You don't need to fear strong light so long as there's no glare. In fact, the light in homes is rarely more than 100 foot-candles, and most homes have a good deal less. Light out-of-doors is far brighter. It's as much as 1,000 foot-candles in shaded places.

Care of your eyes. With good care your eyes will last your entire lifetime. The things to avoid are: (**1**) not enough light; and (**2**) too much strain. When you're using your eyes, be sure you have enough light. Rest them every half hour or so by relaxing. If you notice that they burn, or tend to get red, see a doctor at once. If you find you're not seeing things as clearly as you used to, have them examined.

You may need glasses. Use common sense in regard to your eyes and they'll reward you with good sight.

How your ear works. Many of your experiences depend on hearing sound. Your ear is the structure which receives sound waves and sends the messages to the brain. Look at Fig. 55-3. You'll see in general how this is done.

Your *outer ear* consists of an ear flap and a tube leading into the side of the head. Then comes the *middle ear*. Across its entrance is the *eardrum*, which vibrates when sound waves strike it. The vibrations are carried across to the *inner ear* by three small bones. Notice that a *Eustachian* (yoo-*stay*-kee-an) *tube* connects the throat with the middle ear.

The inner ear contains two structures. One of them is an *organ of hearing*. The other is an *organ of bal-*

ance. Both of these structures send messages to the brain.

Ear troubles. You probably know that some people are born deaf. Other people become deaf later.

In many cases deafness is due to injury of the middle ear. The real organ of hearing in the inner ear can still do its work. But sound vibrations just don't reach it. In such cases a hearing aid makes sounds heard.

An ear can be damaged by a blow on the side of the head. A loud explosion nearby can also do injury. But the action of germs is a greater danger for most people.

Remember how a Eustachian tube leads from the back of the mouth to the middle ear? Normally, this tube serves a useful purpose. It lets air in and out of the middle ear. So pressure on the two sides of the eardrum is kept about equal.

Suppose you get a cold. Maybe you blow your nose too hard. Various germs are forced up the Eustachian tube to the middle ear. Here they multiply and cause trouble. The germs may even get into bony tissue lying next to the middle ear.

A colony of germs in the middle ear can be painful. Sometimes your doctor must puncture the eardrum to drain off the pus. This isn't as bad as it sounds because the eardrum usually heals right up again. If germs keep on living in the middle ear, the damage is apt to become permanent. The victim may become hard of hearing or deaf. You can see that it is wise to get rid of such germs.

Taste and smell. You learned some things about taste in Chapter 45. For instance, you know that the nerve endings of taste are mostly on your tongue. Because of them you can tell the difference between sweet, salty, bitter, and acid substances.

But much of what you call tasting is really smelling. It's really smell that recognizes the delicate flavors of food. The nerve endings of smell are in your nasal passages. They respond to many different odors.

What is touch? When you feel your way around a dark room, you realize that touch is important. Scattered through your skin are a lot of nerve endings. Many of them are sensitive to touch. Others respond to warm sensations. Still others respond to cold in some cases, and pain in other cases.

Such nerve endings, of course, aren't found only in the skin. You know, for instance, that the tip of your tongue is quite sensitive to touch.

CHECK YOUR FACTS . . .

Number 1 to 6 on a sheet of paper. Select the best answer for each of the following items.

1. A Eustachian tube connects the throat with the (outer, middle, inner) . . . ? . . . ear.

2. Many of the nerve endings in the skin are sensitive to (smell, taste, touch) . . . ? . . .

3. The colored part of the eye around the pupil is the (iris, retina, cornea) . . . ? . . .

4. Nerve endings which are sensitive to odors are located in the (nose, mouth, Eustachian tube) ...?...

5. When you read, you need at least (5, 20, 10) ...?... foot-candles.

6. A convex lens corrects a (far-sighted, nearsighted) ...?... condition.

CHAPTER 56

Your Nerves Control Many Body Actions

Jim was batting ground balls to Ed. Ed got every ball that came near him. Jim was quite impressed.

" Do you think about how you hold your hands when you go after the ball? " he asked.

" Why, no," replied Ed, " I guess I don't think about that. I just try to get to the ball. But I used to think about my hands when I was learning."

What Ed said might be repeated for many things you do. You think about the details, perhaps, when you're learning. But once you've learned, a good many of your actions are largely automatic.

Behavior includes all of our actions. What is it that directs the actions of your muscles? One thing is the nervous system. It's part of the story in almost anything you do. To a large extent, your nervous system determines your behavior. Behavior includes all of your actions. These actions are in response to things and forces in your environment.

Now let's go back to Ed and the batted ball. The ball coming toward him was a *stimulus* (*stim*-yoo-lus). It aroused him to do something. His actions in catching the ball were a *response* to the stimulus. This response, in turn, was a part of Ed's behavior.

Nerve cells and behavior. Ed used his special senses in getting the stimulus. He saw the bounding ball and heard the crack of the bat. His sense of touch was used in running and catching the ball. His muscles worked together so that he could run and catch the ball.

The work done by his nerve cells made all this possible. One type of nerve cell is shown in Fig. 56-1. You can see that it has a *cell body* with a

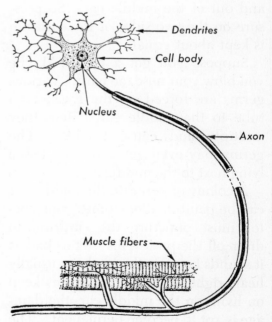

Fig. 56-1. Diagram of one kind of nerve cell. Messages are received by the dendrites. Messages go to muscle fibers through the axon.

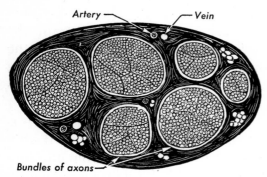

Fig. 56-2. This diagram shows a cross section of a nerve. Note that small arteries and veins are present.

nucleus. Several *dendrites* (*den-drytes*) are attached to the cell body. These dendrites receive messages from another nerve cell. Let's think of a dendrite as a *receiving part*.

Now look at the *axon* (*aks-uhn*) in Fig. 56-1. Such an axon may be two or three feet long. It may run through a nerve to a muscle in some part of the body. Messages from the nerve cell go through the axon to the muscle. This causes the muscle to contract. You can think of an axon as a *sending part*.

What, then, is a *nerve?* Why, it's a bundle of axons, for the most part. The bundle is held together by an outer covering of tissue. This is shown in Fig. 56-2. You see also that a nerve may include small arteries and veins.

Look at Fig. 56-3. You'll see the nerve centers of the human body. Note that the larger nerves are connected with the spinal cord or the brain. The spinal cord and the brain act as central controls of the nervous system.

Involuntary controls. Before you think about actions that you can control, think about some that you don't try to control. Suppose you decide to

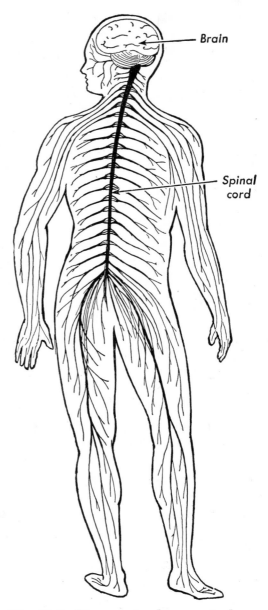

Fig. 56-3. Diagram to show control centers of the nervous system. These centers are the brain and the spinal cord.

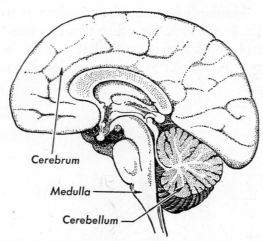

Fig. 56-4. This diagram shows the regions of the human brain.

run. Do you first have to tell your heart and lungs to work harder?

Of course not. But when you start running, your heart and lung motions speed up. The change is automatic. You *can* think about it, but you don't really *need* to.

If you're in good health, you don't worry about your internal organs. They do their work just the same. As a result, you can use your thinking for other problems.

The spinal cord and the brain. Most of the main nerves in your body connect with your *spinal cord.* It's an important center for the control of involuntary actions. But it's also a pathway to and from the brain.

Fig. 56-4 shows you what the brain looks like. The part of the brain joined to the spinal cord is the *medulla* (meh-*duhl*-uh). The medulla controls some involuntary acts. For example, it affects your breathing rate, and the rate of your heart beat.

The *cerebellum* (ser-uh-*bel*-um) lies below the back portion of the cerebrum. It main use is to make the muscles work together. For instance, it has a great deal to do with your actions when you catch a ball.

The *cerebrum* (*seh*-ruh-brum) is the largest part of the brain. It's the control center for your voluntary actions. It's also the center for memory, thought, and intelligence.

Injuries of nerve centers. When you cut a finger, skin and muscle tissues soon grow back in place. But if a nerve is destroyed, it's not replaced. Now you can see that damage to the nerve centers may be lasting and serious.

A blow on the head, for instance, may make a person unconscious. If the blow isn't heavy, and the brain isn't injured, the victim soon " comes to." But if the blow is heavy and at the base of the brain, the breathing center of the brain may be paralyzed. This causes death.

Also, a blow on the head may break blood vessels in the brain. The result is serious if a large vessel is broken. The blood which escapes presses on the brain. If a small vessel is broken, the result is less damaging. But head injuries are a good thing to avoid.

Quite a different story is the effect of infantile paralysis, or " polio." It's a disease caused by a virus. The disease may cause damage to some of the nerve centers in the spinal cord. When the nerve centers are destroyed, the muscles which they control are paralyzed.

CHECK YOUR FACTS . . .

Number 1 to 6 on a sheet of paper. Match the items in Column A *with the best answers in* Column B.

Column A	Column B
1. Medulla	*a.* Part of a nerve cell which may carry a message to a muscle cell
2. Axon	
3. Stimulus	*b.* Part of the brain responsible for memory and intelligence
4. Cerebellum	
5. Cerebrum	*c.* Reaction to a thing or force in the environment
6. Dendrite	
	d. Part of a nerve cell which may receive a message from another nerve cell
	e. Part of a muscle cell which is responsible for contraction
	f. Part of the brain which exercises involuntary control over your breathing actions
	g. Part of the spinal cord which controls the rate of heart beat
	h. Part of the brain which makes the muscles work together
	i. Thing or force of the environment which causes you to make a response

CHAPTER 57

How Smart Are You?

" Women have smaller brains than men," announced Jim, " and the bigger the brain the smarter you are."

" Oh, is that so? " replied Ann. " I suppose you think that makes men smarter? "

What do you think of this argument? Who was right?

Well, better finish reading this chapter. Then you can give the right answer.

Memory is the ability to remember past events. You learned in Chapter 56 that your ability to remember depends on cells in your cerebrum.

What about a dog or a cat? Do they remember past events? Probably you'll agree that they do, at least in some cases. Certainly their actions suggest that they gain from experience.

But suppose your dog gets too fat. Does he know this is bad for his health? Does he decide to stop eating and go on a diet? Definitely he doesn't. Such a decision and change in behavior call for more than just memory. You, of course, could make such a decision yourself.

How you make decisions. When you do make a decision, you're using *intelligence.* You're faced with a problem. You draw on your memory for related facts. Such facts can include things you read in books or learned in school. You relate the facts to your problem. Then you make a

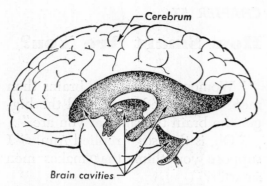

Fig. 57-1. Diagram of the human cerebrum and the brain cavities.

get it by plugging away at the facts. But such people may not use their facts in solving problems.

What does the cerebrum do? From reading Chapter 56 you know that the cerebrum is the center for memory. It's also the center for intelligence. In the cerebrum are two kinds of matter: (*1*) gray and (*2*) white. The **gray matter** covers the surface of the cerebrum. There are also masses of gray matter near the center of the cerebrum.

Cell bodies of nerve cells are found in the gray matter. The rest of the cerebrum is **white matter.** It's made up of axons, which carry messages from one cell to another.

The brain of an average man weighs about three pounds. The brain of an average woman weighs about two and three-fourths pounds. Scientists know that intelligence doesn't depend on brain size alone. It depends also on the perfection of the cell and axon structure. Messages must go along certain pathways if the brain is to work properly.

decision which is in line with these facts.

Man has great ability to stop and think. He has great ability to use his past experiences in solving problems.

Now you may ask: " Is intelligence the same as knowledge? "

The answer is no. The facts or experiences you can remember are your knowledge. People can be quite intelligent and not have much knowledge. This happens when they haven't had much chance to learn. Likewise, people with low intelligence can have a lot of knowledge. They

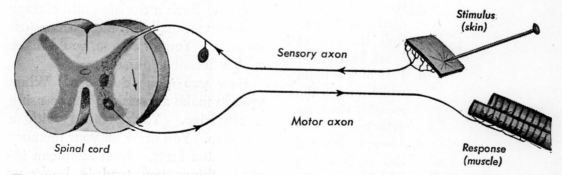

Fig. 57-2. Some reactions are automatic. This diagram shows how they work. When a pin pricks the skin, a message goes along a nerve to cells in the spinal cord. A response message goes along another nerve to muscles.

Fig. 57-3. When you've learned to ride a bicycle, you've formed a habit. You no longer think about the way you pedal or balance.

Forming habits. Everyone has certain habits. *Habits* are responses that you make so often you don't realize you make them.

Let's go back to the boy catching the ball. When he's learning, he has to think of a lot of things. No wonder he often seems awkward.

He finds or is told ways to use his hands. He tries them, and finds that they work. So he keeps on using them. After a lot of practice, he doesn't have to think about his hands any more. He's formed a habit of using them in certain ways.

The same thing happens when you learn to ride a bicycle. At first you find yourself thinking of all sorts of things: turning the handlebars, using the pedals, doing this, and doing that. But in time the job becomes easier. You do a lot of necessary things without thinking about them. You've formed riding habits.

Now suppose you ask: "Are habits a good thing?"

Before you answer, you must admit that there are good habits and bad habits. It's possible to form bad habits of catching a ball, or driving a car. You can form bad habits of studying, and bad habits of just about everything you do. That's one reason why you have teachers and coaches. They help you form good habits. You can see that bad habits are a handicap.

Good habits are a different story. They're the habits that work. When they work, your mind is left free to think of other things. Your responses will be more intelligent.

CHECK YOUR FACTS . . .

Number 1 to 6 on a sheet of paper. Mark each of the following items True *or* False.

1. Good habits are an advantage, because they free the mind for other uses.

2. The cerebrum contains both gray and white matter.

3. Intelligence depends on the size of the brain alone.

4. The cerebellum is the center for memory.

5. Knowledge and intelligence are just about the same thing.

6. Memory is the ability to recall past events.

CHAPTER 58

Chemical Messengers Affect Your Behavior

Ever see a person eight feet tall? There are such people. Sometimes they travel with circuses and shows. "A real giant," you might say.

Yes, but how do they get that way? Well, their height usually is due to a hormone (*hor*-moan). It's a growth hormone, produced by a small gland at the base of the brain. If too much of this hormone is produced, a giant results. If too little is produced, a midget develops.

How ductless glands affect you. You have a number of *ductless glands* in your body. From the name you can tell that they don't have ducts. Some of them are separate structures, off by themselves. Some are masses of gland tissue in various organs of the body. But in either case, their secretions, or *hormones,* are carried by the blood stream.

Hormones have been called "chemical messengers" of the body. They regulate the ways in which parts of your body develop and function. So

they have an effect on your behavior, just as the nervous system does. But the effect produced by these hormones is more gradual.

When ductless glands produce normal amounts of hormones, the effect on the body is normal. But too much

Fig. 58-1. A giant and a midget. The difference in size is caused by too much (giant) and too little (midget) of a hormone.

or too little of any one hormone may cause trouble.

The thyroid gland. Fig. 58-2 shows one of the ductless glands. It's the *thyroid* (*thy*-royd) *gland,* in the tissues of the neck around the windpipe. The hormone from this gland contains iodine. It affects the rate of oxygen use in your body. This is another way of saying that it affects the rate at which you use energy.

When the thyroid gland becomes greatly enlarged it forms a *goiter* (*goy*-ter). This happens when there isn't enough iodine in the diet. It's common in regions where there is little iodine in the soil and water. One way to prevent it is to add iodine to the diet. As you know, iodine is sometimes added to common table salt.

The thyroid gland sometimes produces too much or too little of its hormone. A partial lack of this hormone means that the body uses less than a normal amount of energy. Body motions slow down. The skin becomes dry and rough. Tissues under the skin thicken, and fat is deposited. A lack of thyroid hormone can be corrected by taking thyroid extract. But do this only on the advice of a doctor.

Too much thyroid hormone has opposite effects. It causes loss of weight. The eyeballs protrude, and the heart action becomes fast and irregular. Doctors can correct the condition by removing part of the thyroid gland.

The adrenal glands. You have two *adrenal* (ad-*ree*-n'l) *glands.* One is located at the upper end of each kid-

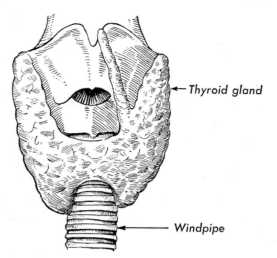

Fig. 58-2. The thyroid gland.

ney, as shown in Fig. 58-3. An adrenal gland produces more than one hormone. We'll just describe the hormone secreted by inner tissues of the gland. A trade name for this hormone is *adrenalin* (ad-*ren*-uh-lin).

When you're excited for any reason, your adrenal glands give off adrenalin. It goes into the blood vessels and soon reaches the digestive organs. Blood vessels in the walls of these organs contract. Digestion slows down for the time being. More blood goes to your head, arms, and legs. Your heart action is speeded up. Your liver gives up sugar to the blood. This sugar is a source of energy.

What's the result of these changes? They seem to make your muscles work faster. Your mind also works faster. You can meet an emergency.

Adrenalin has several uses in medicine. One of them is to contract small blood vessels. As a result, bleeding from such vessels can be reduced.

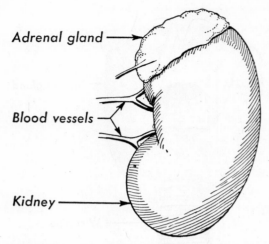

Fig. 58-3. An adrenal gland lies at the upper end of each kidney. Hormones are secreted by these glands.

Ductless glands of the pancreas. You read about the pancreas in Chapter 45. Some of its tissues produce a digestive fluid. But there are also groups of cells in the pancreas which act as ductless glands. They produce a hormone called *insulin* (*in*-suh-lin).

A normal amount of insulin in the blood seems necessary to good health. If there isn't enough insulin, cells of the body can't use sugar. Sugar begins to appear in the urine. At the same time, oxidation of fats in cells is faulty. Acid products are formed, and these products act like poisons. The victim now has the disease *diabetes* (dy-uh-*bee*-tez).

People who have diabetes can be treated successfully. They're given enough commercial insulin (not natural insulin) to offset the failure of their pancreas glands. Their bodies can now use sugar again. Insulin checks diabetes and keeps it under control so

people can lead normal lives. But it doesn't cure the disease.

Other ductless glands. We shall not try to study all the ductless glands and their hormones. As a matter of fact, some of them are still more or less a mystery. But scientific study goes on, and we shall know more about them in the years ahead.

CHECK YOUR FACTS . . .

Number 1 to 6 on a sheet of paper. For each of the items in Column A *select the best answer in* Column B.

Column A	Column B
1. Pancreas	a. Produces a hormone which contains iodine
2. Hormones	b. Disease in which oxidation of fats is faulty
3. Adrenal gland	c. Secretion from this gland prepares you for an emergency
4. Thyroid gland	d. Produces a hormone which digests sugar
5. Insulin	e. Located at base of the brain and affects rate of growth
6. Diabetes	f. Produces insulin
	g. Prevents but does not cure diabetes
	h. "Chemical messengers" in your body which regulate your various activities
	i. Enlarges for a period of 5 hours after meals

Your special senses make you aware of things around you. These senses are sight, hearing, taste, smell, and touch.

Behavior includes all the things that you do. It's influenced by your nervous system. Nerve cells receive and send out stimuli. Muscle cells make responses. Some controls of the nervous system are more or less automatic. Others are directed by what you think.

The spinal cord and brain are control centers. Many of these controls are automatic, but the cerebrum is the center for memory and intelligence. The medulla has more or less control over breathing and the rate of heart beat. The cerebellum is a control center for muscle actions. The spinal cord is a pathway for messages going to and from the brain. It is also a control center for many involuntary actions.

Memory is the ability to recall facts, or past events. When you use these facts to solve a complex problem, your behavior is intelligent. Habits can be either good or bad. Good habits are useful, because they free the cerebrum for more important work.

Various ductless glands also have an effect on behavior. They secrete hormones which pass through the blood to cells of the body. These hormones are the "chemical messengers" of the blood. Too much or too little of a certain hormone may affect normal growth. It may also keep your body from functioning properly.

W H A T   D O   T H E S E   W O R D S   M E A N ?

Adrenal gland	Farsightedness	Memory
Axon	Habit	Nearsightedness
Behavior	Hormone	Nerve
Cerebellum	Insulin	Nerve cell
Cerebrum	Intelligence	Pupil (eye)
Dendrite	Iris (eye)	Response
Diabetes	Knowledge	Spinal cord
Ductless glands	Lens (eye)	Stimulus
Eustachian tube	Medulla (brain)	Thyroid gland

ASK YOURSELF . . .

1. (a) How can farsightedness be corrected? (b) How can nearsightedness be corrected?
2. What kind of light should you have for reading?
3. (a) In what ways are people likely to become hard of hearing? (b) How can they avoid this?
4. (a) Where are the nerve endings of smell, taste, and touch located? (b) How much do you depend on these senses?
5. (a) What do the dendrites of a nerve cell do? (b) The axon?
6. (a) What kind of responses are automatic or largely so? (b) Where are the control centers for such responses?
7. (a) What controls the rate of your heart beat? (b) Your rate of breathing?
8. How does " polio " affect the nerve centers of the body?
9. Why can a person be intelligent and not have much knowledge?
10. Why are good habits an advantage to the person who has them?
11. When you make a decision why are you using intelligence?
12. (a) Why do some people develop into giants? (b) Midgets?
13. In what way does the thyroid hormone affect the body?
14. What effect does adrenalin have on the body?
15. How can diabetes be controlled?

GETTING THE FACTS . . .

1. Focus a microscope on a drop of culture containing some Paramecia. Add a tiny amount of red stain or red ink at one side of the culture. See what the Paramecia do as the red stain spreads. The stain is the stimulus. What the Paramecia do is the response. Is the response always the same? Are any Paramecia killed by the stain?

2. Examine models or charts of the eye and ear. Learn to recognize the parts described on pages 246 to 248. Study how these parts work together so that you can see and hear.

3. Have a member of the class roll up his left sleeve. Blindfold him, and put a pencil in his right hand. Now take another pencil and touch him lightly on the forearm. Have him try to touch the same spot on his forearm. Try different spots up and down the arm, and on both sides. Are nerve endings of touch evenly distributed through the skin?

4. Get a piece of cardboard or heavy paper about a foot square. Using a sharp pointed knife, cut out a square, a right triangle, a circle, a rectangle, a half circle, and a quarter circle. Blindfold a member of the class. Time him while he puts the cut-out pieces back in their proper places. Repeat the experiment two or three times. Normally, the

subject would use his sense or sight in doing the job. But he soon learns to depend upon his sense of touch. His first attempts are slow and halting. Soon, however, they get faster and more certain.

5. Study the behavior of a pet or laboratory animal for several days. Make a record of behavior that you believe to be (a) automatic, and (b) influenced by past experiences.

6. Get a calf, pig, or sheep brain from a butcher. Locate the cerebrum, cerebellum, and medulla. Cut into the cerebrum with a razor blade. Where is the gray matter? The white matter? See if you can find the internal cavities.

7. Make up ten True-False items based on the picture on page 245. Have half of them true and half false. You can begin with these two samples: 1. The policeman had a revolver in his right hand (false). 2. A young man had climbed a lamp post to see what was going on (true). Now have three or four friends study the picture for 30 seconds. Tell them in advance that they are going to take a test on the picture. Give them the test and see what happens. What does this tell you about how well we observe and remember?

8. Fig. 57–2 on page 254 is a diagram to show how some automatic acts take place. The kind of action shown here is a reflex act. The nerve cells and muscle cells shown make up a reflex arc. Look up reflex acts in the books at the end of this unit. Report on reflex acts that are automatic or largely so. Find out what is meant by a conditioned reflex.

9. Sit in a dimly lighted part of a room with your back to the windows for two or three minutes. Look at your eyes in a mirror. Note the size of the pupils. Now go to a window and look out at the light for two or three minutes. Note the size of your pupils again. This change in the size of the pupils is the result of a reflex act. It is an automatic response over which you have no control.

Books You May Like . . .

American National Red Cross. FIRST AID TEXTBOOK. The Blakiston Company, Philadelphia. 1945. First aid treatment for shock, wounds, injured bones and muscles, poisons, injuries caused by heat and cold, and other emergencies. It includes a general discussion of the human body.

American National Red Cross. CIVIL DEFENSE SUPPLEMENT TO THE AMERICAN RED CROSS FIRST AID TEXTBOOK. The Blakiston Company, Philadelphia. 1951. This deals with the treatment of injuries related to bomb explosions.

Barnett, Anthony. THE HUMAN SPECIES. W. W. Norton & Company, New York. 1950. A discussion of modern biology and how it relates to everyday social problems.

Brownell, Clifford L., and Williams, Jesse Feiring. THE HUMAN BODY AND HOW IT WORKS. American Book Company, New York. 1946. A standard book on the human body and its functions, for the highschool student.

Gerard, Ralph Waldo. THE BODY FUNCTIONS. John Wiley and Sons, New York. 1941. The emphasis in this book is on the way functions are carried out in the human body. A useful reference book for the student who has special interests in this field.

Young, Clarence W., and Stebbins, G. Ledyard. THE HUMAN ORGANISM AND THE WORLD OF LIFE. Harper and Brothers, New York. 1951. Part I of this book is a good reference on the structures and functions of the body.

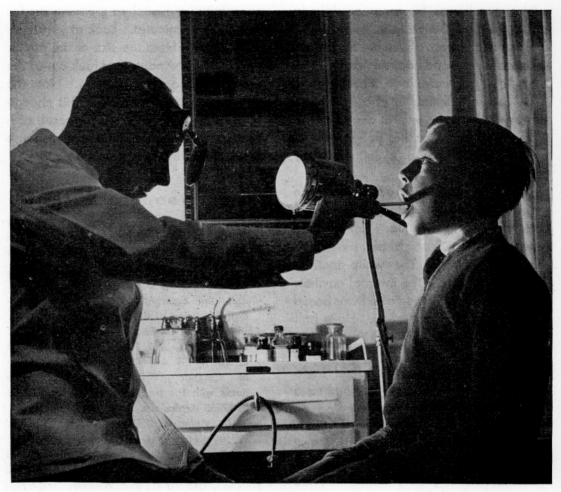

Fig. 58-4. A regular medical check up should be part of your health program.

HIGH LIGHTS OF UNIT 5

The skeleton supports your body and is a place of attachment for muscles. It also protects vital organs.

Your digestive system includes a mouth, esophagus, stomach, small and large intestines. Foods are acted on by digestive enzymes. The foods are then broken down into soluble substances which are carried to cells of the body.

Foods contain vitamins which are necessary for good health. A balanced diet provides for energy needs. It also supplies materials for growth and repair.

Human blood includes plasma in which there are red and white blood cells. The blood carries absorbed food and oxygen to the cells. It carries waste products away from the cells. In the lung tissues the blood receives new supplies of oxygen, and gets rid of carbon dioxide waste.

Solid wastes leave the body through the large intestine. Liquid wastes and water leave the body in the urine. Excess heat and water also leave the body through the skin and in the breath.

Your special senses make you aware of things. Your behavior consists of responses you make to various stimuli.

The spinal cord and brain are central controls of the nervous system. Some of these controls are automatic, or largely automatic. In other cases, memory and intelligence direct your responses.

Hormones from ductless glands also have effects on behavior. They regulate various functions in the body.

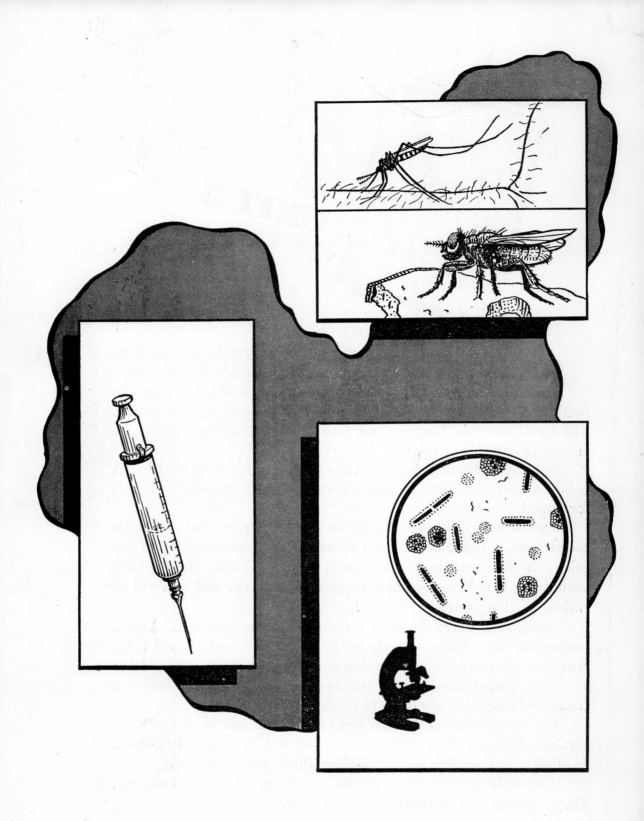

Unit 6

Most Diseases

Can Be

Controlled

Ed got a bad cut on his finger. It was bleeding a lot in spite of the bandage Jim put on for him.

"Guess we better take you down to see Doc Jones," Jim told him. "I don't think my first-aid work is so hot, and it's better to be safe."

The doctor looked at the cut finger and put on a better bandage. "I'm going to give you a shot of penicillin," he said. "Miss Smith, please get the hypo ready."

Miss Smith, the nurse, handed the doctor a loaded hypo. "This won't hurt you a bit, Ed," the doctor said as he jabbed the needle into Ed's skin. "I just want to make sure I kill any germs that may have entered through that cut. You see, you might get a bad infection, and I want to fight it with penicillin. It's better to protect the body from germs than to cure the infection once it's taken hold. If you'd stepped on a nail, I'd be giving you another kind of shot."

"Gee, thanks a lot, Doc," Ed smiled as he and Jim left.

Topic 1

GERMS CAUSE MANY DISEASES

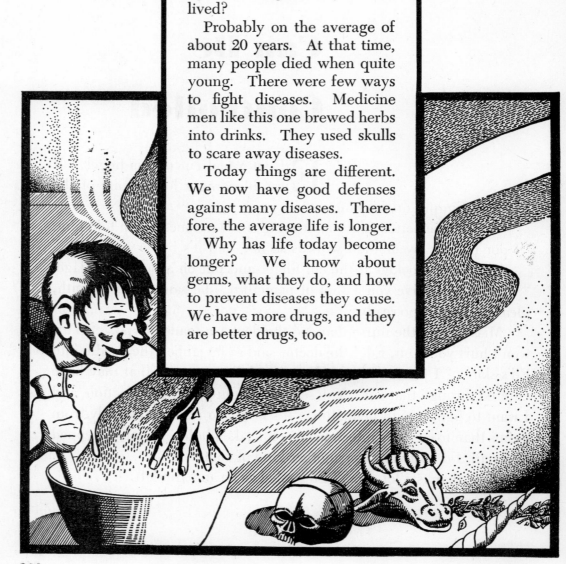

If you'd been born 400 years ago, how long would you have lived?

Probably on the average of about 20 years. At that time, many people died when quite young. There were few ways to fight diseases. Medicine men like this one brewed herbs into drinks. They used skulls to scare away diseases.

Today things are different. We now have good defenses against many diseases. Therefore, the average life is longer.

Why has life today become longer? We know about germs, what they do, and how to prevent diseases they cause. We have more drugs, and they are better drugs, too.

AMONG THE NEW WORDS FOR THIS TOPIC

- **ANTISEPTIC** (an-tih-*sep*-tik).   A substance which destroys germs or checks the activity of germs.
- **EPIDEMIC** (ep-ih-*dem*-ik).   An attack of disease which affects many people in a certain area.
- **IMMUNE** (im-*yoon*).   Not subject to a certain disease.
- **INFECTION** (in-*fek*-shun).   Condition due to the presence of germs in a living tissue.

CHAPTER 59

What Are Disease Germs?

Ed and Jim were arguing about diseases.

"You can't see germs," said Ed.

"That's right," answered Jim, "all germs are bacteria."

"Oh, no, they're not," Ed told him, "some other things are germs, too."

There are many kinds of germs. You probably will agree with both boys on one point. Germs are small. That's why they were a mystery for so many years. Until microscopes were invented, scientists couldn't study germs. They couldn't see them.

Are all germs bacteria? By no means! Many germs, to be sure, *are* bacteria. But some of them are one-celled animals or protozoa. Some of them are related to the molds and yeasts. And some of them are in-between types. They might be either bacteria or protozoa. Then too, there are the viruses, which you read about in Chapter 6. Viruses cause some diseases, such as colds and influenza.

If you look at Fig. 59-1, you'll see two general types of disease-producers. One is a group of bacteria. The other is a protozoan. Viruses, as you know, are like liquids. They're not like cells.

You should remember also that not all diseases are caused by germs. You've read about some of these non-germ diseases in Unit 5.

Germs are all around us. "Can I avoid contact with germs?" you ask. No, not if you lead a normal, active life. There are many different kinds of germs, and they're around you all the time.

Germs may be in foods and in liquids. They may be on drops of moisture in the air. They're on and in the bodies of your pets, your domestic animals, and your cultivated plants. They're in the dust and out-of-doors.

Germs in plants? To be sure! Sometimes one of the farmer's biggest problems is to protect crop plants against germ diseases. And the farm-

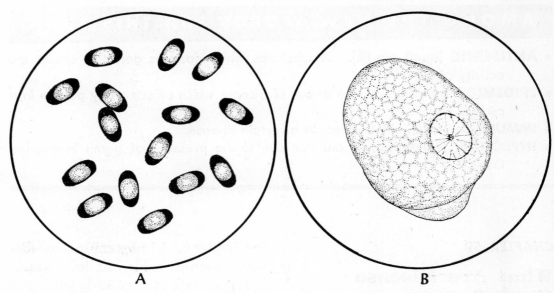

Fig. 59-1. Two types of germs. The germs shown in A are one-celled plants (bacteria). The germ shown in B is a one-celled animal (protozoan).

er must also protect his animals against germ diseases.

"But," you say, "if germs are in air, dust, liquids, foods, plants, and animals, how do we escape them?"

The answer is you don't escape them completely. They're even in your body. Did you know that various bacteria and protozoa live in your digestive canal at all times? It's a fact. Some of them don't cause diseases — they're not germs. Others can cause disease if they're enough of them and if your resistance is poor.

Yet with all these germs in and around you, it's quite possible that you may not get sick. How can this be?

The answer is that everybody has certain defenses against germs. You'll read more about these in Chapter 61. As a result, everybody is more or less

immune (im-*yoon*) to some diseases. This means that he's not likely to develop the diseases in question. But remember one thing. An immunity usually is for *one disease* and for *that disease only*. Being immune to smallpox doesn't make you immune to typhoid fever, too.

You should also remember that some immunities are only partial. They protect you if you don't get too many germs of a certain kind in your body. Also, some immunities are only temporary. You have protection for a time, but it doesn't last. So it's a good rule to avoid germs as much as possible. This is why everyone favors sanitation, pure foods, and public health.

Epidemics of disease. Did you ever hear of an *epidemic* (ep-ih-*dem*-ik)? In an epidemic a large part of the pop-

Fig. 59-2. An old drawing of a plague doctor. This type of costume was worn hundreds of years ago. The beak of the face mask was filled with spices. But no one really knew what caused the plague.

ulation in an area gets a certain disease. This can happen when a disease to which many people aren't immune is spread.

The worst epidemics happened centuries ago, before scientists knew anything about germs. One of the epidemic diseases was the so-called plague. This disease struck ancient Rome, and for a time, 10,000 people died every day. Later on, in the Middle Ages, Europe and even England were visited by the plague, or "black death" as it was called.

Back in those days people didn't know what caused such diseases.

They suspected all sorts of things. Some thought that comets, earthquakes, and eclipses were related to plagues. Others believed that the heavens were angry, and that the plagues were a punishment. Still others blamed people who were supposed to poison the wells or to cast an evil spell on other people. These people were tortured and often killed.

It wasn't until much later that the truth came out. And it proved to be a story of germs, rats, and fleas. The famous fire of London put an end to one plague because it burned out the rats and fleas.

House rats, as well as man, are attacked by the bacteria that cause plague. These rats often have rat fleas on their bodies. The fleas live by biting the rats and sucking their blood. Now when a flea bites a rat that has plague, some of the plague germs get into the flea's body. Later on, if the flea bites a man, some of the germs, in turn, get into his body.

So the plague or "black death" has

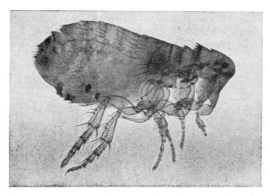

Fig. 59-3. An enlarged photograph of a flea. It is the rat flea which carries the germs of plague.

stopped being a great killer. We now know how to guard against it. But the disease still goes on in some parts of Asia. Do you see now why care is taken that rats from incoming ships don't enter our seaports?

The conquest of germs. Science has conquered many diseases. They include many of the childhood diseases. People live much longer today. But we still have our problems. Against some diseases we have few defenses. Others are checked only by constant effort.

CHECK YOUR FACTS . . .

Number 1 to 6 on a sheet of paper. Select the best answer for each of the following items.

1. Plague is carried from rats to men by (mosquitoes, rat fleas, lice) . . . ? . . .

2. Germs include (all bacteria, certain bacteria, all protozoa) . . . ? . . .

3. A person who isn't made ill by the germs of a certain disease is (immune, parasitic, resilient) . . . ? . . .

Fig. 60-1. Joseph Lister explaining to his fellow doctors how wounds can be kept free of infection.

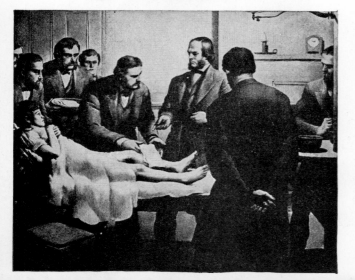

4. A person who is immune to one disease (is, isn't) . . . ? . . . necessarily immune to another disease.

5. Immunities may be (partial and temporary, good and bad, large and small) . . . ? . . .

6. In the following list, disease germs may attack (domestic animals, crop plants, both crop plants and domestic animals) . . . ? . . .

CHAPTER 60

How You Can Get Diseases

How do disease germs get into your body?

The answer is, in various ways. It depends partly on the germ and its habits. Let's consider some of the possibilities.

Contact with germs. Everyone gets cuts and scratches now and then. They're wounds, but not very serious ones.

Wounds are an old story, especially in time of war. But until about 100 years ago people didn't know that wounds could become places of infection (in-*fek*-shun). *Infection* means that germs have gotten into living tissues. In other words, people didn't know that germs could get into wounds. They didn't know that red, swollen skin and pus were due to the presence of germs.

As a result, even minor wounds sometimes led to the loss of a leg or an arm. Half the unfortunate people

Fig. 60-2. When you sneeze, a nasal spray is thrown out several feet in front of you.

who had arms or legs removed died from wound infection.

How did the germs get into wounds? They got in from the blades of bayonets or swords, or from dust on the ground. They even entered from the unclean bandages that often were used. In other words, the germs got in through various types of plain contact.

An English doctor named Joseph Lister changed all this. He was worried about the high death rate in many kinds of operations. He knew that in France, Louis Pasteur had blamed certain diseases on bacteria.

So Lister used dilute carbolic acid to treat a compound fracture. In such a fracture a broken bone end is pushed out through the skin. He was pleased to find that the injured part healed without infection. There was no *pus,* which is a sure sign of an infection.

Here was something new. From it came the use of antiseptics (an-tih-*sep*-tiks). An *antiseptic* is a substance that you can use to kill germs in wounds. Today you use merthiolate, mercurochrome, and other antiseptics to kill germs that may get into your cuts and scratches.

Nose droplets are one kind of contact with other people. Take a look at Fig. 60-2. It's a photograph of a man sneezing. But not an ordinary photograph! It was taken at such

Fig. 60-3. The hairs and bristles which cover a housefly are ideal lodging places for dirt. This dirt is almost sure to contain germs.

high speed that the nose spray became part of the picture.

When you sneeze you throw out such a spray. When you breathe or talk, you throw out a smaller spray, but it's still a spray. This spray is made up of little droplets. Certain germs " ride " on or in such droplets. In that way it's possible for them to get from one person to another.

Now you see being in a crowd of people isn't a good idea, especially when certain diseases are common.

Germs in foods and liquids. Another way in which dangerous germs

get into your body has to do with what you eat and drink. In Chapter 49 you read about food poisoning. You learned that germs are sometimes present in cans or jars of preserved foods. You also learned that germs may get into foods in various ways.

How can this happen? Let's suppose dust is blown into food. Dust may contain germs. The food may be handled by people who have germs on their hands. The dishes in which food is placed may contain germs. A housefly or a cockroach, covered with germs, may crawl over the food. There really are all sorts of possibilities.

Of course, germs can get into milk and water in much the same way. But there's a special danger in the case of water. Human wastes are sometimes dumped into streams. Then the water isn't safe to drink until it's been boiled or treated chemically. One germ that often enters the human body in water is the germ of typhoid fever. Germs which cause various intestinal diseases may also be in water as well as in foods.

There's a special danger in the case of milk. Cows which produced the milk may have such diseases as tuberculosis or undulant fever. Of course *pasteurized* (*pass*-ter-yzed) *milk* is safe to drink. This is milk that has been heated enough to kill dangerous germs. But in the country, people still drink a lot of milk that hasn't been pasteurized.

Germs and biting insects. In Chapter 34 you learned that the dreaded diseases malaria and yellow fever come to us through mosquito bites. The malaria germs — and there are at least three types — are protozoans. Yellow fever, however, seems to be caused by a virus.

We get plague from the bites of rat fleas. Typhus fever and some other diseases are brought to us by lice. All these insects are bloodsuckers. They carry the disease germs from the blood of one person to the blood of another person. One way to fight these diseases is to kill the insects that carry them.

What are your chances? Can you go through life and avoid all germ diseases? By this time you'll probably agree that the chance is slim.

But cheer up! Your body has defenses of its own. Modern science can also add special defenses to these. Your chances are still good, as you'll learn in the next chapter.

CHECK YOUR FACTS . . .

Number 1 to 6 on a piece of paper. Select the best answer for each of the following items.

1. A substance which is used to kill germs in wounds is a(n) (vaccine, antiseptic, sedative) . . . ? . . .

2. Malaria is a disease due to the presence in the body of certain (bacteria, viruses, protozoa) . . . ? . . .

3. We get typhus fever as a result of being bitten by (ticks, lice, mosquitoes) . . . ? . . .

4. Scientists believe that yellow fever is caused by a (virus, bacterium, protozoan) . . . ? . . .

Fig. 60-4. This is one of the many types of mosquitoes. It is a species which carries the virus of yellow fever.

5. You'd be most likely to get typhoid fever from (contaminated water, nasal spray, contact) . . . ? . . .

6. Milk that has been heated enough to kill dangerous germs is (vaccinated, immune, pasteurized) . . . ? . . .

CHAPTER 61

Your Body Can Fight Disease Germs

What, then, are the defenses which make your body able to ward off many germs?

A number of things, some of them quite surprising. But let's begin with

Fig. 61-1. Your skin serves to keep many germs out of your body. But even the skin has small openings through which some germs can enter.

something you know about, like your skin.

The skin is one protection against germs. You learned about the skin in Chapter 53. The skin, as you know, covers your entire body. Its tough coating forms a protection against the entrance of many disease germs.

Some germs, of course, do get into the skin. For the skin has various openings. If you examine Fig. 61-1, you'll see that there are openings through which hairs grow out. There are also openings where the ducts of skin glands reach the surface. Germs can work down into these openings.

Then too, some germs can get through thin membranes such as the lips. Also, the skin may get cracked,

scratched, or cut. But in general, the skin keeps many germs out of your body.

Defenses in the digestive canal. As you've learned, germs may enter the digestive canal with food. Does the entrance of a few germs mean that you'll get sick? By no means. It usually takes a lot of germs to produce an active case of disease. The germs that do get into your body must keep on living. They must multiply and become more numerous.

This doesn't always happen. For one thing, the stomach juices normally contain an acid. This acid isn't strong, but it kills some germs. In the intestines, invading germs must survive another test. They must live

SOME FACTS ABOUT COMMON DISEASES

Diseases	How Spread	Cause	Notes
Chicken pox	Contact	Virus	Common, but generally mild disease of childhood
Common cold	Contact	Virus or viruses	Common cause of discomfort and loss of efficiency
Diphtheria	Contact	Bacterium	Formerly a common cause of death in childhood
Influenza	Contact	Virus or viruses	Has appeared in epidemic form. Often followed by pneumonia.
Malaria	Mosquitoes	Protozoa	Several types of this disease
Measles	Contact	Virus	Most common children's disease
Mumps	Contact	Virus	Causes swelling of glands in neck region
Polio (Infantile Paralysis)	One of the big questions	Virus	Feared because of its crippling and other effects
Pneumonia	Contact	Bacteria (virus)	Over thirty different types including virus pneumonia
Scarlet fever	Contact	Bacteria	Can cause serious aftereffects
Smallpox	Contact	Virus	Formerly a common cause of death
Sore throat (septic)	Contact	Bacteria	Some types can cause serious aftereffects
Tetanus	Contact (wounds)	Bacterium	Causes disease known as lockjaw
Tuberculosis	Contact	Bacterium	X-ray reveals infection
Typhoid fever	Food and drink	Bacterium	One good reason for not drinking polluted water
Typhus fever	Lice	Borderline organism	Head and body lice are not just harmless little pests
Yellow fever	Mosquitoes	Virus	A dreaded disease in warm countries
Whooping cough	Contact	Bacterium	Common disease of children

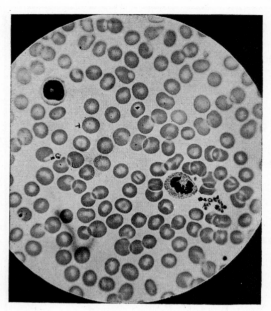

Fig. 61-2. The two large cells in this greatly enlarged photograph are white blood cells. Notice that these white blood cells have nuclei.

in competition with the bacteria and protozoa which normally live there. No one knows just how effective this test is. But it probably results in the death of many of these invading germs.

Defenses in the blood and tissues. Some germs which enter the body through the mouth stay in the digestive canal. Others enter the blood stream and so get into the body tissues. And of course some germs don't enter through the mouth. In this case they get directly into the blood and body tissues.

"What happens now?" you ask. "Are there any defenses in the blood stream, or in the various tissues of the body?"

Yes, fortunately there are. Your blood contains several kinds of white blood cells. (See Fig. 61-2.) Such cells can destroy some invading germs. The white blood cells collect at a place where there's an infection. They destroy the germs which cause the infection if these germs aren't too numerous. White blood cells even leave the blood vessels. They pass out among the cells of a tissue to reach the seat of infection.

And as a matter of fact, white blood cells aren't the only cells that can destroy germs. Some tissue cells can also do this useful work.

And finally, there are substances in blood and tissues that kill germs. Or, in some cases, they keep germs from multiplying. Some of these germ-killing substances were present when you were born. Others were developed in the course of your life. They're the reason you're somewhat or largely immune to certain diseases.

How immunity is developed. You probably know that you're apt to get some diseases only once. When you have such a disease, immune substances are formed in your blood. These substances stay there after you get well. They're a more or less permanent defense against that disease.

However, you don't develop this lasting immunity for all diseases. Consider, for instance, the common cold. The common cold isn't a dangerous killer, but it causes a lot of discomfort and lost school days.

Do you develop immune substances for the common cold? Possibly. But if so, they're not very lasting. Or perhaps there are many kinds of colds, and being immune to one kind doesn't protect you against other kinds.

You must remember that these immune substances are definite in their action. A substance which protects against one disease usually doesn't protect against other diseases.

People vary in their resistance to disease. No two people are exactly alike. This is true when we compare their structures. It's also true when we study their ability to resist diseases.

As you might guess, one person may be more or less immune to diseases A, B, C, and D. If he gets them at all, he gets them only in mild form. Another person may be more or less immune to diseases C, E, F, and G. But he's a ready victim for diseases A, B, and D.

Remember too, that some immunities come and go. And for some diseases there are no effective immunities.

So you see how your body has a number of defenses against germs. But these defenses aren't always complete. However, science has given us other defenses. We have special drugs and similar things that destroy germs after the germs are in our bodies.

CHECK YOUR FACTS . . .

Number 1 to 6 on a sheet of paper. Mark each of the following items True *or* False.

1. Certain chemical substances in human blood and tissues kill invading germs.

2. Most people have about the same resistance to diseases.

3. White blood cells commonly gather in tissues which are infected.

4. As long as the skin layer is unbroken, germs can't get into it.

5. Acid in stomach juices favors the survival of invading germs.

6. Some tissue cells can destroy invading germs.

Germs cause some of our most dreaded diseases. Such diseases affect not only ourselves, but also the plants and animals that we raise. Germs are tiny plants, animals, and viruses. They're all around us and even in our bodies.

Germs get into your body as a result of contact. They get in with the things you eat and drink. They're brought to you by certain biting insects.

Fortunately, your body has defenses against germs. Your skin forms one protection. Acid in your stomach juices is another. Bacteria and protozoa in your intestines compete with invading germs. White blood cells and some tissue cells kill germs.

In addition, your body is largely or partly immune to certain diseases. This is because of special substances in your blood and tissues.

W H A T   D O   T H E S E   W O R D S   M E A N ?

Antiseptic	Germ	Pasteurized milk
Bacteria	Immune	Pus
Epidemic	Infection	Virus

ASK YOURSELF . . .

1. (a) What kinds of living things are properly called germs?   (b) In what ways are they alike?
2. Why is it practically impossible to avoid all germs?
3. (a) Where are the substances located which make you immune to certain diseases?   (b) Are all of these immunities complete?   (c) Are all of them permanent?
4. (a) Why were people afraid of the " black death " during medieval times?   (b) Would you fear such a disease as much today?
5. (a) Name two or three antiseptics.   (b) For what purposes do you use them?
6. When you say that you get germs by " contact," what do you mean?
7. Why is it unwise to stay in an unventilated room that is crowded with people?
8. Would you be as likely to get germ diseases if all people around you were healthy?
9. (a) What germs may enter the body with foods?   (b) With liquids?
10. Why is chlorine sometimes added to city water?
11. Why is it unsafe to drink from open brooks and pools?
12. From the health standpoint, why is it unwise to discharge sewage into rivers?
13. Why are mosquitoes, lice, houseflies, and cockroaches a threat to your health?
14. What protection does your own body have against invading germs?
15. Do all people have equal resistance to diseases?
16. (a) Are all diseases caused by germs?   (b) Name some that aren't.

GETTING THE FACTS . . .

1. With the aid of your teacher, examine lantern slides or microscope slides of germs. Different types of bacteria and protozoa may be included.

2. With the aid of your teacher, make several agar surfaces for the growth of bacteria. Use Petri dishes and nutrient agar. Figure 61-3 shows two agar sur-

faces on which colonies of bacteria have developed.

3. Put scrapings from your teeth on two or three agar surfaces. Put a little dust from the floor on two or three other agar surfaces. Cover these preparations. Keep them in a warm place for several days. Note the bacterial colonies which develop.

4. Put scrapings from your teeth and dust on different agar surfaces. Then flood the surfaces with iodine solution or 70% alcohol. Pour off any surplus iodine. Cover the agar surfaces, and keep them in a warm place for several days. See how the results differ from those in No. 3.

5. Consult with public health officials. Find out which germ diseases are most common in your community. Compare

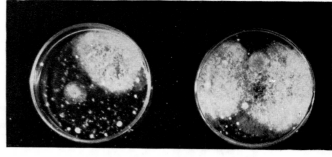

Fig. 61-3. Two Petri dishes with colonies of bacteria growing on agar surfaces.

the records of three or four recent years. What diseases have become less common?

6. Visit a garden or a field. See if you can find some plants that are being attacked by diseases. Many plant diseases are caused by molds, rusts, mildews, and bacteria.

7. If you have Riker mounts of life histories, study the development of houseflies, cockroaches, fleas, and lice. Report on the ways in which you can control these insect pests.

Topic 2

YOUR DOCTOR CAN PROTECT YOU FROM MANY DISEASES

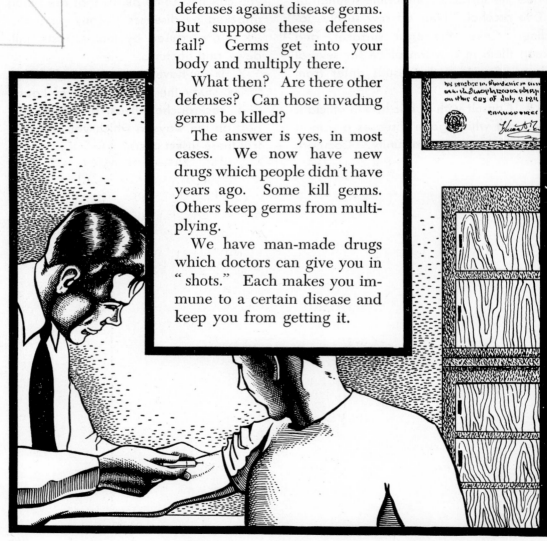

Everyone has certain natural defenses against disease germs. But suppose these defenses fail? Germs get into your body and multiply there.

What then? Are there other defenses? Can those invading germs be killed?

The answer is yes, in most cases. We now have new drugs which people didn't have years ago. Some kill germs. Others keep germs from multiplying.

We have man-made drugs which doctors can give you in "shots." Each makes you immune to a certain disease and keep you from getting it.

AMONG THE NEW WORDS FOR THIS TOPIC

- **ANTIBIOTICS** (an-tee-by-ot-iks). Drugs obtained from bacteria and fungi, which limit the growth of germs in the human body.
- **CANCER** (kan-ser). An overgrowth of tissue which may spread from the place of origin to other parts of the body.
- **SULFA** (sul-fuh) **DRUGS.** A group of drugs used to control various germs.
- **TETANUS** (tet-uh-nus). A dangerous type of wound infection caused by a certain kind of bacteria.
- **VACCINATE** (vak-sih-nayt). To put cowpox material in the skin, and thus make a person immune to smallpox.
- **VACCINE** (vak-seen). A substance used to provide immunity to a germ disease.

CHAPTER 62

What Is Immunity?

In Chapter 59 you learned that some people are immune to certain germ diseases. Either they're born that way, or develop the immunity by having a mild case of the disease. In Chapter 61 you read some things about defenses of the body.

Now you're ready to ask "How can I become immune?"

Of course, you have to go a little further with your question. You have to say what disease you have in mind. You must remember that immunity to one disease doesn't provide immunity to other diseases. Then too, there doesn't seem to be any immunity for a few diseases. Or, if there is, the immunity lasts so short a time that it has little value.

The case of smallpox. Suppose the disease you have in mind is smallpox. Then a rather lasting immunity exists.

You can get this immunity without having the disease.

Let's look at the story of smallpox for a moment. It's a disease that has killed people for centuries. Even Egyptian mummies 3,000 years old show the pits of old smallpox sores. From 1700 to 1800 sixty million Europeans died from the disease.

At about this time a way to prevent smallpox was brought to Europe from Asia. Material from old pox sores was put in scratches on the skin. People who were treated this way developed mild cases of smallpox. Usually they got well, and then they were immune. But one problem remained. The people with mild cases of smallpox were carriers of the disease. In other words, they spread the disease among people who weren't immune.

Shortly before 1800, Dr. Edward Jenner found a better solution. That was to *vaccinate* (*vak*-sih-nayt) people with cowpox material. He merely applied cowpox material to small

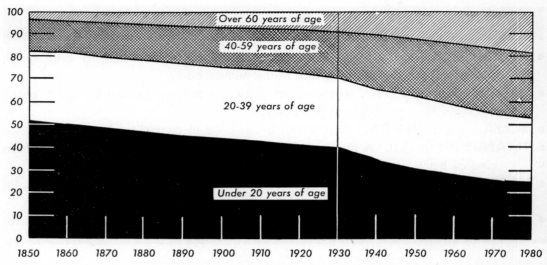

Fig. 62-1. Here's a graph which shows how the human population is changing. The figures on the left give the per cent of the population. Those below give ten year periods. Note that the data show probable changes as far in the future as 1980. People are living longer today. In 1850, people under 20 years of age made up more than half of the total population in this country.

scratches in the skin. Cowpox is a disease of cattle. Humans get cowpox only in a mild form. But if you're vaccinated with cowpox you become immune to smallpox which is a dangerous disease. The immunity lasts five years in many cases. In a few cases it's good even after 20 years.

The good thing about Jenner's method was that it made people immune to smallpox. But it did more. People who were vaccinated with cowpox weren't a menace to other people. They weren't carriers of smallpox.

Vaccination for smallpox did much to change health conditions. The disease was no longer a great killer. But we still have outbreaks of smallpox here and there. This is because there are some who don't get vaccinated.

The case of typhoid fever. Another great killer in times past was typhoid fever. This disease is caused by a kind of bacterium which forms colonies in the human intestines. The body wastes of someone who has the disease contain these bacteria. If any part of these wastes get into food, water, or milk, the disease may be passed on to other people. Flies can also carry the germs.

Some people who recover from typhoid fever have the germs of this disease in their bodies for years. They're carriers of the disease. This means that germs from their bodies can get into the bodies of other people.

Years ago typhoid fever was greatly feared, especially by soldiers. In the Spanish American War, during a period of three and a half months, about

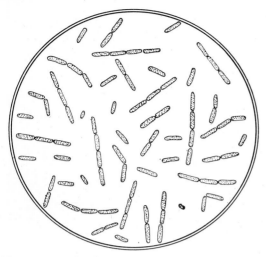

Fig. 62-2. This is a drawing taken from a microscope slide. It shows the bacteria which cause typhoid fever.

20% of the United States soldiers had typhoid fever. But in World War I and World War II the story was different. By this time a way of making people immune to typhoid fever was in use.

How, then, can you become immune to typhoid fever? The answer is simple. Scientists raise cultures of typhoid bacteria in the laboratory. The bacteria are killed and put in a typhoid vaccine (*vak*-seen). A *vaccine* is a substance used to produce immunity. The vaccine is then injected into human tissues. Typhoid " shots " are injections of the vaccine.

Since the typhoid bacteria have been killed they can't multiply. So the person who receives the vaccine can't get a case of typhoid fever. But his blood develops substances which make him immune to the disease. This immunity lasts for one or two years. Then the person should get another " booster shot " to be fully protected.

The case of tetanus. Have you heard of a person who stepped on a nail and then developed lockjaw? Lockjaw is the disease *tetanus* (*tet-uh*-nus). It's caused by a kind of bacterium. One of its features is a tightening of the jaw muscles. Hence the name " lockjaw."

The germ of tetanus lives in the intestines of horses. But it seems to do horses no harm. It's present in horse manure, so it's likely to be found in the surface soil wherever horses have been. There is one interesting thing about this tetanus germ. It won't grow well if it is exposed to plenty of air. Therefore, tetanus germs are most likely to develop in deep wounds, such as you get in stepping

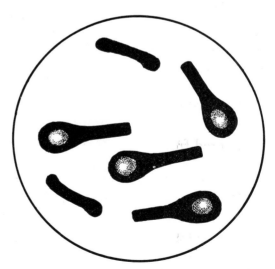

Fig. 62-3. The germs shown here cause the disease tetanus or "lockjaw." This disease is really one type of wound infection.

Fig. 62-4. Modern laboratories like this have become very important in the detection and control of disease.

on a nail. Doctors have a tetanus shot which will protect you against the disease.

But suppose you haven't had tetanus toxoid and you get a deep wound of the puncture type. What are your chances? Well, there's another defense measure. In this case a doctor gives you a shot of tetanus antitoxin (an-ti-*tok*-sin). In most cases this antitoxin will protect you against the disease. An *antitoxin* is another substance used to produce immunity.

Active and passive immunity. The fact is that immunity can be either active or passive. You have *active immunity* when your own blood has formed the substances that protect you. This is what happens when you get a shot of tetanus vaccine or have recovered from an attack.

We get tetanus antitoxin from the blood of horses which are immune to tetanus. It contains the substances which prevent development of the disease. When it is added to your own blood, you have *passive immunity*. Your own blood hasn't formed the protecting substances. Also, passive immunity usually doesn't last as long as active immunity.

Immunity to other diseases. Smallpox, typhoid fever, and tetanus aren't the only germ diseases to which you can be made immune. Similar protection can also be given, at least for a time, against cholera, diphtheria, yellow fever, plague, and various other diseases. But for some germ diseases there is no such protection. However, scientists are at work on these problems. There's no doubt that they will find ways of providing immunity to some other diseases.

CHECK YOUR FACTS . . .

Number 1 to 6 on a sheet of paper. Select the best answer for each of the following items.

1. When your own blood develops substances which protect you from a disease, you have (active, partial, passive) ...?... immunity.

2. The scientist who discovered a method of vaccinating for smallpox was (Pasteur, Jenner, Hooke) ...?...

3. You would be most likely to get typhoid germs from (air, soil, water) ...?...

4. Tetanus germs don't live successfully in the presence of (air, soil, moisture) ...?...

5. Smallpox is due to a (kind of bacterium, protozoan, virus) ...?...

6. A person whose body contains germs that may be carried to other people is a (mutant, carrier, vaccine) ...?...

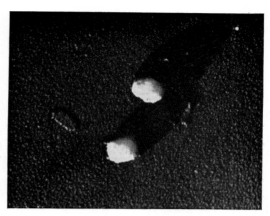

Fig. 63-1. This is what the virus of smallpox looks like when it is magnified 29,000 times.

CHAPTER 63

Public Health Concerns Everyone

What happens when all people are immune to disease? Does the disease cease to exist? Is it no longer a problem?

Think carefully before you try to answer.

Why are some diseases controlled? Making people immune to germ diseases is one way to conquer these diseases. Let's take a look at the record. In years past smallpox, diphtheria, and typhoid fever were great killers. But it's different today. What has brought about the change?

For one thing many people are now made immune to these diseases early in life. Thus the public health is improved. Fewer people actually get the diseases. There are fewer sources of germs that can attack other people. These diseases are nearly conquered.

But is the conquest complete? Unfortunately, we have to say no. This leads you to the question "Why not?"

Perhaps you can think of the answer yourself. Smallpox, diphtheria, and typhoid fever are diseases against which people can get protection. But for one reason or another some people don't get the protection. For instance, they may not worry about a disease because it's not common any more. The first thing you know some of them get the disease.

Animals carry germs. It's not possible to get rid of diseases even though defenses are good. There are always some people who carry the infection. We could come closer to conquering the diseases if we used all the knowledge and defenses we have.

Fig. 63-2. A Health Department warning. Some diseases are easily spread by contact.

Then too, there's another problem. Some of the germs that attack us also attack wild and domestic animals. We have some of the same germs as cattle, pigs, horses, and other livestock do. You know that rats may carry germs that affect our welfare. Even our pets are sources of some germs. So getting rid of germs in all the people won't get rid of all germ diseases.

The problem of disease carriers. But at least we can greatly reduce the number of germs around us. One way to do it is to keep our people healthy. If you come in contact with people who don't have dangerous germs, you are fairly safe yourself.

This is why you're quarantined when you have a disease that you can spread by contact. It's why many hospitals have special wards for people with such diseases. In such cases, the idea is to keep well people from coming in contact with germs.

One function of your state or local Board of Health is to deal with quarantines. In some cases only the person who has the disease is quarantined. In others, all people who have been near the sick person are also quarantined. The United States Public Health Service does the same kind of thing on a broader scale. It quarantines people from foreign lands who have, or may have, germ diseases. It

Fig. 63-3. A town dump. All sorts of things are found in it. Such a dump is often a good refuge for rats. In this case, the pool of water is also a good breeding place for mosquitoes.

co-operates with state agencies to prevent the spread of germ diseases.

The sewage and garbage problem. You probably know that one of the main public health problems is garbage and sewage. People have to get rid of garbage and sewage. The question is, how to do it safely and cheaply?

In the past, many cities and towns took the "easy way out." They dumped garbage in nearby vacant lots. They discharged sewage into nearby rivers. Both these practices are dangerous to public health.

Let's consider the "garbage dump" first. Often it contains everything from worn-out furniture to food scraps. It provides a shelter for rats and mice. It also provides food for these animals. And you know that both rats and mice are a source of disease germs.

Garbage dumps also become a breeding place for flies. If the manure of horses is included, the dumps are a breeding place for houseflies. Any of these flies are a menace if they enter your home. They usually have dirt clinging to their bodies and feet. This dirt contains germs which may get into your food.

How about the sewage? You can guess that it often contains a lot of germs. It may also contain the eggs and young of worm parasites. The stream into which the sewage is discharged becomes polluted.

If people swim in the polluted water, they're apt to come in contact with dangerous germs. Suppose people drink the water. They take germs into their bodies.

So you can see that the "easy way out" is not the safe way. Today some cities have solved this old prob-

Fig. 63-4. Part of a modern sewage disposal plant. Dangerous germs are killed and useful by-products are recovered from the sewage.

lem. They have built sewage and garbage disposal plants. These plants get rid of the germs in sewage and garbage. Solid materials are removed and used as fertilizers. Other useful by-products are also obtained. In some cases the sale of by-products more than pays for operating the plants. And the problem of getting rid of the germs is solved.

The insect problem. Another public health problem, as you can guess, has to do with insects. You've read how mosquitoes, flies, lice, and fleas convey certain diseases to man. In places where such diseases are common, the insects which carry them to man must be controlled.

CHECK YOUR FACTS . . .

Number 1 to 6 on a sheet of paper. Mark each item True *or* False.

1. Some of the germs that cause diseases in man are also found in the bodies of domestic animals.

2. A person who has a disease not caused by germs is usually quarantined.

3. Today, diphtheria, smallpox, and typhoid fever are the most common causes of death.

4. Every person in the United States is now made immune to typhoid fever.

5. The fewer the number of people around you who have germ diseases, the less are your chances of getting a germ disease.

6. All cities and towns should build sewage and garbage disposal plants.

CHAPTER 64

Why We Have Pure Food and Drug Laws

Are quarantines, garbage, and sewage the only public health problems?

By no means. You've learned that a lot of germs enter your body by way of your mouth. Many of them come in with the things you eat and drink.

Years ago, the people of Europe would flee from cities and towns when an epidemic of disease came. They didn't know why, but life seemed to be safer in the country. At the time they were quite right.

Today modern cities protect public health. In some cases the protections aren't as good as they might be. But public health in cities has been greatly improved. In fact, it's now better than public health in many country areas.

A safe water supply is important. Water isn't a food, of course, but we do drink it. The human body must have a regular supply of water.

In Chapter 63 you learned that sewage can pollute streams. There are other ways in which germs can get into water supplies. Look, for example, at Fig. 64-1. On some farms, wells are too close to sources of germs to be safe. The water may be cool and clear, but this doesn't mean that it's free from germs. Actually, it may contain the germs of cholera and typhoid fever, as well as other diseases. The Board of Health should check wells to make sure that their waters do not contain dangerous germs.

City water supplies come from various sources. Sometimes cities get water from lakes or rivers. Other cities use a system of reservoirs that collect water which comes from rainfall and melting snow. Still others use one or more deep wells which tap water supplies far down in the earth. Of course, streams, lakes, and reservoirs from which cities get their water must be guarded against pollution.

Ground water

Fig. 64-1. Water in shallow wells is sometimes polluted by surface drainage.

Fig. 64-2. Water is sprayed up in the air to get rid of bad tastes and odors.

Water from these sources usually has to be filtered. It may be sprayed up into the air to get rid of unpleasant tastes and odors. Many cities often add chlorine to the water to kill bacteria. You will read more about water supplies in Unit 8.

You can easily see that a safe city water supply is necessary. If the water is full of living germs, there will always be danger of disease epidemics.

A safe milk supply is also important. We often say that milk is the near-perfect food. It contains all the substances needed for growth and development. But milk can also be a real source of danger. This happens when the milk is full of germs.

Germs in milk can come from cattle. Milk cattle may have the germs of tuberculosis and undulant fever. We can get either or both of these diseases by drinking the "raw" milk of such cattle.

But there's one odd thing about the tuberculosis that people get from milk. It usually doesn't cause tuberculosis of the lungs. Rather, it causes tuberculosis of other tissues in the body. In some ways this is worse than tuberculosis of the lungs.

Undulant fever is also a disease you wouldn't enjoy. An attack of this disease may last for years. The victim has fever, chills, and pain in the muscles and joints. Goat's milk as well as cow's milk may contain the germs of undulant fever.

So you see that germs can be in milk as it comes from cows and other animals. There's an added danger. Germs can get into the milk during milking and handling. For instance, germs can be on the milker's hands, in milk pails, and in milk bottles.

Here you see why we have laws dealing with the milk supply. Health officials inspect herds of cattle to see if any animals have tuberculosis. Other health officials inspect dairy farms, bottling plants, and stores. They try to make sure that the milk is handled in a sanitary way.

Fig. 64-3. Clean barns and clean handling tend to assure a pure milk supply.

We have laws to regulate our food and drugs. Milk is only one of many foods. You can see that safety measures in the case of milk must be observed in the case of other foods as well. This is why there are various laws dealing with foods and markets.

In many cases cattle and pigs that are to be slaughtered are inspected for disease. Health inspectors are also interested in the cleanliness of markets and restaurants. Canned foods are inspected, among other things, to find out if any harmful preservatives have been put in them.

The federal *Pure Food and Drug Law* passed in 1906 and the federal *Food, Drug, and Cosmetic Act* passed in 1938 are concerned with such safety measures. They provide for the inspection of animals that are used as food. They set up standards of purity for foods, and provide that foods be free from harmful preservatives. They also provide for accurate labeling of packaged goods, including drugs.

In the case of drugs, for example, the manufacturer must do certain things. He must show on the label how much of any habit-forming drug, such as morphine, is in the medicine. He must not make any false or misleading statement that the medicine will cure a certain disease.

Health conditions are sometimes better in cities than in the country. The reason for this is partly a matter of pure foods and better sanitation.

Germs are apt to be found wherever there's food material, moisture, and favorable temperature. They're sure to be present in manure, garbage, and other decaying materials. Therefore, great care should be taken that the water which drains from manure piles, cesspools, and outdoor toilets doesn't get into wells.

Dirty stables and manure piles are a menace in another way. Houseflies breed in horse manure. They're always apt to carry disease germs to the foods you eat. One way to get rid of them is to keep stables clean and to spread the manure out on fields. Dry manure or manure that has been plowed into a field isn't a breeding place for flies.

Each female housefly lays from 100 to 200 eggs on horse manure. The eggs hatch in about a day and the young pass through several stages. In about two weeks adults develop and are ready to fly and start breeding again. This goes on from spring until cold weather in the fall. It's estimated that over 2 billion flies can hatch in one season as a result of the mating of two flies in the early spring! Now do you see why it is important to get rid of houseflies in the summer season?

CHECK YOUR FACTS . . .

Number 1 to 6 on a sheet of paper. Mark each of the following items True *or* False.

1. Today, health conditions are always better in country areas than in the city.

2. We usually get germs of undulant fever from impure water.

3. It's possible for the germs of cholera and typhoid fever to be in water.

4. Germs are killed when chlorine is added to city water supplies.

5. The housefly generally breeds in or on decaying meat.

6. Tuberculosis germs from milk usually cause tuberculosis of the lungs in man.

CHAPTER 65

Drugs Are Used in Fighting Diseases

When you don't manage to keep free from germs, and when you're not immune, what happens?

By this time you know the answer. The germs are likely to get into some of your organs or tissues. Here they may multiply. When there are enough germs, the symptoms of disease appear.

Do we have any other defenses against these germs? The answer is yes, in a good many cases. For example, you already know that you use antiseptics, such as merthiolate solution, to kill germs in surface wounds.

But antiseptics are only used on the *outside* of the body. What about germs that are in the stomach, the intestines, or the blood?

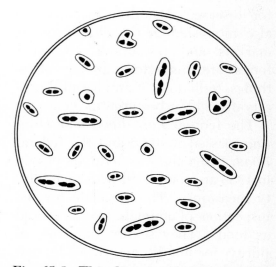

Fig. 65-1. This diagram shows one type of bacterium that causes pneumonia.

In such cases you still need a substance that will kill germs. But it must also be a substance that won't hurt any part of your body or at least do no lasting harm. Such substances aren't always easy to find.

Quinine and malaria. One of the first useful germ killers to be discovered was quinine. It cures the disease, malaria.

Malaria was a common disease in Ancient Greece and Rome. It kept on being an important cause of sickness and death right down through the years. You've read in Chapter 26 how the bark of a South American tree was brought to Europe. Chewing this bark relieved people of malarial chills and fevers. But it was many years before they found out the bark contained quinine.

We still use quinine to prevent malaria and to cure it. We now get this drug from cultivated cinchona trees. But we also use other drugs that are made chemically. Some of them are as good or better than quinine for the treatment of malaria.

How the sulfa drugs were discovered. The last 20 years have brought new chemical weapons for the war on germs. In 1932 a German scientist began to make tests with a sulfa drug. He called it that because it contained some sulfur. He tried it out on mice which had pneumonia. Results were fair, but not as good as he thought they would be.

Then an English drug company set to work on the problem. They made up a lot of different sulfa drugs. They tested these on diseased laboratory animals. Other scientists and other drug firms began to experiment with the sulfa drugs. Before long, several very useful substances were identified.

These sulfa drugs are now widely used. They've proved quite effective against the germs of pneumonia and scarlet fever, as well as some other diseases and some kinds of wound infections. One good thing about the sulfa drugs is that they can be made chemically. So they can be supplied whenever they're needed. You should only take sulfa drugs under the direction of your doctor. Some people react unfavorably to them.

Germs sometimes get more resistant. For a time scientists hoped that sulfa drugs would be effective against all kinds of germs. But this didn't prove true. Also, another disappointment came along. A certain sulfa drug would be effective against certain germs for a time. Then it would become less effective.

What had happened? No one can be sure about it, but perhaps the story is like this. At first the drug affected almost all the germs in question. People with the disease were cured. But the drug didn't affect a few of the germs which were immune to the drug. So these surviving germs lived and multiplied. They gave rise to a special type of germ that could resist the action of the drug.

So you see that our chemical warfare against germs is likely to go on and on. If one chemical defense fails against a resistant germ, another may

Fig. 65-2. The mold from which we get penicillin. Penicillin is one of our most useful antibiotics.

succeed. This is why scientists keep testing out new drugs. We can hardly have enough weapons in this kind of warfare.

Penicillin — a new chemical defense. *Penicillin* (pen-ih-*sil*-in) has just about become a household word. It's another newcomer among the drugs. Its history goes back to the British scientist, Alexander Fleming, and the year 1929. Fleming was raising some cultures of bacteria. A green mold got into his cultures. The growth of some bacteria came to a sudden stop. Among the bacteria affected were various disease germs.

There the study rested until World War II began. Then some other British scientists took up the trail. They took out penicillin from the green mold. British and American scientists began to test the new drug against various germs. They soon found that penicillin was a brand new chemical weapon. It was the first of the *antibiotics* (an-tee-by-*ot*-iks). These are substances obtained from molds and bacteria used to check the growth of disease germs.

There was one trouble at first. Not nearly enough penicillin could be made to meet the demand. The first move was to improve ways of growing the mold. As a result, there was more mold to employ as a source of the drug. Then in 1946 scientists began to produce penicillin chemically in the laboratory. Thus a good supply was assured, and we have plenty of it today.

Like the sulfa drugs, penicillin is used to fight a number of different germs. It's used in cases of pneumonia and about a hundred other diseases. Many germs don't seem to get more resistant to penicillin.

But penicillin won't cure everything. There are many germs which it doesn't seem to affect. So it's a good thing that scientists have found other antibiotics.

Some other antibiotics. Only a few years ago an American scientist named Waksman and his assistants were studying bacteria taken from the soil. They found a new antibiotic and called it *streptomycin* (strep-toh-*my*-sin). It's now used to fight a number of germs, including those which cause bubonic plague or "black death." Another group of scientists found a third antibiotic called *chloromycetin* (klor-oh-my-*see*-tin). This one is used to cure typhus fever, typhoid fever, and some other diseases.

Still other useful antibiotics have been found. *Aureomycin* (*oh*-ree-oh-my-sin) is one. Some of the known antibiotics can now be made chemically. Others come from bacteria rather than molds. There are still some germs against which we don't have good drug defenses. But our defenses are better than they were a few years ago. And we may be sure that new discoveries will add to them as research goes on.

CHECK YOUR FACTS . . .

Number 1 to 6 on a sheet of paper. Match the items in Column A *with the best answers in* Column B.

Column A	*Column B*
1. Antiseptic	*a.* First obtained from a mold
2. Penicillin	*b.* Used only on the outside of the body
3. Sulfa drugs	
4. Quinine	*c.* Discovered by the French scientist Pasteur
5. Soil bacteria	
6. Bubonic plague, called "black death"	*d.* Obtained from molds and bacteria
	e. Used internally but not antibiotics
	f. Now treated by using an antibiotic
	g. Obtained from the bark of a tree
	h. The source of some antibiotics

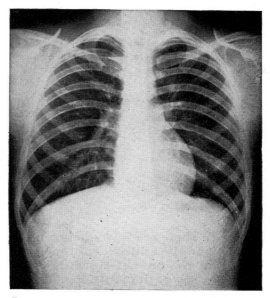

Fig. 65-3. This is an X-ray photograph of the lungs. Such photographs are useful in locating certain causes of illness.

CHAPTER 66

Not All Diseases Are Caused by Germs

When you're sick, are germs always the cause? No, not always, and at least not the direct cause. But germs are often a part of the story just the same. A tissue may not do its work because it has been hurt by germs earlier.

To understand this better, let's give a little thought to the most common cause of death today. This is *heart disease,* or rather, *heart diseases.*

The heart diseases. You probably know that heart disease is a general term. You also know that the work

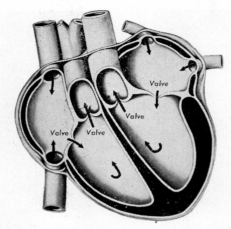

Fig. 66-1. There are valves between the auricles and the ventricles of the heart. Valves are also present at points where the blood leaves the ventricles. These valves regulate the flow of blood through the heart.

of the heart is related to that of the blood vessels. The heart pumps the blood to the tissues through arteries. Veins return the blood to the heart.

In Chapter 51 you learned that your heart has four chambers. Two of them are auricles which receive incoming blood. Two are ventricles. The right ventricle pumps blood to the lungs, and the left ventricle pumps blood to the rest of the body. Contraction of muscle in the heart wall does the pumping.

If you look at Fig. 66-1, you see that there are valves between the auricles and the ventricles. There also are valves at the point where blood leaves the ventricles. The valves prevent back-flow of the blood. You can see that if a valve leaked, and back-flow took place, the heart would have to work harder to pump a normal amount of blood.

Now what would make a valve leak? Well, sometimes germs get in the blood stream. Sometimes they cause the heart valves to be deformed. The germs may all die in time, but the damaged valves stay damaged.

There's some back-flow of blood. The heart may enlarge, so that it pumps a normal supply of blood in spite of the back-flow. If the valves aren't badly damaged, there may be no serious result. But there are limits to the amount a heart can enlarge. If the valves are badly damaged, the circulation may fail. Or if the body is put under a heavy strain by some later attack of germ disease, the circulation may not be good enough.

Here you have a case of heart disease which begins with a germ attack. The germs may be cleared out of the body. But years later the heart may fail. Remember that this is just *one type* of heart disease. There are many others. Some of them have their origins in germ attacks. Others seem to have no relation to germs.

High blood pressure and hardened arteries. The welfare of the heart depends closely on the condition of the blood vessels and the organs of the body. Let's take an example that includes the heart, the arteries, and the kidneys.

In some people, the pressure of blood in the arteries is higher than normal. It stays that way most or all of the time. The fact that the smaller arteries are contracted seems to cause this. Being contracted, they resist normal blood flow.

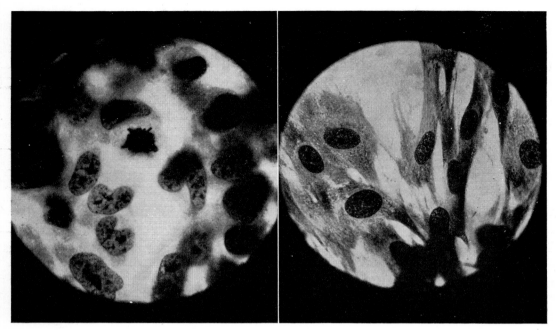

Fig. 66-2. On the right you see the cells of a normal tissue. But on the left the same tissue has developed cancer. Cells are dividing rapidly and the tissue is enlarging.

One of the things that can cause high blood pressure is the failure of circulation in the kidneys. Steady high blood pressure leads to hardening of the arteries. The arteries become less elastic. They tend to be stiff and brittle like an old garden hose.

The work of the heart is increased when blood pressure is high. As before, the heart enlarges, and pumps hard enough to offset the high pressure. But again, you see that the reserve strength of the heart is reduced, perhaps to the vanishing point.

What can happen now? Almost surely diseased kidneys. An artery may rupture or the heart may fail.

What is cancer? Another common cause of death is *cancer* (*kan*-ser).

Heart and kidney diseases and cancer have become the greatest killers. All these diseases are more common among middle-aged and old people than among young people. Probably they're more common than they were a hundred years ago. No doubt this is because people today live long enough to get such diseases.

There are various types of cancer. Some cancer growths form on the outside of the body — in the skin. Other cancer growths form deep in the body tissues. We can best understand the subject if we consider the growths called tumors (*too*-mers).

A *tumor* is an overgrowth of tissue. You can recognize it by a lump, or enlarged mass of cells. You know that the cells of a tissue divide now and then. In this way, worn-out cells are replaced. But sometimes the division "runs wild." Cells divide to form three, rather than two new cells. The result is an overgrowth of tissue. Often a wall surrounds this overgrown tissue. This wall develops and stays in one place. A doctor can usually remove it and that's the end of the matter. It's just a simple tumor.

Sometimes an overgrowth of tissue results in cancer. A wall doesn't form around the growing mass of cells. The cells keep on multiplying. Cancer cells get into the blood and are carried to various parts of the body. Cancerous growths begin to develop in other tissues. This is the real danger. These growths destroy tissues and organs.

One of the bad things about cancer is that it isn't painful in the early stages. So it's likely to be overlooked. Early treatment is more likely to cure the disease. So everyone should be examined by a doctor from time to time. And you should always be on the lookout for signs like these:

(1) Changes in the color or size of moles and warts, from which cancerous growths may develop.

(2) The development of any unusual lump of tissue.

(3) Unusual bleeding from any opening of the body.

(4) Sores which don't heal up as they should.

(5) Continued indigestion which doesn't yield to treatment.

(6) Sudden loss of weight which isn't due to diet or increased exercise.

Sometimes the question is asked: "Do other animals and plants develop cancers?"

The answer is yes. Scientists study unusual growths of cells in various animals and plants. In the laboratory it is possible to produce tumors and cancers. It can be done by long irritation of a tissue. Friction, irritating chemicals, and heat sometimes produce cancer growths.

So you see that the war against diseases goes on. Over some diseases we have gained a partial victory. It would be an almost complete victory if all people got proper treatment. Many germ diseases of childhood, for instance, have ceased to be a general menace.

Against some other diseases our defenses are not so good. Among the remaining great problems is the conquest of cancer.

CHECK YOUR FACTS . . .

Number 1 to 6 on a sheet of paper. Mark each of the following items True *or* False.

1. The cells of a simple tumor usually spread to many parts of the body.

2. If you lose weight suddenly, this may mean the presence of cancer in your body.

3. The walls of hardened arteries are usually too stiff and brittle.

4. A hardened artery is more likely to rupture than is a normal artery.

5. Man is the only organism known to develop cancer.

6. Heart valves can be damaged by germs in the blood.

Science now has ways to make us immune or partly immune to smallpox, typhoid fever, diphtheria, tetanus, cholera, yellow fever, plague, and other diseases. Not all of these immunities, however, are equally lasting. Some are active; some are passive.

People whose bodies contain certain germs act as carriers of disease. Our pets and our domestic animals are likely to be sources of some disease germs. Sanitary disposal of sewage and garbage is an important way to control germs. So is a safe water supply, and a pure food supply, including milk. Federal, state, and local laws and agencies see that we have pure water, food, and drug supplies. We quarantine people who have germ diseases that are spread by contact. The idea is to keep the germs from reaching a lot of other people.

When germs get into your body, you have several chemical defenses. Quinine and certain synthetic drugs control malaria germs. Sulfa drugs are used to fight a number of bacteria that cause diseases. Penicillin and other antibiotics are effective against many germs that resist the sulfa drugs. But some germs seem to get more resistant to drugs after a time. They develop what we call resistant strains. For this reason, the search for new and better drugs goes on.

Two of the great killers today are heart diseases and cancer. There are many kinds of heart diseases. Sometimes the original damage to the heart or the blood vessels is done by germs. Diseases of the heart and blood vessels may affect other organs of the body. Cancer is due to an overgrowth of tissue cells. Cancer cells can be carried to all parts of the body. Early diagnosis of cancer and early treatment are important. Heart diseases, cancer, and diseases of the kidneys are the big health problems today. In part, this is because people now live long enough to get these diseases.

WHAT DO THESE WORDS MEAN?

Active immunity	Immunity	Sulfa drug
Antibiotic	Passive immunity	Tumor
Cancer	Penicillin	Vaccinate
Carrier	Resistant	Vaccine

ASK YOURSELF . . .

1. How were people made immune to smallpox before the discovery of Jenner's method?

2. Typhoid fever, diphtheria, and smallpox are diseases for which immunity can be given. Why do we still have cases of these diseases in our communities?

3. (a) What is the difference between active immunity and passive immunity? (b) Which is likely to last longer?

4. How could you get the germs of typhoid fever or tetanus?

5. What are three of the most common causes of death in our country today?

6. (a) What is a typhoid carrier? (b) Why may such a person be a menace to other people?

7. If you got rid of all germs in the human population, could you still get germ diseases?

8. What are some good ways and some bad ways to get rid of sewage and garbage?

9. (a) What germs can you get from impure water? (b) Are all sources of water supply equally safe? (c) What makes the difference?

10. (a) What germs can you get from impure milk? (b) Where do they come from? (c) How can you avoid them?

11. (a) What special problems of germ control are apt to be found in country areas? (b) Are farm food supplies and water supplies always as safe as city supplies?

12. (a) What is the advantage in being able to make a drug chemically? (b) What is the advantage in having more than one drug to fight a certain type of germ?

13. In what way may germs develop special varieties that are resistant to a certain drug?

14. (a) From what kind of plants did the original antibiotics come? (b) Are these antibiotics effective weapons against all germs? (c) Do we have good drug defenses against all germs?

15. (a) What diseases cause the greatest number of deaths today? (b) Are they germ diseases?

16. How may the improper working of the kidneys affect the heart?

17. Why are regular medical examinations necessary?

18. What is the difference between a simple tumor and a cancer?

19. (a) How do cancer cells divide? (b) How does this differ from the division of normal cells?

20. Why is cancer likely to be overlooked in early stages?

GETTING THE FACTS . . .

1. Take six culture surfaces like those described on page 279. Rub the fingers of your unwashed hand lightly across three of the surfaces. Wash your hand thoroughly, and rub the fingers lightly on the other three culture surfaces. Now cover all surfaces, label them, and put them in a moderately warm place. After a few days see where the largest colonies of bacteria have developed.

2. Carry out one or more field trips to study (a) your local water supply, including the source of the water, how it is tested, and how it is cleaned and purified; and (b) the methods used in getting rid of garbage and sewage in your community.

3. From your local Board of Health find out what policies are followed in quarantining. Try to relate these policies to the ways in which germs get into your body.

4. Visit a farm if possible. Study the sources of water and food supply. Study the ways used to get rid of garbage and sewage. Discuss the general problem, and decide (a) which practices are good; and (b) which practices should be changed.

5. After consulting the references on page 302, report on: (a) discoveries made by Ehrlich and Koch; (b) the infantile paralysis (polio) problem; (c) soil bacteria and antibiotics.

6. Collect some plant galls like the one shown in Fig. 66-3. Plant galls are tumorous growths. Cut them open and see if you can find out what caused the original irritation.

7. Plant six young sunflower plants in flower pots. Wait until they're about six inches tall. Then paint an area on each stem several times with a solution that is about one-fifth ammonia and four-fifths water. See if you can cause tumorous growths to form.

Fig. 66-3. Galls or tumerous growths on a sugar beet. Such growths are formed in many plant tissues.

Books You May Like . . .

American Public Health Association. *THE CONTROL OF COMMUNICABLE DISEASES.* American Public Health Association, New York. 1950. A booklet which is a mine of information on germ diseases, their effects, sources of the diseases, immunity, and methods of control.

Haggard, Howard W. *DEVILS, DRUGS AND DOCTORS. Harper & Brothers, New York. 1944.* A fascinating history of man's fight against diseases. This is a good reference on health conditions from the days of Ancient Greece to the present century. It features the plagues which swept over Europe.

Haggard, Howard W. *THE SCIENCE OF HEALTH AND DISEASE. Harper & Brothers, New York. 1938.* A very readable discussion of the human body and the diseases which affect it.

Marriott, H. J. L. *MEDICAL MILESTONES. The Williams and Wilkins Co., Baltimore, Maryland. 1952.* An excellent source of facts about the antibiotics and some other newcomers among drugs.

Tanner, Fred Wilbur, and Tanner, F. W. *BACTERIOLOGY. John Wiley and Sons, New York. 1948.* A standard textbook which includes discussions of bacteria and disease, water, food and milk supplies, sewage disposal, and immunity.

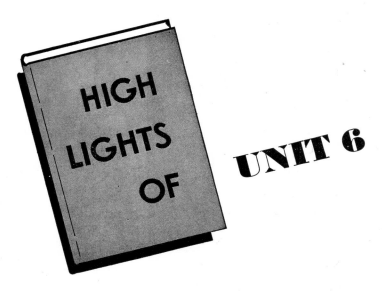

HIGH LIGHTS OF UNIT 6

Germ diseases and diseases that act like germ diseases are caused by certain bacteria, protozoa, and viruses. You get the germs of these diseases through contact, in the things you eat and drink, and in some cases by insect bites.

Your body has various natural defenses against germs. You improve these defenses by becoming immune to a number of diseases. You're protected from germs by quarantines, and by pure foods and liquids. You also fight germs by getting rid of sewage and garbage in a sanitary way.

Another line of defense against germs is the use of drugs. Quinine and some modern chemical drugs are used to fight malaria. Sulfa drugs and antibiotics are useful in controlling many germs.

Some diseases aren't caused by germs. There are, for example, many diseases of the heart and blood vessels. Some of them may be caused by germ attack. But some aren't related to germs.

Diseases of the heart, blood vessels, and kidneys, and cancer are the common causes of death today.

Unit 7

All Living

Things

Reproduce

It was the middle of October, but there had been no frost so far. Ed and Jim were working in the family garden one Saturday.

" This row of tomatoes has been a mess all summer. Curled up leaves and small tomatoes. But that next row is swell. Nice healthy plants and lots of big tomatoes. Wonder why? " Jim asked Ed.

" You've got me," Ed replied. " Maybe we just got stung. We got a dozen of those good plants at one place. Then we bought the other dozen a week later."

Just then Ann came out. The twins asked her what she thought.

" It's easy! " she said. " Those sickly plants aren't disease-resistant. The healthy ones are."

" What's disease-resistant? " Jim asked her.

" Well, biologists breed different varieties for their good qualities. Disease-resistant means they won't get diseases. That sickly row wasn't bred for the best qualities so you've got duds. Nothing you can do about it, though. You just got stung."

Topic 1

REPRODUCTION DEPENDS ON CELL DIVISION

How do living things reproduce their kind?

There are several ways, and some are quite surprising.

What's this in the picture? It's a sea horse, an odd kind of fish. It lives in shallow seas. The male sea horse has a brood pouch as part of its body.

When a female sea horse is ready to lay her eggs, she seeks her mate. Then she forces the eggs into the brood pouch of the male. He acts as a "mother" until the eggs hatch.

Just the opposite of what you'd expect? Read on, and see the other ways that living things reproduce their kind.

AMONG THE NEW WORDS FOR THIS TOPIC

- **CHROMATIN** (*kroh*-mah-tin). Material in the nucleus that forms chromosomes.
- **CHROMOSOMES** (*kroh*-moh-sohms). Bodies which form from chromatin in the nucleus during cell division. They carry the genes.
- **EGG CELL.** A mature female sex cell.
- **EMBRYO** (*em*-bree-oh). A stage in the early growth of some plants and animals.
- **GENES** (*jeens*). Tiny bodies in the nucleus of a cell that determine what kind of living things that cell will produce.
- **HEREDITY** (*hair*-ed-ih-tee). What any living thing inherits from its parents and ancestors.
- **MITOSIS** (my-*toh*-siss). A special but common type of cell division.
- **REGENERATE** (ree-*jen*-er-ayte). To develop new parts to replace those that have been destroyed.
- **REPRODUCTION** (ree-pro-*duck*-shun). The process of producing offspring.
- **SPERM.** A mature male sex cell.

CHAPTER 67

What Is Reproduction?

When you read Chapter 5 you learned that cells divide. Amoeba, for instance, grows until it's full size. Then it divides to form two Amoebas. Other one-celled plants and animals do much the same sort of thing.

When a new living thing is produced by cell division, we call it *reproduction* (ree-proh-*duck*-shun). But when cell division occurs in tissue cells, it may be only a process of growth or repair.

The cells of tissues divide. Suppose you get a small scratch or cut. Probably it heals up in a few days. What happens to make it heal?

Among other things, new cells are produced to take the place of cells that have been destroyed. Cells in the injured tissue divide to form the new cells that are needed. This process is called *regeneration* (reh-jen-er-*ay*-shun). You can see that regeneration is a process of repair. New parts are developed to take the place of parts that were destroyed.

Even if you don't get scratches or cuts, your body needs new cells. For one thing, new cells are needed to make you grow. For another, old cells wear out. Then they must be replaced. Cells of your outer skin get rubbed off all the time. But younger cells in the skin keep on dividing. The new cells take the places of those cells that are lost.

What are sex cells? Now let's come back to reproduction. How do the larger plants and animals produce offspring?

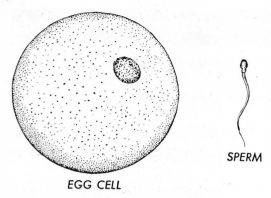

SPERM

EGG CELL

Fig. 67-1. An egg cell or female sex cell, and a sperm cell or male sex cell.

Bodies of larger plants and animals are made up of billions of cells. You generally find that there's *division of labor* among these cells. Some cells do one thing, and some cells do another. Thus, in the animal body, certain cells are sex cells. *Sex cells* are those which contain characters for maleness or femaleness. In female animals, they're found in the *ovaries* (*oh*-vah-rees) or female sex organs. In male animals, they're found in the *testes* (*tes*-teez) or male sex organs. In other words, sex cells are the cells in the sex organs. They do nothing but reproduce the animal.

Before they're ready to reproduce, cells in the sex organs must mature. They develop until they're like the cells in Fig. 67-1. You see that the mature male sex cell is a *sperm.* The mature female sex cell is called an *egg cell.*

You can see in Fig. 67-1 that the egg cell is quite large. Usually it contains a lot of stored food. The sperm cell is small and active. Both cells contain nuclei. The nucleus plays a

part in heredity. *Heredity* (hair-*ed*-ih-tee) is the process of inheriting characteristics from one's parents and ancestors.

Stages in the life cycle. Most living things are either born alive, hatched from an egg, or developed from a seed or a spore. They pass through a period of youth in which they develop and grow. Then they become mature. Finally they get old and die.

The mature plant or animal may reproduce. The cells which reproduce the offspring are cells from the sex organs.

Youth, maturity, and old age: these are the stages in the life cycle. The body cells die in time. But some of the sex cells and the cells that come from them live on in the new generation.

What are chromosomes? When you look at a stained cell through a microscope, you may see something like Fig. 67-2. The cell shown here is a muscle cell. But notice the dark spots or little granules in the nucleus. They're masses of chromatin (*kroh*-mah-tin). *Chromatin* is the material in the nucleus that forms the chromosomes.

When such a cell is ready to divide, the chromatin material begins to look different. It's grouped together in

Nucleus

Fig. 67-2. Diagram of a muscle cell. The small dark spots in the nucleus are masses of chromatin.

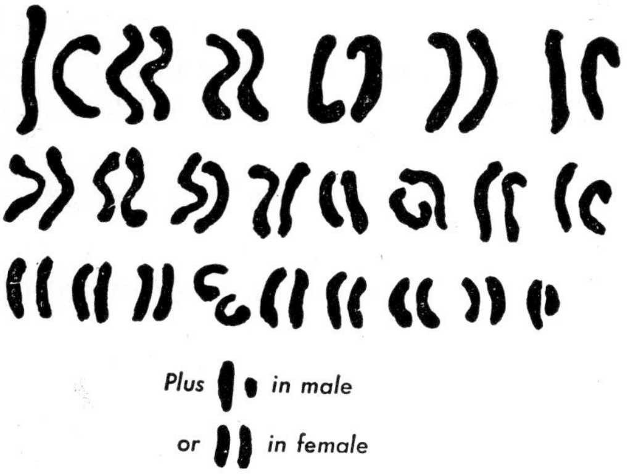

|(C }} }} ( ))))(
}> }})))(((((((((((((( )))(

Plus (in male

or () in female

Fig. 67-3. Chromosomes of a human sex cell. Note that they are in pairs, and that there is a difference between the male and the female.

rod-shaped pieces and forms *chromosomes* (*kroh*-moh-sohms). In Fig. 67-3 you see the chromosomes of a human cell. Note that there are quite a few of them. They're in pairs, and have several different shapes.

The thing to remember is that chromatin and chromosomes are the same thing. The difference is largely in form. Before the division of a cell, the hereditary material appears as chromatin. But when the cell is ready to divide, it appears as chromosomes.

Every living cell with a nucleus contains chromatin material. And when chromosomes appear during division, the number is the same for *all individuals of a species.* For instance, this number is 6 for one species of mosquito, 12 for all houseflies, 18 for all chickens, 20 for all corn, 26 for all bullfrogs, and 42 for all wheat. Man has 48.

What are genes? There's one interesting fact about chromosomes. Each of them may contain a number of units called *genes* (*jeens*). These genes go in pairs. In heredity, a certain characteristic such as eye color is determined by a pair of genes. Or a characteristic may be determined by two or more pairs of genes. And you see that a pair of chromosomes may determine the heredity of more than one characteristic.

Genes aren't just scattered here and there in a chromosome. Rather, the different pairs of genes seem to be in a series along the length of a chromosome.

CHECK YOUR FACTS . . .

Number 1 to 6 on a sheet of paper. Select the best answer for each of the following items.

1. One common difference between an egg cell and a sperm cell is that the egg cell is (larger, more active, smaller) . . .?. . .

2. The process of repairing or replacing an injured part of a plant or animal is (reproduction, fertilization, regeneration) . . .?. . .

3. Eye color in man is determined by (diet, genes, environment) . . .?. . .

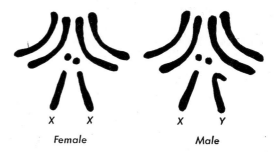

X X   X Y

Female   *Male*

Fig. 67-4. Chromosomes of female and male fruit flies. Notice again that there is a difference between the two sexes.

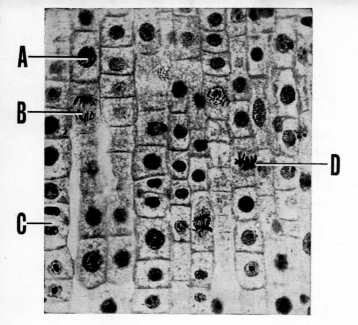

Fig. 68-1. A greatly magnified photo of tissue cells. A is a cell that is about to divide. B, C, and D are cells that are dividing.

4. When the sex cells of an ovary are mature they're (egg cells, chromosomes, sperms) ...?...

5. When the sex cells of testes mature they're (eggs, chromosomes, sperms) ...?...

6. Chromatin is the material that forms (eggs, sperms, chromosomes) ...?...

CHAPTER 68

How Cells Divide

"An Amoeba never dies," announced Joe.

"Nonsense," Harry replied, "suppose some other animal eats it. Doesn't the Amoeba get digested?"

"Well, that's so, of course," Joe agreed, "but I mean natural death.

An Amoeba just grows to full size and then forms two new Amoebas."

From what you've already learned, you know there's a good deal of truth in Joe's idea. Growth and reproduction are related. A good many one-celled plants and animals grow to full size. Then they divide to form two offspring. These two offspring separate and lead their own lives.

Divisions of tissue cells. Much the same thing happens to many cells in your own tissues. Some of these cells become mature. Then they divide. Two new cells are formed. But instead of separating, they stay together. This production of new cells is necessary for growth and repair in the higher plants and animals, and in man.

Tissue cells divide in a special way. We call this kind of division *mitosis* (my-*toh*-siss). It results in the chromosome material of the parent cell dividing equally.

What is mitosis? Let's look at Fig. 68-2. It shows the story of mitosis. A is an early stage. The chromatin material has come together in the nucleus.

Now look at B. Here the chromatin material has actually formed chromosomes. You can see how the chromosomes have divided or split to form two equal groups. The wall around the old nucleus has disappeared during this stage.

In C, the two groups of chromosomes have gone to opposite ends of the cell. The cell itself is beginning to divide.

In D you see the final stage. Two

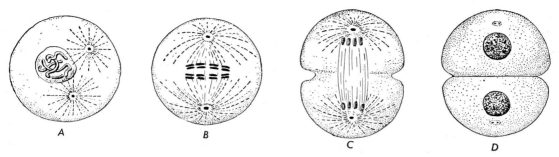

Fig. 68-2. Diagram to show the type of cell division called mitosis. Division of the chromosomes is equal. Two new cells are formed.

new cells have formed. Two new nuclear walls have appeared. You can't see the chromosomes any longer. But the genes are still there in the chromatin, which again looks like tiny granules.

Now suppose you're asked: "What is mitosis?" What would you say? You'd say that it's cell division of a special type. It divides the chromosomes exactly equally. But it seems to be a very common type. Two new cells are formed. Half of the chromatin, or hereditary material, goes to one cell. Half goes to the other cell. Thus each new cell gets an equal amount of the chromatin.

Cell division makes growth and repair possible. This division of cells makes growth and repair possible. When a body cell divides, two new cells are formed. Each of them contains the same number of chromosomes. Each of them grows until it is full-sized.

Regeneration rebuilds or forms new parts. In some of the simple plants and animals this ability to rebuild tissues is striking. Fig. 68-3 shows an

example. The animal is a flatworm which lives in ponds and streams. What happens if you cut the body of this animal in two? Both halves may grow into complete, new flatworms.

When you think of animals which can form new parts, you think of starfish. These animals of the shallow oceans have an unusual ability. Look at Fig. 68-4. What you see there is a starfish developing new arms. In fact, just a single arm with some of the central part of the body attached can grow into a complete starfish.

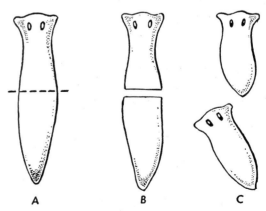

Fig. 68-3. When the body of this flatworm is cut in two, each half may become a complete flatworm.

Fig. 68-4. A starfish regenerates two new arms.

In Chapter 31 you read how starfish open oyster shells and eat the oysters. They're a great pest to oyster raisers. At one time in the past, oyster raisers used to dredge starfish from the bottom. Then they chopped the starfish up and dumped the pieces back into the sea. You can guess what happened. Many of the pieces grew into complete starfish. Soon there were more pests than before.

As you might expect, not all animals have such good powers of forming new parts. But tissues of all animals become repaired to some extent. In your own case you know that cuts, scratches, and other wounds will heal.

Many plants also have good powers of repair. We take advantage of this fact in raising plants. Sometimes just a small part of a plant will grow into an entire new plant.

For instance, consider the white potato. The part you eat is really an underground stem. Food is stored in this potato, and it develops buds or "eyes."

We raise new potatoes by planting pieces of old potatoes. Each piece must contain an "eye." Such a piece placed in good soil will develop into a new potato plant. And of course we do the same kind of thing with bulbs and stems to raise various vegetables and flowers.

We also use a process known as *grafting* when we raise some plants. Here again we take advantage of the plant's ability to form new cells and repair injuries. Fig. 68-5 shows some ways to graft stems on plants. Usually, the purpose is to graft on a stem which will produce a better yield. As a rule, the stem and the plant upon which it is grafted must belong to the same species.

But growth from parts doesn't always work to our advantage by any means. A good many of our worst weed pests can develop from small pieces of roots or stems. When we plow our fields and gardens, we uproot the plants. We check their growth for a time. But often we don't really destroy them. New plants soon grow from pieces of the old plants.

CHECK YOUR FACTS . . .

Number 1 to 6 on a sheet of paper. Select the best answer for each of the following items.

1. Starfish may become pests because they eat (young fish, oysters, sponges) . . .?. . .

2. When a starfish develops a new

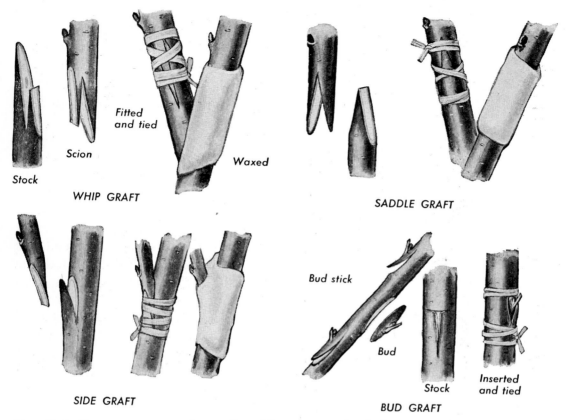

Stock

Scion

Fitted and tied

Waxed

WHIP GRAFT

SADDLE GRAFT

Bud stick

Bud

Stock

Inserted and tied

SIDE GRAFT

BUD GRAFT

Fig. 68-5. Four ways to make grafts. The stem or bud that is grafted on the plant is one that gives a better yield.

arm to replace an arm that has been lost, the process is called (reproduction, mitosis, regeneration) ...?...

3. A cell which contains eight chromosomes divides by mitosis. Each of the resulting cells contains (eight, sixteen, four) ...?... chromosomes.

4. When we graft a stem on a plant, we take advantage of the plant's ability to (repair tissues, bear flowers, produce seed) ...?...

5. Growth and repair of plants and animals is made possible by (injury, cell division, necessity) ...?...

6. Mitosis is a special type of (cell division, heredity, growth) ...?...

CHAPTER 69

Living Things Start as One Cell

At this point you'll want to ask a few questions. You know that some plants can be grown from stems or pieces of roots. "But," you say, "what about corn, beans, and peas? Don't we raise them from seeds? And what about chickens or ducks? Don't they come from eggs?"

The answer is yes. Some living things like starfishes and certain weeds

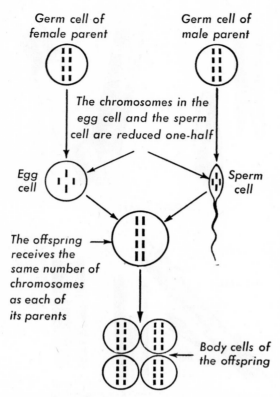

Germ cell of
female parent

Germ cell of
male parent

The chromosomes in the
egg cell and the sperm
cell are reduced one-half

Egg
cell

Sperm
cell

The offspring
receives the
same number of
chromosomes
as each of
its parents

Body cells of
the offspring

Fig. 69-1. When a sex cell matures, its chromosome number is reduced by one-half. Then two mature sex cells unite. The offspring has the same number of chromosomes that its parents had.

can grow from parts. But this isn't true of all living things, by any means. Some plants and animals reproduce by sex cells only. And so does man. **Sex cells become mature.** You know that the number of chromosomes is always the same for all members of a certain species. Let's take as an example the fruit fly that has eight chromosomes. A member of this species has eight chromosomes (or the same material in the form of chromatin) in every cell of its body. If you look at cells from an ovary

of this fruit fly, you'll find eight chromosomes. When you look at cells from a testis or male sex organ, you get the same result. In each case the eight chromosomes form four pairs of similar chromosomes. See Fig. 67-4 on page 309.

Now you know that an egg cell from an ovary and a sperm cell from a testis unite to form a new offspring. But here we seem to have a problem. In our example the chromosome number is eight. If an egg cell has eight chromosomes, and a sperm cell has eight, what then? If they united, the resulting cell would have 16 chromosomes, or eight pairs.

But it just doesn't happen that way! A cell from an ovary first becomes mature. It becomes an egg cell. During this process the chromosome material is reduced by one-half. You see a diagram of this process in Fig. 69-1.

Now the same thing happens to a cell in the testis. It's changed into a sperm cell. During the change the chromosome material is reduced by one-half also.

So in our example of the fruit fly an egg cell has four chromosomes. A sperm also contains four chromosomes. What happens when these two cells unite? The resulting cell has eight chromosomes. These eight chromosomes again form four pairs.

What happens when sex cells unite? When a sperm and an egg cell unite, a new life begins. The new cell is called the *fertilized egg*. This process is called *fertilization*.

In Fig. 69-2 you see how a sperm

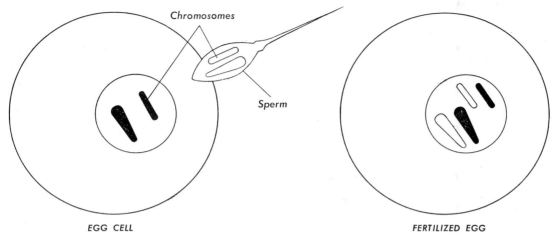

Fig. 69-2. A mature sperm cell unites with a mature egg cell. This is known as fertilization.

unites with an egg cell. Many sperms may come to an egg cell. But only one of them actually gets in.

Notice one thing about the fertilized egg. Half of its chromosomes came from the sperm cell. Half came from the egg cell. So half of the inheritance came from the male, and half from the female.

After an egg cell is fertilized, it may enter a resting stage. Then it begins to divide and forms more cells by mitosis. Development of the offspring is now under way. The cells of the new body divide by mitosis. It's the same process you read about in Chapter 68.

What is development? Can you say that a complex body may begin life as one cell?

Yes, you certainly can. The human body is an example. In the adult stage this body contains billions of cells. These cells are of many different types. They form various tissues, organs, and systems. You can trace back every one of them to one cell — the fertilized egg.

How does such an egg give rise to a large complex body? First of all, you can see that it must divide to produce more cells. As the body develops, many of these cells must be of special types. They must be the kinds of cells that are found in adult tissues.

What is an embryo? In general, an *embryo* (*em*-bree-oh) is a very young plant or animal. Thus the chicken embryo is a developing chicken in an egg. You see such an embryo in Fig. 69-3. It has been developing or hatching for about two days.

Now this embryo began life as one cell —— the fertilized egg. But this cell has divided again and again and again. After two days there are thousands of cells. The cells are being grouped to form organs and systems. After 21 days the new chicken breaks out of the egg shell. It keeps on grow-

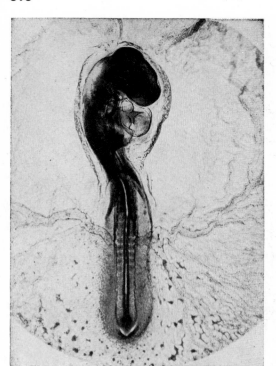

Fig. 69-3. A chicken embryo that is about two days old. By this time many cells have formed. Tissues, organs, and systems are developing.

ing and developing. Then it becomes an adult.

"But what about a seed?" you ask. Well, a seed contains the plant em-bryo. For the time being, develop-ment has stopped. But if you put the seed in a warm moist soil, devel-opment of the embryo begins again. Cells divide by mitosis and form more cells. Soon the seed sprouts. A new plant is developed. This plant also began life as one cell. It was once just a fertilized egg cell.

CHECK YOUR FACTS . . .

Number 1 to 6 on a sheet of paper. Mark each of the following items True *or* False.

1. The human body begins life as one cell — the fertilized egg.

2. In a species whose cells contain eight chromosomes, a mature sperm cell or egg cell will also contain eight chro-mosomes.

3. When a sperm cell and an egg cell unite, a fertilized egg results.

4. Half the chromosomes in a ferti-lized egg come from the male parent.

5. A sperm cell is one from an ovary which has become mature.

6. Embryos are developed by many animals, but aren't found in plants.

IN A NUTSHELL

Living things produce offspring. The basic process is cell division. Among simple plants and animals cell division produces new members of many species. But cell division also goes on in the tissues of other plants and animals. It provides new cells for growth and repair.

Many plants and animals develop sex cells. Cells from ovaries become egg cells. Cells from testes become sperms. It is these sex cells that form the offspring.

All body cells contain chromatin which forms chromosomes during cell division. The number of chromosomes in a cell is usually the same for all members of a certain species. Chromosomes contain genes, which are responsible for heredity.

When a sex cell or a body cell divides, the division of chromosomes is equal. Half of the chromosome material goes to each new cell. This kind of cell division is called mitosis.

Mitosis makes possible the growth and repair of tissues. In some animals and plants, this power of repair is well developed. Some plants can grow again from pieces of stems or roots.

Before a sperm cell and egg cell can unite, each must lose half of its chromosomes. Then the sperm cell joins with the egg cell. The process is fertilization.

A fertilized egg passes through a period of development. More cells and special types of cells are formed. Tissues, organs, and systems are developed. Finally, a new individual is produced.

WHAT DO THESE WORDS MEAN?

Body cell	Fertilization	Ovary
Chromatin	Gene	Regeneration
Chromosome	Grafting (plants)	Reproduction
Division of labor	Heredity	Sex cells
Egg cell	Mitosis	Sperm
Embryo	Nucleus	Testis

ASK YOURSELF . . .

1. What do we mean by the saying " all life comes from life "?
2. Why must new body cells be produced throughout life?
3. What is the relation of chromatin to chromosomes?
4. What are genes and where would you look for them?
5. Is the chromosome number the same for all cells of a body? For all members of a species?
6. Is mitosis a common or a rare process?
7. (a) What happens to the chromosomes when a cell divides by mitosis? (b) What does this mean in terms of heredity?
8. (a) How do we take advantage of growth from parts among plants? (b) In what cases is this growth from parts a nuisance to us?

9. (*a*) How are plant parts grafted? (*b*) In what ways does grafting help the orchardist?

10. (*a*) What are some examples of animals which have good powers of tissue repair? (*b*) Do tissues of your own body have any ability to repair themselves?

11. (*a*) What happens to the chromosome number in a sex cell when the cell becomes mature? (*b*) Why is this important?

12. (*a*) What do we mean by fertilization? (*b*) How many sperm cells can unite with an egg cell?

13. What general things happen during plant or animal development?

14. What conditions are necessary to make an embryo in a seed begin to grow?

GETTING THE FACTS . . .

1. Fill a culture bowl with sugar water. Add some yeast, and let it stand in a warm place for 48 hours. Now examine drops of the culture through a microscope. You will see the yeast cells budding. This is one way in which yeast cells reproduce.

2. With the aid of a microscope, examine slides which show Paramecium dividing. The one-celled animal divides to produce two new animals.

3. Put the cap of a mushroom on a piece of paper with the gills downward. Leave it for a day or two. See if you get a "spore print." Examine the spores with the aid of a microscope.

4. With the aid of a microscope, examine a slide which shows a section of an onion root tip. In such a growing root tip cells are likely to be dividing. See if you can find cells in some of the stages shown in Fig. 68-1 on page 310.

5. Plant some bulbs, geranium slips, pieces of potato, and green willow shoots in moist, sandy soil. Keep them watered, and in a warm place. See if complete plants develop from these plant parts.

6. Make some practice grafts on plant stems like those shown in Fig. 68-5 on page 313.

7. Study any slides or models you may have which show early development of fish, frog, or chick embryos.

Topic 2

HOW PLANTS AND ANIMALS BEGIN LIFE

Everyone knows that the snapdragon is a flower. It's very pretty and makes a fine bouquet for the house.

But what about the grasses? Do they have flowers? Would you pick a bouquet of grasses?

Both snapdragons and grasses bear flowers. Flowers are the reproductive organs of a plant. They contain the sperms and the egg cells in special parts. Wind carries the parts of grasses containing sperms to the egg cells. Insects carry the parts of snapdragons containing sperms to the egg cells. Many higher plants reproduce in this way.

AMONG THE NEW WORDS FOR THIS TOPIC

- **ANNUAL** (*an*-yoo-ul).   A plant which completes its life cycle in a single growing season.
- **BIENNIAL** (by-*en*-ih-ul).   A plant which completes its life cycle in two growing seasons.
- **FRUIT.**   A ripened plant structure which is mainly an ovary and its contents.
- **GERM LAYER.**   One of three layers formed in the early development of an animal.
- **SEED.**   Structure produced by a seed plant which includes a plant embryo.

CHAPTER 70

How Are Seeds Formed?

Did you ever wonder just how fruits and seeds come from flowers? Of course you know some things about this already. You read about flowers, fruits, and seeds in Chapter 20.

The sex cells of flowers. Look at Fig. 70-1. It shows parts of a flower which produce sex cells. Notice that there are several *stamens* (*stay*-mens). These stamens are the male parts of the flower. *Pollen* (*pah*-len) *grains* are formed at the ends of the stamens. Pollen grains contain some special cells which give rise to sperm cells.

Let's turn now to the female parts of the flower. They make up the *pistil* (*pist*-il). At the base of the pistil is a swollen structure called the *ovary.* Mature egg cells are formed within this ovary. From the ovary a tube called the *style* leads upward. At its tip is a *stigma* (*stig*-muh).

But remember one thing. Flowers aren't all alike. Some types have more than one ovary. Some have ovaries but no stamens. Some have stamens but no ovaries.

What is pollination? You've heard that flowers are pollinated (*pahl*-ih-nayt-ed). You know, of course, that it is one step in the reproduction of flowering plants.

Well, *pollination* (pahl-in-*nay*-shun) is actually just a transfer of pollen grains from the male part to the female part of the flower. A pollen grain must go from the stamen, where it was formed, to a stigma. In some cases it goes to a stigma on the same flower. Then we say the flower is *self-pollinated.* In other cases, the pollen goes to a stigma on another flower. Thus the flower is *cross-pollinated.*

In fact, some flowers can't be self-pollinated. A corn plant, for instance, produces two kinds of flowers. On one flower there are only male parts, the tassels. On the other flower are only female parts, or silk of the ear.

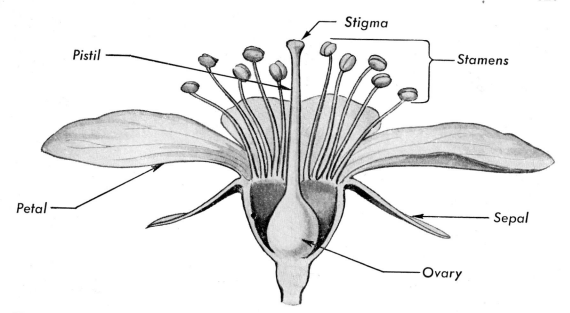

Fig. 70-1. Diagram to show important parts of a flower.

In some other species, such as willow trees, the whole plant bears either male or female flowers, but not both. So pollen from one plant must go to another plant of the same species.

How is pollination brought about? The exact method of pollination differs among plants. It's a subject that scientists have studied carefully. If we're going to raise crop plants, they must be pollinated. If we're to improve their heredity, we must often control their pollination.

Now the pollen grains of some plants can be carried in water. This is the way that some water plants get pollinated. In other cases, pollen grains just drop from a stamen to a stigma on the same flower or another flower.

Ever see "autumn haze?" It suggests another way in which many other plants are pollinated. For the "haze" is at least partly due to pollen grains in the air. They're small and light, and sometimes the wind carries them for many miles.

Finally, insects carry the pollen of a good many flowering plants. This group includes some crop plants, too.

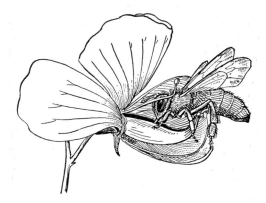

Fig. 70-2. Insects which visit flowers carry pollen from one plant to another. Many plants are pollinated in this way.

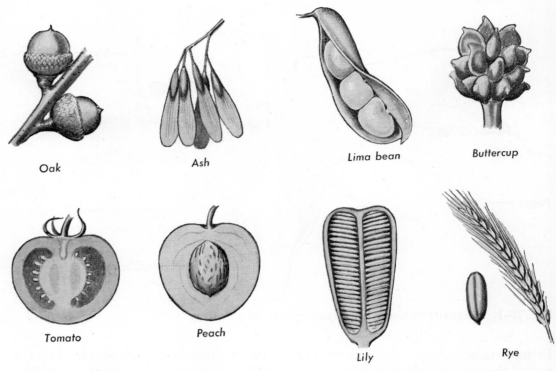

Oak

Ash

Lima bean

Buttercup

Tomato

Peach

Lily

Rye

Fig. 70-3. All of these plant structures are fruits. They include the seeds and other parts which come from the ovaries of flowers.

Insects, which carry the pollen grains, must be present if such plants are to flourish. Snapdragons, for example, are pollinated mainly by bees.

How do the sex cells of flowers unite? When a pollen grain has reached a stigma, the stage is set for other events. The pollen grain develops a tube which grows down the style toward the ovary. In this tube are the nuclei of sperm cells. These nuclei are mature. They contain only half the regular number of chromosomes.

Meanwhile, egg cells in the ovary have become mature, also. They too contain only half the regular number of chromosomes.

When the pollen tube gets down into the ovary, fertilization takes place. A sperm nucleus unites with an egg cell. A fertilized egg is the result. It contains the regular number of chromosomes.

Formation of a seed. The fertilized egg is still inside the ovary. It begins to divide by cell division. New cells are produced. They form a plant embryo.

This plant embryo is what you find in a seed. Much of it is made up of either one or two seed leaves, or of stored food. There are also parts from which the future stem and root develop. A seed case forms around the plant embryo. Now the seed usually goes into a resting period. It doesn't develop further until it sprouts. Often it doesn't sprout until the next growing season. Now the embryo begins to grow again. New cells are formed as are the roots, stems, and leaves of the adult plant.

The relation of fruits and seeds. Fruits are fleshy parts that develop around the seeds of flowering plants. These fleshy parts come from the parts of the old flower, mostly the ovaries.

The things that you commonly call fruits don't include all fruits. Look, for instance, at Fig. 70-3. Of course you know a peach is a fruit. But you're more likely to call a tomato a vegetable although it's really a fruit. And the ash seed is also a fruit enclosing a seed.

CHECK YOUR FACTS . . .

Number 1 to 6 on a sheet of paper. Select the best answer for each of the following items.

1. Pollen grains are developed on the (pistils, petals, stamens) . . .?. . . of flowers.

2. A seed really consists of a plant (sex cell, embryo, ovary) . . .?. . .

3. Fruits are fleshy parts that develop around the (pollen grains, petals, seeds) . . .?. . . of flowering plants.

4. Mature egg cells are developed inside the (stamen, stigma, ovary) . . .?. . . of a flower.

5. The sperm nuclei of flowers are developed from (ovaries, pollen grains, stigmas) . . .?. . .

6. (All, many, few) . . .?. . . plants are pollinated by wind.

CHAPTER 71

How Do Seeds Sprout?

" This ground must be full of weed seeds," Jim said, as he hacked with a hoe in the garden. " I just got rid of all these weeds a week ago."

Jim was learning something that's all too true. Garden soil often contains a lot of weed seeds. Weeds keep coming up as the growing season goes on. Add to them the weeds that grow from pieces of roots and stems, and you've got a real job in gardening.

How plant seeds are scattered. Of course, the plant which produces seeds often is rooted to the ground. But seeds aren't rooted and there are many ways in which they're scattered.

For instance, man brings about much scattering of weed seeds. You may be sure that the settlers of a new country don't bring weed seeds with them on purpose. But the weed seeds come just the same. They're in shipments of goods. They're in soil around the roots of young fruit trees. They even get mixed in with the seeds of crop plants.

Some of the structures of seeds and fruits which make it easy for them to be scattered are shown in Fig. 71-1. Winds carry the hairs on dandelion and milkweed seeds long distances. Some fruits have hooks which stick to clothing or to the fur of animals. Some fruits burst open when the seeds are ripe. Then the seeds are thrown off from the parent plant. Some fruits and seeds are carried in water. And

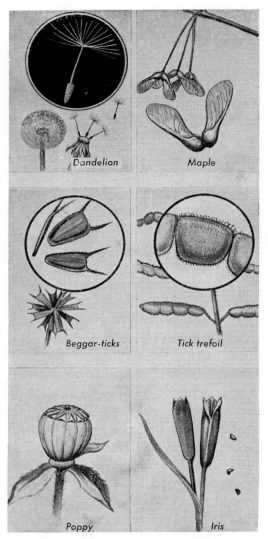

Dandelion

Maple

Beggar-ticks

Tick trefoil

Poppy

Iris

Fig. 71-1. Structures of many seeds and fruits make it likely that seeds will be scattered far and wide.

of course animals are likely to carry any seeds which they eat.

Remember that these seeds are really plant embryos. This is one stage in the life cycle when they can be moved about. You can see the advantage of this scattering. If all seeds remained under the parent plant, the

new plants would be crowded. Also, scattering of seeds gets plants into new places for growth.

Remember that a place favorable for growth one season may not be favorable the next season. At the same time, a different location may become favorable.

A seed sprouts. When the growing season arrives, seeds start to sprout. This really means that the embryos in the seeds begin to grow again.

Certain conditions favor sprouting. The temperature must be right and water and oxygen must be present.

In Fig. 71-2 you see a seed that has sprouted and continued to develop. The new root system pushes down into the soil. Gravity and water in the soil affect the direction of its growth.

Meanwhile, the new stem pushes up into the air and sunlight. New leaves begin to form. This is necessary because the supply of stored food in a seed is limited. The new plant must soon begin to make its own food.

The plant life cycle. Some seed plants live their whole life cycle in a single growing season. The seed sprouts in the spring. By autumn it produces flowers and seeds. The old plant dies, and only the seeds remain. Such a plant is called an **annual** (an-yoo-ul).

Other seed plants need two growing seasons to complete their life cycle. In the first season they develop stems and leaves, but don't bear flowers. Often the parts above ground die off during the next winter. But

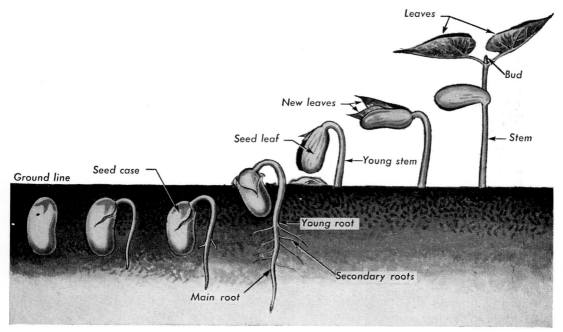

Fig. 71-2. The sprouting and early growth of a bean plant. The two seed leaves are full of stored food.

the plant grows up again from its underground parts during the second season. In this second growing season it produces flowers and seeds. Then it dies. Such a plant is a *biennial* (by-*en*-ih-ul).

Finally, there are the *perennials* (per-*en*-ni-als). These are plants which live through a number of growing seasons. Some crop plants and some flowers you raise are of this type. You can think right away of many kinds of trees that live for years. In fact, some species of trees are known to have lived for hundreds and even thousands of years. Perennial plants may produce flowers and seeds through many seasons.

Plant reproduction in general. Before we leave the plants, we should recall that they reproduce in several ways. Some of the simple, one-celled plants simply divide. Yeast cells divide, but they do it by forming buds. Other simple plants like the bacteria and molds you read about in Chapters 14 and 16 can form spores. Each spore cell can develop into a new individual. In some cases, however, spores only develop when living conditions aren't favorable.

A good many of the seed plants can grow from parts, like the white potato. But they also can produce sex cells and seeds. The seed plants or flowering plants are among the *higher plants*. They're generally larger and more complex than the *simple plants* which include plants like yeasts, bacteria, and molds.

CHECK YOUR FACTS . . .

Number 1 to 6 on a sheet of paper. Mark each of the following items True *or* False.

1. If a plant's seeds are widely scattered, that plant species is likely to survive.

2. A perennial plant completes its life cycle in one growing season.

3. The presence or absence of water in the soil can affect the direction of root growth.

4. A seed contains no stored food, and the new plant must begin food manufacture as soon as it sprouts.

5. Some plant fruits and seeds are carried by animals.

6. A biennial plant completes its life cycle in two growing seasons.

CHAPTER 72

How Do Animals Reproduce?

Many one-celled animals, like one-celled plants, simply divide when they've grown to full size. You may remember that Amoeba and Paramecium can reproduce in this way.

Animal spores. But sometimes Amoeba divides in a different way. This happens when conditions of life aren't favorable. The Amoeba contracts and forms a cyst, which is a protective covering. The cell contents then divide to form 500 or more tiny cells. These tiny cells are a type of spore.

When conditions of life are again favorable, the Amoeba spores break out of the cyst. Each of them is capable of growing into a full-sized Amoeba. You see, then, that spore-like cells are found among animals as well as plants.

Budding. Some of the many-celled animals can divide also. One of them is Hydra. Look at Fig. 72-1. It's a diagram of a Hydra dividing. Division begins at the end of the body where the mouth opening is located. In time, two Hydras are produced.

This kind of division in Hydra, however, seems to be rare. The process you're more likely to see is budding. The bud forms as a bulge in the body wall. It develops a mouth opening and tentacles as you can see in Fig. 72-2. Then it separates from the parent Hydra. Of course Hydra also reproduces by means of sex cells.

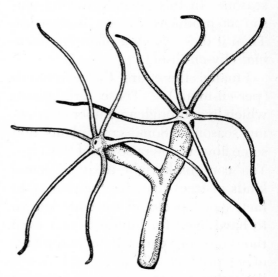

Fig. 72-1. Hydra is a many-celled animal. However, it may divide, as shown here.

Fig. 72-2. Diagram to show how a Hydra bud develops. After a time the bud breaks away from the parent Hydra.

Some animals are hatched from eggs. A good many animals are hatched from eggs. In this group are such types as many worms, clams, oysters, crayfish, lobsters, most insects, most fishes, frogs, toads, many reptiles, and birds. Strangely enough, there are two mammals which are also hatched from eggs. They are the duckbill and the spiny anteater from the Australian area.

Such eggs are usually laid by the female parent. But not always! Among some simple animals an individual may be both male and female. Its body contains both testes and ovaries.

You read about the way in which frog eggs develop in Chapter 36. Toad eggs develop in much the same way. But there's an interesting exception. It's the case of the Surinam toad.

This little South American animal doesn't lay its eggs in the water like most frogs and toads. Rather, the eggs are spread over the back of the female. Then a little hole in the skin develops around each egg. The egg sinks into this hole, and a sort of lid is formed over it.

The eggs hatch in the holes on the back of the female toad. You see the toad in Fig. 72-3. The tadpole stage takes place in these holes. After a time young toads come out. Thus the normal water-dwelling stage of the life cycle is avoided.

Some animals are born. We sometimes get the idea that only higher types like mammals bear their young. This isn't strictly true. To be sure,

Fig. 72-3. A female Surinam toad. Young toads are coming out of the skin "pockets" on its back.

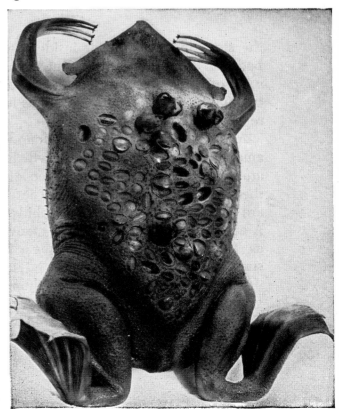

Fig. 72-4. A group of aphids on a plant stem. Some aphids produce about 20 groups of young each year.

the steps in development inside the body of the parent vary. But even some of the roundworms, such as the trichina worm, bear their young as a regular practice.

Another striking case is found among the *aphids* (*ay*-fids), which are tiny, bug-like insects. Some of them are shown in Fig. 72-4. There are many different kinds of aphids. A certain type may produce as many as 17 to 20 groups of young each summer.

The odd thing is that most of these groups of young contain only females. These females bear young aphids.

Moreover, they do it without being fertilized. So the offspring have only one parent. When autumn comes, a last group of offspring is produced. This group contains both males and females, and the females lay eggs. These eggs hatch to produce the first group of new offspring when spring comes again.

Probably you know the little tropical fish known as guppies. Guppies and some other fish bear their young alive. So do some species of snakes. Of course some snakes like bull snakes and black snakes lay eggs, but water snakes and garter snakes bear their young.

The three germ layers. When you study animal development, you learn something that may surprise you. It's true of animals that lay eggs, and it's also true of animals that bear their young.

At an early stage in development each offspring develops three cell layers. They're called the three *germ layers*. One is on the outside of the developing body, one is on the inside, and one is in the middle.

These three germ layers develop into the tissues, organs, and systems of the adult. And in all animals each germ layer gives rise to the same adult structures.

Thus, in all animals the outer skin layer and the nervous system come from the outer germ layer. The skeleton, muscles, and sex organs come from the middle layer. The linings of internal organs come from the inner layer.

CHECK YOUR FACTS . . .

Number 1 to 6 on a sheet of paper. Select the best answer for each of the following items.

1. Some animals reproduce by means of: (*a*) budding; (*b*) spores; (*c*) sex cells; (*d*) all of these.

2. In animals, the linings of internal organs develop from: (*a*) the outer germ layer; (*b*) the middle germ layer; (*c*) the inner germ layer; (*d*) all of these.

3. Reproduction of a Surinam toad is unusual because: (*a*) there is no tadpole stage; (*b*) the young are born; (*c*) the tadpoles do not live in ponds or streams; (*d*) the female toad lays her eggs in the water, and the male toad guards the eggs of the female toad.

4. Which of the following statements is true of guppies: (*a*) they are reptiles which lay eggs; (*b*) they are one-celled and produce spores; (*c*) they are insects which bear their young; (*d*) they are fish which bear their young?

5. Which of the following statements is true of aphids: (*a*) all female aphids bear young; (*b*) some female aphids bear young; (*c*) all aphids have two parents; (*d*) all aphids are hatched from eggs throughout the summer?

6. The duckbill is unusual because it's a: (*a*) mammal which lays eggs; (*b*) bird which has scales and claws; (*c*) mammal which bears its young; (*d*) bird which bears its young.

Pollen is formed on the stamens of flowers. Two sperm nuclei develop in pollen grains. These sperms unite with mature egg cells in ovaries. The fertilized eggs then develop. They become seeds, which contain plant embryos.

An embryo contains one or two seed leaves and parts from which the root and stem develop. Parts of a flower (mainly the ovary) may form a fleshy fruit around the seeds.

Man scatters many plant seeds. Others are carried by wind and water, or by animals. Some plant fruits burst open and "throw" their seeds when they're ripe. The scattering of seeds favors plant survival.

An annual plant lives and dies in a single growing season. A biennial completes its life cycle in two seasons. A perennial lives through more than two seasons.

In reproducing, some one-celled plants merely divide. Some simple plants form spores from which new plants come. Other plants reproduce by means of sex cells.

Many one-celled animals also divide, and some animal cells form spores. Some simple animals can reproduce by budding. Many animals, however, reproduce by the union of sex cells.

Some of the better-known animals are hatched from eggs. Others, however, develop within the bodies of female parents and are born.

But all of the more complex animals develop three germ layers early in life. In all species the same kinds of adult structures come from these three germ layers.

WHAT DO THESE WORDS MEAN?

Annual	Germ layers	Seed
Biennial	Perennial	Spore
Budding	Pistil	Stamen
Fruit	Pollination	Stigma

ASK YOURSELF . . .

1. (a) What part of a flower produces pollen grains? (b) How does this pollen reach the egg cells of a flower?
2. (a) What is cross-pollination? (b) Self-pollination? (c) Can all plants pollinate themselves?
3. What is one way in which certain insects are necessary to the success of plants?
4. What structures are present in a seed?
5. (a) How are plant seeds scattered? (b) In what way is this related to the control of weeds?
6. What is an advantage in raising perennial plants?
7. What are some of the ways in which plants and animals reproduce without the aid of sex cells?
8. Why are so many seeds useful as food?
9. Name three seeds that you use as food.
10. (a) Name three perennial fruits or vegetables. (b) Name three annual vegetables.
11. (a) What kinds of animals are hatched from eggs? (b) What kinds are born?
12. (a) What are the three germ layers in animal development? (b) What kinds of structures come from each of these layers?
13. In what way is the reproduction of a Surinam toad unusual?
14. What are some ways in which we ourselves may scatter weed seeds?
15. What is unusual about the ways in which aphids reproduce?
16. What do people mean when they say that a plant " seeds itself "?

GETTING THE FACTS . . .

1. Examine several microscope slides which show early development of a starfish or sea urchin. Your teacher will help you do this. You will need a microscope or a projector. Starfish and sea urchin eggs divide equally during early stages. Find 2-cell, 4-cell, 8-cell, and 16-cell stages. See if you can find out how the three germ layers are formed.

2. Examine a Hydra which has a bud. Is this bud formed by sex cells or by body cells? Consult the books at the end of this unit. See if you can find three different ways that a Hydra reproduces.

3. Examine a flower. Using Fig. 70-1 and the description on page 320, identify its structures. Locate the pollen. Cut an ovary in two and examine the contents of the ovary.

4. Plant some bean and corn seeds in moist, sandy soil. Study them in various stages of sprouting. Find out what structures give rise to the roots and stems. Find out how the seed leaves of beans and corn differ.

5. Arrange a visit to a fish hatchery if one is nearby. Observe the ways in which fish are hatched and raised.

6. If you have an incubator, hatch a dozen fertile hen eggs. Open an egg a day for several days. Study the way in which development goes on.

Topic 3

WHY LIVING THINGS VARY

What fish are these? They're codfish in the ocean.

A female codfish may lay as many as four million eggs a year. About half of these eggs hatch into male codfish. The other half hatch into females.

Let's assume that a female codfish begins laying her four million eggs when she's three years old. Suppose all the eggs hatch and all the young codfish live.

Now start with one pair of codfish. How many young fish will this pair produce in two years? In four years? In five years? Does anything like this really happen in nature? Does the sea become filled with codfish?

AMONG THE NEW WORDS FOR THIS TOPIC

- **ACQUIRED CHARACTER.** A character that isn't inherited. It results from effects of the environment on body cells.
- **HEREDITY.** The process in which characters are passed from one generation to the next.
- **HYBRID** (*hy*-brid). A plant or animal which has genes of different type for any character.
- **MUTATION** (mew-*tay*-shun). A new character which can be inherited.
- **SELECTION.** A process used to develop better types of domestic plants and animals.
- **VARIATION** (vair-ee-*ay*-shun). The differences between members of a species.

CHAPTER 73

How Do Living Things Vary?

If you planted corn seeds and they grew up to be onions, would you be surprised?

Of course you would. Things like that just don't happen. Offspring tend to resemble their parents. Corn seeds grow into new corn plants. Radish seeds give rise to more radishes. Cats give birth to kittens, and dogs to puppies.

The members of a species vary. Are all the corn plants, radish plants, kittens, and dogs exactly alike? By this time you know that they're not. Even identical twins aren't really identical in all ways.

We call the differences among members of a species *variation* (vair-ee-*ay*-shun). Look around you. You see variation among your friends and relatives. Some are taller than others.

Some are brunettes. Others are blonds. Some have blue eyes and others have brown or hazel eyes. These differences are what you depend on to tell your friends apart.

Fig. 73-1. Even leaves from the same plant vary in form. These are leaves from the sassafras tree.

Fig. 73-2. Dogs all belong to the same species, but there are many breeds of dogs. Here you see a greyhound and a basset hound.

And it's easy to do because you're used to noticing differences among people.

Probably the birds in a flock of chickens look more nearly alike to you. Or, perhaps you don't see much difference among bean plants in a garden. But if you studied any plant or animal type you'd be surprised. The differences are there in all cases. Few of us are trained to notice them.

In fact, variation is one of the most certain things in nature. You find that no two members of any species are exactly alike.

Why plants and animals vary. Now you may want to know what causes this variation in nature. When you think about it, this is a useful thing to know. By knowing this you can raise better plants and animals.

When you study the subject, you soon find that variation isn't caused by one thing alone. Rather, there are two general groups of causes. One of these groups includes the things that are inherited. In other words, the variations that are *inherited*. The other group is made up of variations that are *acquired*. They result from reactions to things and forces in the environment. Such acquired variations aren't inherited.

Variations that are inherited. Let's consider a variation that is inherited. A good example is human eye color. It's caused by genes in the male and female sex cells which unite to produce the offspring. One combination gives blue eyes. Another gives brown eyes. Still another gives hazel eyes. They keep on reappearing.

The point is that eye color is caused by the genes in the sex cells. Blue, brown, and hazel eyes are well known. You might say that they're old variations that have been present for many generations.

Old and new variations. Now you may ask: "Are there ever any new variations? Are there any characters that appear for the first time?"

This is a good question. The answer is yes. New variations due to changes in the genes do appear in all sorts of plants and animals. And some of them are useful to us. We call these new inheritable variations *mutations* (mew-*tay*-shuns).

For instance, all Hereford cattle once had horns. Often the horns were a nuisance. They injured cattle, and hurt other animals. Then in 1889 one hornless Hereford calf was born on a farm in Kansas. The hornless condition was a mutation. This calf then gave rise to a long line of hornless Hereford cattle. They're common today.

Variations that aren't inherited. How about the variations that aren't inherited? Well, there are a lot of these. We call them *acquired characters.* They result from contact with the things and forces of the environment. They're due to changes in the body cells, not in the sex cells.

Perhaps you've seen a tree growing on a rocky ledge. Its roots spread out over the rocky surface, and then go down into the soil. The result is a root system that's far from normal.

Now suppose you planted seeds from this tree. Let's say you planted them in soil where there were no big rocks. Would you get trees with the same unusual type of root system?

Of course you wouldn't. The genes in the sex cells of the parent tree weren't changed. Seeds from the parent tree will continue to produce trees with normal root systems.

But remember this. Every new plant or animal is more or less plastic. At first it has certain abilities to grow and develop. These abilities are affected by things and forces of the environment. The result is a variety of

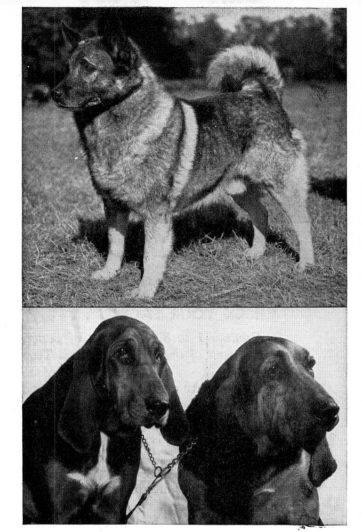

Fig. 73-3. An elkhound (above) and two bloodhounds (below). Careful selection has developed many different breeds of dogs.

characters which differ from those typical of the species.

Part of the variations you see around you, then, are inherited. Part of them come from contact with the environment. The result is a variety of individuals in every species. No two of them are exactly alike.

Each individual is affected by both heredity and environment. These forces shape development.

Fig. 73-4. An albino robin. This is a variation in which the feathers are white and the eyes are red. Albinos also occur in other types of animals.

CHECK YOUR FACTS . . .

Number 1 to 6 on a sheet of paper. Mark each of the following items True *or* False.

1. There are many cases in which two members of the same species are exactly alike.

2. A mutation is a new, inheritable variation.

3. Some differences among the members of a species are due to contact with the environment.

4. The color of human eyes is determined by heredity.

5. Acquired characters are almost always inherited.

6. Hereford cattle have always been hornless.

CHAPTER 74

How Living Things Struggle to Exist

Remember the little problem of the codfish on page 332? Remember that all members of a species differ from one another? These are two important facts about plants and animals.

How fast does a species increase? Let's think about the codfish problem for a minute. If all codfish eggs produced new codfish, what would happen?

In a few years the oceans would be filled with codfish. There would be no room for anything else.

In the same way, a single species of land plant might cover the surface of the earth. That is, it would if all its spores or seeds grew into new plants.

But nothing like this actually happens. The question is: Why not?

The answer is that many of the offspring don't survive. Some of them are eaten by animals or killed by parasites. If they get too numerous some of them can't find food. Thus, they die of starvation.

The rate of survival. The *possible* rate of increase for many plants and animals is very high. But in such cases many of the young fail to survive. In other words, the *rate of survival* is low. If it wasn't, there would soon be too many plants and animals.

Of course, some of the higher animals care for their young. Then the rate of survival is generally higher. But such animals also produce much smaller numbers of offspring.

Of course there are cases in which some species have increased very rapidly. This often happens when a species arrives in a new place. There it may find food and few natural enemies. All the English sparrows, starlings, cabbage butterflies, and Japa-

Fig. 74-1. Some animals, like this bird, provide care for their young. In such cases, the rate of survival is likely to be fairly high.

nese beetles have come from a few individuals that came to our country at various times. They haven't always been here.

The struggle for existence. Billions of spores, seeds, eggs, and young are produced by living things each year. Most of them don't grow up to be adults.

Remember also that the young, like their parents, vary from one another. They're faced with the problem of survival. This is partly a problem of finding food. It's also partly a problem of keeping away from natural enemies.

Such being the case, scientists believe that a *struggle for existence* takes place. In the long run, the young that are best fitted to survive *do* survive.

This leaves us the question: " What makes a plant or animal ' fit '? " Clearly the plant or animal must be able to get along with the conditions of life. It must be able to get food. It must be able to survive among natural enemies. In a word, it must be adapted to its environment.

Environments change. The environment in one place isn't like the environment in another place.

To be sure! For these reasons fitness varies also. The plant that survives in a desert may not survive in a more fertile spot. The animal that survives in one place today may not be able to get food a year or ten years

Fig. 74-2. One of the dinosaurs which lived millions of years ago.   For reasons not known to us today, none of these reptiles has survived.

from now. So you see that fitness depends on the things and forces of the environment. It varies from time to time and from place to place. Being fit is being well adapted.

What about heredity? Heredity is part of the story, too. Many of the variations that plants and animals have can be inherited. If the fittest survive, they can pass on to their young some of the characters which made them fit.

Does this tend to improve the species? Does it make the species better adapted? What do you think?

Probably you'll say " yes." And this answer seems to be true, but we have to allow for some exceptions. For instance, if the environment changes very much, fitness changes also. The variation that was once useful may be of no value another time.

The theory of natural selection. Now what does all this add up to? Scientists call it the *theory of natural selection.* Or you could just call it **selection in nature.** It's an attempt to explain how plant and animal species change.

Let's see what we have. *First,* more plants and animals are produced than can possibly survive. *Second,* all of these plants and animals are different because of variation.

This being the case, a struggle for existence takes place. In the long run, the fittest plants and animals tend to survive. They pass on to their offspring those inherited characters which made them fit.

The general result is to keep all species adjusted to conditions of life. Or, you might say, adjusted to the environment. The environment changes, of course, but when this happens, the nature of selection changes also.

Can we use selection? Do you see any way to use this theory of natural selection to our advantage?

Maybe you can see that we do use selection. In fact, men used a kind of selection long before there was any such theory. Centuries ago the early farmers began to keep seeds from their "best" plants. They planted these seeds and slowly but surely began to improve the plants.

We do the same kind of thing today. But we do it faster and better. We know a lot more about heredity. Thus we're able to get results in less time and with less effort.

Fig. 74-3. **Study of fossils suggests that the first birds looked like these.**

CHECK YOUR FACTS . . .

Number 1 to 6 on a sheet of paper. Select the best answer for each of the following items.

1. The environment is: (*a*) the same in all places; (*b*) a thing that never changes; (*c*) favorable to all plants and animals; (*d*) an influence in selection.

2. Variations which can be inherited are those due to: (*a*) genes in the sex cells; (*b*) accidental injuries; (*c*) forces of the environment; (*d*) changes in the environment.

3. The thing that determines fitness is the nature of the: (*a*) species; (*b*) environment; (*c*) heredity; (*d*) acquired character.

4. A species which provides parental care for its young usually: (*a*) produces large numbers of offspring; (*b*) fails in the struggle for existence; (*c*) produces relatively few offspring; (*d*) becomes adapted to the environment.

5. The result of variation is that: (*a*) all members of a species are alike; (*b*) only a small number of offspring can survive; (*c*) all members of a species are different; (*d*) plants and animals can get foods.

6. To survive, an animal must obtain food and: (*a*) kill its natural enemies; (*b*) be small and hard to see; (*c*) live in underground burrows; (*d*) avoid destruction by its natural enemies.

Fig. 74-4. From fossils like this we learn about plants and animals that lived before our own time.

CHAPTER 75

How You Inherit Your Traits

The story of how scientists learned about heredity is interesting. Some 100 years ago men knew little about heredity. In a European garden, a studious monk named Mendel was raising peas. He crossed tall plants with short plants. That is, he mated tall plants with short plants. He was on the trail of one of the great discoveries of science.

Now if you cross tall peas with short peas you may expect the offspring to be average in size. But not so! Mendel found that the offspring of pure tall and pure short peas were always tall! Here was a surprising thing. It called for more study and experiments.

Mendel tested other characters of peas in the same way. He crossed peas which had yellow pods with peas which had green pods. He also crossed peas which had round seeds with peas which had wrinkled seeds.

Heredity becomes a science. Mendel's discovery caused no excitement back in 1865. Scientists didn't know enough about heredity to appreciate what Mendel found. But at the beginning of the 20th Century the story was different. Meanwhile Mendel had died just about unknown, but other scientists took up the trail.

"Here," they said, "are very important laws of heredity, if they're true." So as the years passed, they made other experiments. They learned that Mendel was right.

What's more, his laws were true for all sorts of plants. They were true for all sorts of animals, as well. They even worked in the case of man.

So heredity became a science. It was now possible to predict what kinds of offspring would be produced. It was possible to develop better types of plants and animals. Plant and animal breeders could do this faster than ever before.

Mendel's law. Today you hear a good deal about Mendel's law. It's the basic law of heredity. Let's go back to the garden peas and see what it means.

A pure tall pea has received a gene for tallness *from both* its parents. We can label this pea *TT*. A pure, short pea has gotten a gene for shortness *from both* of its parents. We'll label it *ss*. Now if you cross *TT* with *ss*, the offspring inherits *T* from one parent and *s* from the other parent. Or you can show what happens like this:

$$TT + ss = 4\,Ts$$

You assume that there are four offspring, but it actually doesn't make much difference. A thousand offspring would all be the same.

What does a *Ts* look like? Well, it looks as tall as a *TT*. But actually, it is not *pure* tall. It is a *hybrid*. A **hybrid** (*hy*-brid) is the offspring from two parents of different characters. It has a gene for both tallness and

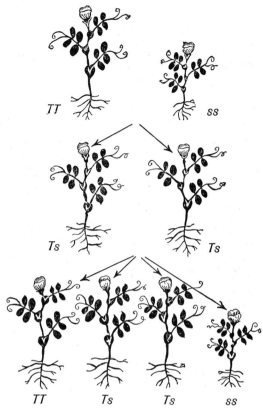

Fig. 75-1. How tallness and shortness are inherited in garden peas. TT is pure tall, Ts is hybrid, and ss is pure short. Notice that only the ss plants *are* short. The TT and Ts plants *appear* equally tall.

shortness. And this makes a difference when a *Ts* reproduces.

So let's see what happens when you cross two *Ts* peas. Now each parent can give either the tall or the short gene to its offspring:

Male = *T* or *s*
Female = *T* or *s*

A *T* from a male may combine with either a *T* or a *s* from a female. You can show what happens by using the square on page 342.

Genes from male parent

            T   *s*

Genes   *T*
from
female
parent   *s*

Now fill in the gene combinations. For each square take one gene from each margin. The result is:

TT	*Ts*
Ts	*ss*

The filled in squares are the offspring. One is *TT*, which looks tall and is pure tall. Two are *Ts*'s, or hybrids, which

look tall, but carry the gene of shortness. One is *ss*, which looks short and is pure short.

What happens when you cross pure tall peas? Why, you keep right on getting pure tall offspring. No gene but the *T* gene is present. And what about a cross of two pure short peas? Why, the offspring are also pure short. They have only the *s* gene.

Dominant genes. We say that in peas *tallness* is **dominant** over *shortness*. It's a dominant character. Or, we say that shortness is the **recessive** character, or one that is weaker. You find many similar cases among other plants and animals.

Some of them are shown in the table on page 343.

A given member of any species is made up of a lot of different charac-

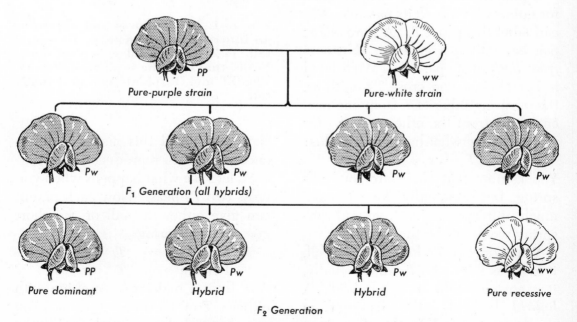

Pure-purple strain   PP

Pure-white strain   w w

Pw   *Pw*   *Pw*   *Pw*

F₁ Generation (all hybrids)

Pure dominant   PP   *Hybrid*   Pw   *Hybrid*   Pw   *Pure recessive*   w w

F₂ Generation

Fig. 75-2. Another example of how Mendel's law works. Here, purple is dominant, white is recessive. F₁ means first generation; F₂ means second generation.

SOME DOMINANT AND RECESSIVE CHARACTERS IN LIVING THINGS

Type	Character	Dominant	Recessive
Cattle of various breeds	Horns or no horns	Hornless	Horned
Cotton plant	Lint	Colored	White
Fruit fly	Eye color	Red	White
Guinea pig	Fur	Black	White
Guinea pig	Fur	Short	Long
Man	Eye	Brown	Blue
Man	Hair	Curly	Straight
Man	Fingers	Webbed	Normal
Pea plant	Seeds	Smooth	Wrinkled
Silkworm	Cocoon	Yellow	White
Snapdragon	Flower	Red	White
Sunflower	Stalk	Branched	Unbranched

ters. Some of these characters are inherited. Others are acquired in the process of living. Many of them depend on both heredity and the effects of living. In any case, all sorts of combinations are possible. Do you see now why one person differs from another? Why the tomato plants in a garden aren't all exactly the same?

And of course you see why knowledge of heredity is useful. It is of great value in raising better plants and animals. We use it every day.

CHECK YOUR FACTS . . .

Number 1 to 6 on a sheet of paper. Answer the following items.

1. *LL* is pure long-haired, and *ss* is pure short-haired. Long-haired is dominant. *LL* is crossed with *ss*. What kind of hair do the offspring have?

2. Same as No. 1 except that *Ls* is crossed with *Ls*. If there are 100 offspring, how many have long hair? How many have short hair?

3. Same as No. 1 except that *LL* is crossed with *Ls*. If there are 100 offspring, how many have long hair? How many have short hair?

4. In man, brown eye color is dominant over blue eye color. *True* or *False?*

5. In guinea pigs, black fur is dominant over white fur. *True* or *False?*

6. In peas, the combination *TT* is a hybrid. *True* or *False?*

CHAPTER 76

How We Get Better Plants and Animals

" Does it help us to know about heredity? " you ask.

Yes indeed! We've found that Mendel's law holds true for all sorts of characters. It holds true in plants and it holds true in animals. But he-

redity of all characters isn't as simple as the case you've just read about.

New domestic plants and animals. We profit when we use what we know about heredity. We can develop special types to raise. Sometimes we want types that resist certain diseases. Sometimes we want a larger type or a smaller type. Or, we may be looking for one that will grow faster.

Men were improving plants and animals centuries ago. They did it by saving seeds from the " best " plants. Also by using the " best " animals as breeding stock. But this was a slow job. It often took many years to get pure breeds of the right kind.

" Why? " you ask. Because there was no known way to sort out the hybrids easily. Suppose *BB* is black and dominant. And suppose *ww* is white and recessive. You want a pure domi-

Fig. 76-1. These two plots show differences in the growth of corn as a result of different soil treatment. Good soil, like good heredity, is very important.

nant breed. In a mixed stock, however, all *BB*'s and *Bw*'s (hybrids) are black and look alike.

Knowing Mendel's law makes all the difference. You can test a group of blacks by crossing them with whites. If your black is really a hybrid, here's what happens:

	w	*w*
B	*Bw*	*Bw*
w	*ww*	*ww*

You see right away that half the offspring are white. But suppose your black is pure, or has both black genes. Then

	w	*w*
B	*Bw*	*Bw*
B	*Bw*	*Bw*

All the offspring are black. Of course these offspring are hybrids and you don't want them. But you do want the black parent for your pure type. You know this parent is a *BB*.

So the use of Mendel's law has greatly speeded up the process of raising better plants and animals. You might guess that a lot of new types have been developed in the last 50 years. This is quite right.

The use of hybrids. Now you may ask "What about the hybrids we raise? Do we always want pure breeds?"

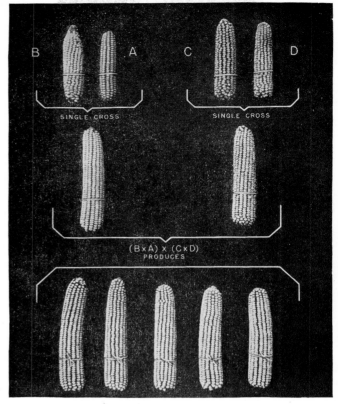

Fig. 76-2. The story of hybrid corn. A and B are crossed to produce AB. C and D are crossed to produce CD. Then AB is crossed with CD. The result is ABCD, as shown by the five ears of corn below.

This is a good question and brings up the case of hybrid corn. What is hybrid corn?

First of all, it isn't just one kind of corn. There are many kinds of hybrid corn. They're developed to meet different needs in different places. But they're all produced in the same general way.

Suppose you want four different characters in a corn plant. You can call them *A*, *B*, *C*, and *D*. Now these characters exist in four different varieties of corn. So you cross the variety which has *A* with the variety which has *B*. And you cross the variety which has *C* with the variety which

Fig. 76-3. A turkey breeding project has resulted in the Beltsville small white turkey. It was developed by selective breeding.

has *D*. Now you have two kinds of hybrids which you can call *AB* and *CD*.

You can guess what the next step is. You cross *AB* with *CD* to get the corn seed you use. You plant this seed. Your crop is corn with all four of the desired characters. You have to get new seed from a seed company each year. Many farmers in the Midwest now raise hybrid corn. Their crops have become much better.

Old characters and new characters. Sometimes it's the hybrid that pays off and other times it's the pure type. But where do the needed characters come from?

Scientists hunt all over the world for these characters. They seek wild relatives of the plants that we raise. Many of these wild relatives are sad-looking specimens. But there's al-

ways a chance that one of them will have a useful character. It may be the ability to throw off an attack of some disease. It may be the ability to mature quickly. Or, it may be some special type of root, stem, seed, or fruit.

The plant with the desired character is crossed with plants already known. Often a scientist has to make a whole series of crosses before he gets what he wants. But by crossing different varieties, and by careful selection, he usually succeeds. He has a new cultivated variety that's actually a " tailor-made " plant.

Some of the useful characters found among plants and animals aren't new. They've existed in certain varieties of these plants and animals for a long time. But others are hereditary characters that have appeared for the first time. They are mutations.

Scientists are always on the lookout for mutations. They find them every now and then. A lot of these mutations are of no practical use. But some have proved to be valuable. In fact, mutations are now produced in the laboratory. Heat, light, X rays, and chemicals are used to change the genes in sex cells. This is another way to get new, and possibly useful characters.

Some products of science. Hornless cattle, wheat that resists rust diseases, special types of fruits, and hybrid corn are only a few of the products of modern science.

In recent years a small type of turkey has been developed. It's about half the size of ordinary turkeys. Such a bird can be canned whole, or put in a small refrigerator. It's not too big for a small family.

We also have a new variety of chicken. It has light, small bones. It has more meat than older types. Special breeds of chickens, pigs, cattle, horses, and sheep have been developed to meet various needs.

In the Southwest native cattle have been crossed with Brahman cattle from India. The hybrid offspring stand the heat of that area well. They resist a number of dangerous parasites.

We now have pigs with more lean meat and less fat. We have blueberries almost as big as golf balls. All these things are produced by using Mendel's law of heredity.

CHECK YOUR FACTS . . .

Number 1 to 6 on a sheet of paper. Answer the following items.

1. Brahman cattle came originally from (Europe, Africa, India) . . .?. . .

2. When *BB* is crossed with *ww* the

Fig. 76-4. This shows a flock of pullets specially bred for heavy egg laying. Rhode Island Reds were mated with white Leghorns.

result is a (hybrid, mutation, pure type) . . .?. . .

3. Not one, but many different types of hybrid corn have been developed. *True* or *False?*

4. Sometimes the plant or animal that we want to raise is a hybrid rather than a pure type. *True* or *False?*

5. If *B* is dominant and *w* is recessive, it's easy to tell a *BB* from a *Bw* just by looking at them. *True* or *False?*

6. Any mutation in a plant or animal that we raise is sure to be useful. *True* or *False?*

Fig. 76-5. On the left is a Brahman cow from India. On the right is a hybrid of a pure-bred Aberdeen-Angus and a Brahman.

All members of a species differ from one another. We call this variation. Some variations are new and some are old. Some are caused by changes in the sex cells and can be inherited. We call these inherited variations, mutations. On the other hand, some variations are due to effects of the environment on body cells. These we call acquired characters.

If all seeds and eggs developed, the world would soon be over-populated. But actually, the death rate among many plants and animals is very high. Scientists believe that a survival of the fittest takes place. Characters which allow the survivors to live are passed on to their offspring by heredity.

About a hundred years ago a European monk named Mendel experimented with garden peas. He found a basic law of heredity. We call it Mendel's law. Other studies show that it explains heredity in many living things.

Today we often use Mendel's law to develop better plants and animals. We hunt for plants and animals which have useful characters. We cross them to produce hybrids. We select pure types. Thus we develop more useful domestic types.

WHAT DO THESE WORDS MEAN?

Acquired character	Heredity	Natural selection
Albino	Hybrid	Recessive
Dominant	Mendel's law	Struggle for existence
Fossil	Mutation	Variation

ASK YOURSELF . . .

1. (a) What do we mean when we say that individuals vary? (b) What use do we make of variations in plants and animals?

2. (a) Do people vary? (b) Why is this important?

3. (a) Why do the members of plant and animal species vary? (b) Are all of their variations inherited?

4. Suppose you're trying to develop a new type of plant. Why is it important to know what characters are inherited?

5. (a) What are acquired characters? (b) Explain why they're not inherited.

6. Why do scientists think that a struggle for existence takes place in nature?

7. (a) What is meant by a " survival of the fittest "? (b) Would all characters that made plants and animals " fit " be inherited?

8. How do we use Mendel's law to develop better plants and animals?

9. What do we mean by " dominant " and " recessive " characters?

10. Describe two cases in which hybrids are more useful than pure types.

11. How do scientists produce mutations in the laboratory?

12. Why are scientists on the lookout for mutations in nature?

13. How is the seed for hybrid corn produced?

14. What methods are used by scientists to develop new types of plants and animals?

GETTING THE FACTS . . .

1. Weigh and measure the height of each of the members of your class. Have your teacher help you make a chart with curves showing the variations in height and weight.

2. Count the members of your class who have: (a) brown eyes; and (b) blue eyes. Don't count " in-between " colors such as hazel. What type appears to be dominant? Explain why two brown-eyed parents might have a blue-eyed child.

3. Visit a farm in your community if you live near one. Find out what special types of plants and animals are raised. Find out *why* these are good types to raise. You'll find that many different factors must be considered.

4. Examine a seed catalogue. Pick out a type of plant which has a number of different varieties. Explain why and where you might wish to raise each of these varieties.

5. If there's an agricultural experiment station nearby, arrange a visit. Find out what scientists have done there and what they're trying to do now.

6. Prepare an exhibit which shows variation in some species of plant or animal.

7. If you can get specimens of fruit flies, your teacher may be able to help you make some crosses. For instance, you can cross flies which have normal wings with flies which have almost no wings. Or you can cross red-eyed flies with white-eyed flies. As you would expect, the results follow Mendel's law.

Books You May Like . . .

Anderson, Edgar. PLANTS, MAN, AND LIFE. Little, Brown Co., New York. 1952. An excellent book giving, in simple language, the story of the origin of our common plants. Dr. Anderson shows how many of our weeds have followed man in his establishment of new areas of the world.

Asch, John. THE STORY OF PLANTS. G. P.

Putnam's Sons, New York. 1948. A useful reference book on plants. Part III deals with *such topics as selection, uses of plants, seed production, grafting, and essentials for* growth.

Beck, Lester F. *HUMAN GROWTH. Harcourt, Brace and Co., New York. 1949. An easy reading reference on the development and growth of the human body.*

Dorrance, Anne. *GREEN CARGOES. Doubleday and Co., New York. 1945. This is the story of how seeds and plants have been carried from their native soil to all corners of the earth and the effect on man.*

Morgan, Anne Haven. *FIELD BOOK OF ANIMALS IN WINTER. G. P. Putnam's Sons, New York. 1939. An introduction to the* ways animals adapt themselves to meeting the hardships of winter.

Platt, Rutherford Hayes. *THIS GREEN WORLD. Dodd, Mead and Co., New York. 1942. This book deals by text and pictures with the trees and flowers — how they live and how we breed them.*

Reed, William and Lucas, May. *ANIMALS ON THE MARCH. Harcourt, Brace and Co., New York. 1937. The history of many familiar types of animals from the earliest forms to the present time.*

Scheinfeld, Amram. *YOU AND HEREDITY. J. B. Lippincott Co., New York. 1950. The contents of this book deals with how and why certain traits are inherited and why others are not.*

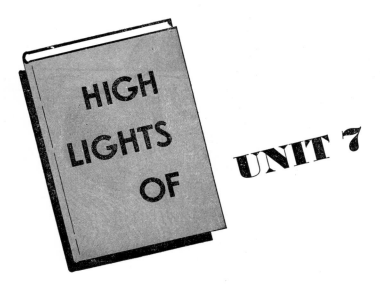

HIGH LIGHTS OF UNIT 7

Cell division in living things results in growth and repair. It's also the basis for reproduction. Many living things have special sex cells. These give rise to egg cells and sperm cells. An egg cell and a sperm cell unite and thus produce a new individual.

The chromosomes of all cells contain genes. These genes are the bearers of the hereditary characters. When a sex cell becomes mature, it loses half of its chromosomes.

Some one-celled plants and animals just divide and form two new cells. Some may divide and form many spores. Each spore can develop into a new cell. In higher plants, egg cells and sperm cells unite and produce seeds. A seed contains a plant embryo. It can also develop into a new plant.

Some of the simpler animals reproduce by budding. Quite a large number produce eggs. Some animals, including most mammals, bear their young alive.

The members of any species vary. Some variations are inherited. Some aren't. Some are new and some are old. A survival of the fittest takes place. Those characters which make the survivors fit are passed on to future generations by heredity.

We use Mendel's law of heredity as a guide to producing better types of plants and animals. Scientists are always on the lookout for new and useful characters in the plants and animals we raise.

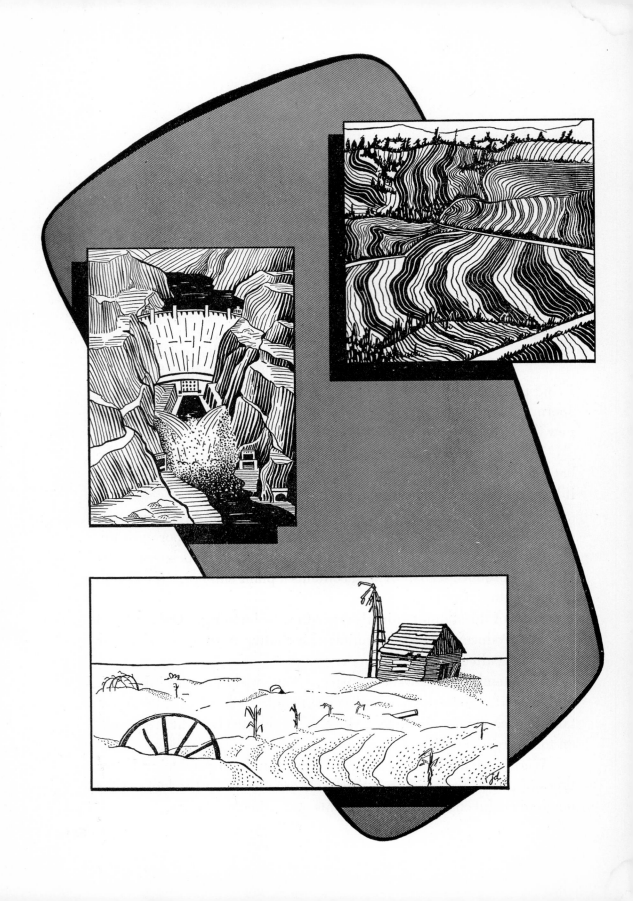

Unit 8

Conserving

Our Resources

Ed and Jim were out for a walk on a crisp October afternoon. They came to a farm that was badly washed away. A tumbled-down shack was the only home the farmer had.

"That farm is a mess," Ed remarked to Jim. "Look at those gullies. The soil is washed away and I don't see how the farmer can grow anything."

"It just proves what Ann said the other night, 'poor soil means poor people,'" Jim replied.

A mile or so beyond, the boys came to a farm that was prosperous. There were no gullies and the crops were good. The farmhouse was large.

"Boy, what a difference!" Jim said. "I wouldn't believe such a thing were possible if I hadn't seen it with my own eyes."

"I wouldn't either," Ed told him. "There sure is something in this conservation business."

Conservation is the science of using our natural resources to the best advantage.

Topic 1

WHAT ARE NATURAL RESOURCES?

Ever watch a freight train come rumbling down the track? There's a refrigerator car. It's full of fresh fruits and vegetables for the city market. These are products of a fertile soil.

Next is a flatcar loaded with lumber. This is a product of the forest. Now comes a tank car full of fuel oil or gasoline. It represents plants and animals of long ago. There's a stock car of pigs, poultry, or cattle. Maybe there's another refrigerator car full of meat.

The train tells a story. It's the story of our natural resources. It's the story of climate, weather, water, soil, plants, and animals.

AMONG THE NEW WORDS FOR THIS TOPIC

- **CONSERVATION.** The science of using natural resources wisely.
- **COVER CROPS.** Soil-binding crops which aren't planted in strips or rows.
- **CROP ROTATION.** The planting of different crops in succeeding years. Thus a crop of corn may be followed for a year or two by clover or alfalfa before corn is planted again.
- **EROSION** (ee-*roh*-zhun). The wearing away of the earth's surface.
- **STRIP FARMING.** The practice of planting alternate strips of row crops and cover crops. The cover crops tend to check erosion.
- **SUCCESSION.** The series of changes through which a plant community goes through in reaching its final growth stage. Successions also take place in animal groups.

CHAPTER 77

What Causes Erosion?

Erosion (ee-*roh*-zhun) often means the loss of the topsoil. Do you have erosion in your community?

"Yes, some," you say. This is to be expected. There's always some wearing away of the land even when it's used wisely. But new soil is being formed. So the loss is made good.

What causes erosion? When our use of the soil is unwise, erosion speeds up. Then you have trouble. The fertile topsoil you read about in Chapter 9 is lost. Crops become poorer and poorer. In time the land is just about worthless.

Now what causes erosion? And what can we do about it? These are good questions because poor soil means poor people. Also, people must have food, clothing, and other things that come from the soil.

Well, if you've ever watched a heavy rain falling you know one answer. Water running over the surface carries away the soil. This is most apt to happen on hillsides. First, there are little *rills*. Later, the rills become *ditches* and *gullies*. Soon, most of the topsoil is gone.

Running water isn't the only cause of erosion. Wind carries the topsoil away, too. Wind erosion goes on everywhere, and is likely to be bad in a dry area. Dust storms result. Fields are stripped bare of topsoil. Buildings are all but buried by shifting sand and dust.

Rapid erosion comes from unwise use of land. If you look around you'll see that plant roots hold the soil in place. Once a hillside is covered with grass or trees, erosion is checked. There's some loss of topsoil, but often it's not serious.

When the settlers first moved into the hill country of New England they

Fig. 77-1. Here you see a case of rill erosion on a bare slope. Running water caused this erosion.

cleared away the forests. Trees were cut on the hillsides as well as in the valleys. The first need was land on which crops would grow. Many of the fields in the valleys were good. There, rainfall and snow didn't run off so rapidly. But it was different on the hillsides. Gullies and ditches soon formed. Topsoil was washed away. One by one the farms were abandoned.

Years later much the same kind of thing happened in the West. In the West there are thousands of acres of *grassland*. It's normally covered and held in place by prairie grasses. The soil is fertile enough, but there isn't much rain. Water for irrigating isn't to be had in some places.

But once in a while there are years when it rains more than the average.

And when this happens the grassland can produce crops of grain. Large tracts are sometimes plowed and planted in the hope that rains will come. When the rains don't come the result is disastrous. Winds sweep over the dry prairie lands. Bits of soil are carried up into the air. They form dust storms. The topsoil is stripped from the land.

Wise use of land stops rapid erosion. Now you may ask, " What can we do to stop erosion? How can we save the topsoil? "

The problem isn't too hard. Rapid erosion has been stopped in many places. It can be stopped in most or all communities. Let's take the case of the hill country first.

Here flat areas can safely be plowed into fields. Why? Because on flat

Fig. 77-2. Erosion of this hillside by running water has made gullies. Crops can no longer be grown.

Fig. 77-3. After wind erosion and dust storms have done their work. Many farms like this have been abandoned.

Fig. 77-4. A combination of terraces, contour plowing, and strip farming. The result is far less erosion.

areas run-off of water isn't fast. Gentle slopes can also be plowed and planted in some cases. But the furrows should run *along* the slope, and *not up and down* the slope. When furrows run up and down a slope, run-off of water is speeded up. It's especially bad when crops are planted in rows. When furrows are run along the slope, instead of up and down, you have *contour plowing.*

"Now what about the steeper slopes?" you ask.

The steeper slopes should not be plowed. Many of these hillsides can be used to grow trees. In other cases they can be pasture land. Either way there are plenty of plant roots in the soil. The soil is held in place. There's one other way out. This is to terrace the land, as shown in Fig. 77-4. Terraces prevent rapid erosion.

Consider the dry-land areas. Many of them shouldn't be plowed at all unless water for irrigation is first brought to them. Some are fairly

good if they're farmed the right way. For instance, they can be *strip-farmed,* as shown in Fig. 77-5. Here alternate strips of land are planted with different crops. Every other strip may have crops in rows. These strips are subject to rapid wind erosion. But between them are strips of crop plants that aren't in rows. These strips tend to check erosion. Not much topsoil is lost.

Row crops and soil-binding crops. You know that corn usually is planted in rows. So are cotton and tobacco. Thus, it's possible to plow them and keep them free of weeds. But land with these row crops on it is likely to erode. Yet we want the things that come from many of our row crops.

Certain crops not planted in rows are soil-binding crops. They're called *cover crops.* They include several types of grasses or hay, alfalfa, and clover. We find use for them in feeding livestock. When land is used properly you usually find both row

Fig. 77-5. Strip farming to prevent erosion. Alternating strips of row crops and cover crops are planted.

crops and cover crops on it. Both kinds of crops can be raised safely and with profit.

CHECK YOUR FACTS . . .

Number 1 to 6 on a sheet of paper. Answer each item.

1. In the following group a cover crop is (tobacco, corn, cotton, alfalfa) . . . ? . . .

2. Wind erosion is likely to be worst where: (*a*) hillsides are covered with grass; (*b*) soil-binding plants are being grown; (*c*) annual rainfall is low; (*d*) topsoil has been carried away.

3. In contour plowing furrows run up and down the slope. *True* or *False?*

4. If farmers didn't plow the soil there would be no erosion. *True* or *False?*

5. Run-off of water is apt to be most rapid on: (*a*) level land; (*b*) a steep slope; (*c*) a gentle slope; (*d*) a valley floor.

6. When a field is strip-farmed, only about half of it can produce useful crops. *True* or *False?*

CHAPTER 78

How We Can Keep Our Soil Fertile

When we have rapid erosion, where does the topsoil go? Is it lost? You can see right away that these are good, practical questions. We depend on the topsoil for crop production.

Various things can happen to the topsoil. None of them is good from our point of view. For instance, consider what happens to soil that is washed from hillsides. It goes down into the valleys and into creeks and rivers. A lot of it is finally carried out into the sea. Some of it, to be sure, comes to rest in the bottom lands. But these lands are swampy. They're flooded every now and then. Often they can't be used to raise crops. So the soil that washes away is usually lost.

Fig. 78-1. Erosion becomes very bad if unchecked. Here the ditches have become canyons.

Can topsoil be replaced? Now maybe you say, "Won't new topsoil form?" You've read enough about soil to know that it will. But the catch is that this takes time. In some places it takes tens or hundreds of years. This is a lot too long to wait. So the best policy is not to lose the topsoil in the first place.

An early remedy is needed. The next best thing is to check erosion whenever it appears. The first thing you have to learn is to know the early warning signs. One kind of erosion is hard to spot. It's erosion where soil particles are carried away from all parts of the surface. It's called *sheet erosion.* The surface may not look very much changed while this is going on.

Rill erosion is easy enough to spot in an early stage. The telltale little rills appear on the slopes. You know that they'll become gullies and ditches

unless something is done about it. But what to do?

The first step is to get rid of the cause. Usually this cause is a soil surface not held in place by the roots of plants. The remedy is to get some soil-binding plants on the exposed surface.

At the same time you may have to do something about gullies that have formed. If they're not too large, you may find soil to fill them. But large gullies often are a problem.

One way to meet the problem is shown in Fig. 78-2. Here, *check dams* to slow down the flow of water have been built across a ditch. Soil-binding plants have been planted. The soil has been covered. In time the ditch will cease to be a menace.

Is rapid erosion the only danger? Don't get the idea that erosion is the only threat to soil. Sometimes the topsoil stays in place but becomes

Fig. 78-2. Farmers often build check dams to slow down rapid erosion.

worthless just the same. This can happen when certain plants are grown on it year after year.

A fertile topsoil contains minerals that plants can use. In fact, the plants must have these minerals to live and grow. Among them are the nitrates you read about in Chapter 15.

Now let's think about crops like cotton and corn. They're fine, useful crops. But when they grow they take a lot of nitrates out of the soil. If they're raised in the same place year after year, crops get smaller and smaller. The soil becomes worn-out.

Keeping the topsoil fertile. One way to do this is to use several different crops. Corn, for example, is raised for a year or two. Then the land is planted with clover; or perhaps with soybeans or alfalfa. In a couple of years corn is raised again. We call this method of growing different crops on the soil *crop rotation.*

"Why soybeans or alfalfa?" you ask.

Because colonies of nitrogen-fixing bacteria grow on their roots. The bacteria make nitrates. Some of the nitrates are restored to the soil. In a year or two the soil will produce another good crop of corn.

Of course, we also use fertilizers on soils. There are two general kinds of these fertilizers. First, there are the *natural products,* such as manures and materials that come from the decay of plants. Men have used such fertilizers for centuries. Second, there are the *chemical fertilizers:* nitrates and phosphates made in factories. These factory products are newcomers. Studies are being made to find out how they affect useful plants and animals in the soil. If these new fertilizers can be made at low cost, they may be used widely in the future.

Can the soil be restored? In the last hundred years a good many farms have been abandoned. But recently some of the eroded, worn-out farms have been put back in business.

Fig. 78-3. Raising soybeans restores nitrates to the soil.

Often this isn't easy, but it can be done.

Erosion is checked, and fields are sometimes leveled off again. Swampy areas may be drained by building ponds to hold the water. Thus the water is saved, and level land is used for fields. Soils are tested to find out what kinds of crops can be raised with profit. Fertilizers, and sometimes lime, are spread on the soil. Crops like clover and alfalfa are used to restore nitrates to the soil. Thus the land is put back in production.

It takes a lot of time and work to wipe out the effects of erosion. It also takes time and work to restore worn-out land. After the land has been restored, the right crops must be raised. They must be raised in the right places.

You should always remember one thing. The plants and animals we raise come from the soil, directly or indirectly. They are **natural resources.** What's more, they're resources that we can raise year after year. Provided, of course, that we save the topsoil and keep it fertile.

CHECK YOUR FACTS . . .

Number 1 to 6 on a sheet of paper. Mark each of the following items True *or* False.

1. Nitrogen-fixing bacteria grow on the roots of crops such as clover and alfalfa.

2. In the process of growing, corn and cotton plants add nitrates to the soil.

3. Some of the topsoil carried away by erosion ends up in the sea.

4. Natural processes will restore a lost topsoil within two or three years.

5. Sheet erosion usually is easier to spot than rill erosion.

6. When crops are rotated, the same crop is raised on one piece of land year after year.

Fig. 78-4. This farm pond was built by throwing up an earth dam across a small valley.

CHAPTER 79

Forests Are Valuable

"Trees are crop plants," said Jim to Ed.

"No they aren't," Ed replied, "trees are just trees."

But Jim stuck to his point, and of course he was right. We know today that forests are among our valuable resources. We have many uses for lumber. More and more we use plant fibers and the other products that come from trees.

You probably know that lumber costs more than it used to. One reason is that the United States passed the peak of lumber production over 50 years ago. But there are a lot more people today than there were 50 years ago. There's more demand for lumber.

We also use forest products to make all sorts of things. For instance, smokeless powder is made in part from wood pulp. The powder in 9,000 rounds for a Garand rifle represents one cord of wood pulp. And this is only one item. There are about 4,500 different uses for tree products today.

The growth of a forest. In one way forest crops aren't like other crops. Trees don't grow to full size in a year or two. When an old forest is destroyed, as many of them have been, a surprising thing happens.

Let's say that the forest is made up largely of pine and hemlock trees. You'll find that an old forest is like this. One or two kinds of trees make up the growth. They're the dominant types. They're the trees best adapted to survive under existing conditions. And in the long run they're the trees that do survive.

Now suppose this forest is cut or burned away. You might expect to find the land covered with young hem-

Fig. 79-1. The first step in harvesting a tree crop is to fell the trees. Here these men are doing the job with the aid of a power saw.

lock and pine trees a year or two later. But not so! Instead, you probably find the land covered with a lot of weeds and shrubs. After four or five years young trees begin to grow up above the weeds. But these young trees aren't just pines and hemlocks. They're a mixture of many kinds of trees.

"What goes on here?" you say.

Well, it's a normal thing in nature. It's what we call *succession.* The young trees get taller and shade out the weeds and shrubs. Then a struggle for existence begins among the trees. Slowly but surely the dominant types begin to win out. They become more and more common, as other types of trees disappear. But this succession is a slow business. The old type of forest may not be restored for two or three hundred years.

This might not make much difference to us if all trees were equally useful. But of course they're not. Many of the trees that come in during early stages of a succession aren't good for lumber. Often they're not good for anything but firewood.

Planting a forest. There's a way to speed up events. This is to plant a forest. You plant the trees best adapted to your needs. And of course they have to be trees that will grow successfully in the area.

It takes quite a while for a forest

Fig. 79-2. Selective cutting keeps forests producing from year to year. Only the trees which have reached their peak growth are felled. The younger trees are left to grow. There is a steady yield of forest products.

crop to mature. But not as long as you might think. Scientists are now at work developing quick-growing types of trees. This can be done best with trees that we use for wood fiber. As you know, many things that we use today are made from this wood fiber.

Our national and state forests. There are over 600 million acres of forest land in the United States. We still have a lot of trees. The trouble is that so many of the more useful trees have been cut out or burned away. As you've seen, they often are replaced by trees that aren't so useful.

About two-thirds of the forest lands are privately owned. The rest make up our national and state forests. You shouldn't get the idea that national forests are just set aside to look at. Or

that they're saved for some distant future. Rather, they're run to protect, develop, and use timber, water, and grazing land. They're run for the benefit of the public.

Trees are cut in our national and state forests. But not just any old trees or all the trees. Actually, only the trees that have reached the peak of their growth are taken. This is called *selective cutting.* The younger trees stay there and grow. The character of the forest isn't really changed. In a few years another cutting can be made. So the forest continues to produce unless it's destroyed by fire, insects, or disease.

We've learned to profit from our mistakes of the past. Not many years ago most private lumbering was

Fig. 79-3. Fires are among the main destroyers of forests. Careless people start most of these fires.

wasteful. Trees of all sizes were cut, and the cutover land was left barren and unproductive. Now the picture is changed. The great destroyers of forest resources today are fire, insects, and disease.

Forest fires. Let's give a little thought to the problem of forest fires. It's the problem that gave rise to the men known as *forest rangers.* Fires have been destroyers of forests since colonial days. Big fires burn off trees. They also burn down into the topsoil and destroy its fertility. The land becomes a charred waste. Erosion and floods follow.

Today forest rangers spend much time in preventing and controlling forest fires. They'll tell you that the best thing to do is to keep fires from getting started. And they're right, because nine fires out of ten could be prevented.

What causes forest fires? One way is by careless people who toss lighted matches, cigarettes, or cigars on the ground. Another way is by building campfires in the wrong places. A third way is by moving on and leaving campfires burning. Only about one fire in ten is due to natural causes, such as lightning.

Once a forest fire does get started, the next best thing is to put it out as quickly as possible. That's why the Forest Service has lookout stations and airplane patrols. Fires can be spotted while they're still small. Fire fighters can be directed to the spot. Roads make it possible to bring modern fire-fighting apparatus into some areas. Fire-breaks are cut through the forests as barriers to the spread of fire. If a fire does break out, quick action may save the day. Too much delay lets the fire get out of control.

Fig. 79-4. Lookout stations are set up in forest areas. Forest rangers locate fires before they have a chance to become widespread.

CHECK YOUR FACTS . . .

Number 1 to 6 on a sheet of paper. Answer the following items.

1. One material used in making smokeless powder is (wood pulp, iron ore, clay) . . .?. . .

2. Most forest fires today are caused by (lightning, spontaneous combustion, people) . . .?. . .

3. The best way to cut lumber is to cut all trees on a given area at the same time. Then a new forest can grow up quickly. *True* or *False?*

4. It is possible for a forest fire to destroy the fertility of the soil. *True* or *False?*

5. The number of different uses for tree products today is about (45, 450, 4,500) . . .?. . .

6. About one-third of the forest lands in the United States are at present a part of our state and national forests. *True* or *False?*

CHAPTER 80

How We Can Save Our Water Supplies

"Water," you say, "is something that I've read about before."

That's right. Water is always part of the story of living things. Water is one of our biggest conservation problems today. When floods come there's too much water. When the land dries out, crops fail for lack of water.

Some of our large cities have a problem of getting enough water. Many acres of dry land in the West and Southwest could be irrigated if there was a water supply to do the job. But you always have the big question: "Where and how do we get the water?" Often it's not easy to find an answer.

Fig. 80-1. An irrigated field. Millions of dryland acres could be in production if we had water to do the job.

Water is a natural resource. You soon find that water supplies have their limits. In many parts of the country the water table has fallen year after year. Then a whole series of things happen.

First, springs begin to dry up. Wells go dry, too. Then the smaller streams dry up in mid-summer. The water level falls in lakes. During hot, dry weather crops fail because the water table is too far from the surface.

You can get an idea of how all these things are related by looking at Fig. 80-3. The key to the whole problem is the run-off of water. Water must soak down into the soil to keep the water table at a high level. If most of the water from rains and snows runs off it's carried away by streams. Floods are the result of rapid run-off.

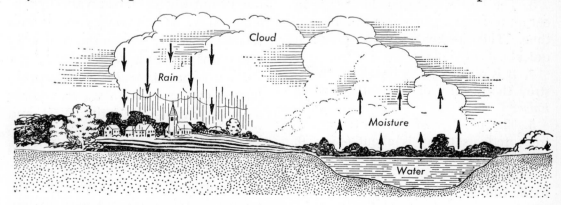

Fig. 80-2. Diagram of the water cycle. Water from the lake enters the air. Clouds form and rains fall. The run-off of rains returns water to the lake.

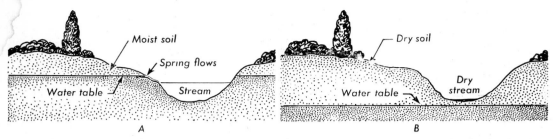

Fig. 80-3. The relation of the water table to springs and streams. In A the spring flows and adds water to the stream. In B the water table has fallen. Now the spring dries up and so does the stream.

You know, of course, that floods do a great deal of damage. You can see the ruined homes and the flooded fields. But there's another serious loss that isn't so easy to see. This is the loss of water. It's water that might have soaked down into the soil. It might have been added to the ground water. It might have kept the springs running and the soil moist.

So the Number One question is how to prevent rapid run-off of water. What you know about erosion control gives you part of the answer. If rapid erosion is stopped there are no gullies to speed up the run-off water. More of the water soaks down into the soil.

In some places reservoirs are built. They hold back flood waters. The reservoirs can do the job if they're big enough. Water from the reservoirs can be used to make electric power.

Fig. 80-4. Floods like this are likely to happen when the run-off of surface water is rapid.

Fig. 80-5. Reservoirs collect and hold water which otherwise might cause floods. Then the water can be used to supply cities, to produce electric power, and to irrigate land.

It can be piped to cities, factories, and farms. It can be used to irrigate land.

All this is good. But you have to remember that it takes time and money to build dams, electric plants, and pipelines. Also, it's not always easy to find a good place for a reservoir. Naturally you don't want to flood towns or good farm land. Finally, a reservoir can hold back the water that might cause a flood. But it can't check rapid run-off of water on the land.

Water and Industry. You may be interested to check up on how much water you use each day. In your community the amount may be about 140 gallons per person. This sounds like a lot of water. But when you start checking, you'll find that the water is used for many things.

It's not just people and farms that need water. A lot of water is used by factories. For instance, about 50,-000 gallons are used to make a ton of smokeless powder, and 100,000 gallons are needed for a ton of some kinds of paper. Fortunately, many factories are able to use the same water over and over in some of their processes.

Water for cities and towns. How does your community get its water supply? It might be in any one of several ways. Some cities get water from natural lakes. Others use man-made reservoirs. Some use wells, and some use streams.

In the early days, a good many towns were built on rivers. The rivers were travel routes. They also supplied needed water. But unfortunately, it was easy to dump sewage and factory wastes in the rivers, too.

As more and more towns grew up, many rivers became polluted with wastes. A good many of them are badly polluted today. If city water is taken from such a stream, the first problem is to get rid of dangerous germs. In addition, there may be other problems of sediment in the water and bad taste.

So it's often necessary to run water into *settling basins.* Here some of the sediment drops out. Chemicals are added to get rid of more sediment. Then the water is filtered. Next it's sprayed up into the air to improve its taste. Other chemicals may be added to stop the growth of algae in the water. Algae, like factory wastes, give water a bad taste and odor. Finally, chlorine is put in the water to kill disease germs. Then it's ready to go into the city water pipes.

Water from the sea. Now you may ask, "What about the sea? Surely, the sea is full of water."

Quite true, but of course you know that it's salt water. Modern ships distill fresh water from salt water. Why not get water in this way for cities and towns?

Well, it has been done. In fact, it's being done in some parts of the world today. Up to now, however, it's been an expensive way to get water. Usually a cheaper way can be found.

Scientists are working on the problem of using water from the sea. That is, using it in large amounts and at low cost. It's now plain to us that water is an important natural resource. Many communities have already had the experience of a water shortage.

CHECK YOUR FACTS . . .

Number 1 to 6 on a sheet of paper. Answer the following items.

1. Which of the following would be most likely to reduce the run-off of water: (a) planting row crops; (b) checking rapid erosion; (c) draining marshes; (d) lowering the water table?

2. Which of the following is apt to cause floods: (a) planting burned-over areas with trees; (b) lowering of the water table; (c) rapid run-off of surface water; (d) building large reservoirs?

3. In the average community the number of gallons of water used per person per day is about (14, 40, 140) . . . .? . . .

4. Which of the following things may happen when the water table falls: (a) springs dry up; (b) surface wells go dry; (c) crops fail; (d) all of these?

5. Germs in polluted water are killed by filtering the water through sand. *True* or *False?*

6. Enough fresh water is available today to irrigate all of our western dry lands. *True* or *False?*

The soil is one of our great natural resources. When erosion speeds up, fertile topsoil is carried away. Running water and wind are two common causes of erosion. Unwise use of land speeds up erosion. Good use of land holds erosion in check.

The best policy is to check erosion whenever it appears. Cover crops serve to check erosion. Their roots hold the topsoil in place. But topsoil can lose its value without being eroded. This happens when crops which take large amounts of minerals out of the soil are raised year after year. One solution of this problem is crop rotation.

Forests are valuable resources. From them we get lumber and material for thousands of products. In nature, a forest develops slowly through a succession. We speed up the natural process by planting the kinds of trees that we desire. Use of forests was once very wasteful. This has been corrected in many cases by selective cutting. The greatest menaces to forests today are fires, insects, and diseases.

Water, like soil, is a natural resource. Rapid run-off of surface water causes floods. Water fails to seep down into the soil. As a result, springs, wells, streams, and lakes dry up. Crops fail in dry seasons. Checking rapid erosion slows down the run-off of surface water.

Many streams have been polluted by sewage and factory wastes. As a result, getting a safe water supply has become more and more of a problem.

WHAT DO THESE WORDS MEAN?

Conservation	Erosion	Selective cutting
Contour plowing	Natural resources	Strip farming
Cover crop	Rill erosion	Succession
Crop rotation	Row crop	Water table

ASK YOURSELF . . .

1. (a) What are two main causes of erosion? (b) Name any others you can think of.
2. (a) What kind of plants should be planted on hillsides in a country where it rains? (b) On dry prairie land? (c) Why?
3. Why does planting of row crops tend to speed up erosion?
4. How are contour plowing and strip farming related to the control of erosion?
5. What are some practical ways to check rill and gully erosion?
6. What is one reason why many farmers use a system of crop rotation?
7. What kind of plants have colonies of nitrogen-fixing bacteria on their roots?

8. (a) What are two general types of fertilizers? (b) Which type is used most commonly today?

9. How would you go about restoring an area of eroded and exhausted farm land?

10. We still have millions of acres of forest in the United States. Why, then, is good lumber hard to get?

11. What grows on the land after a forest has been burned or cut away?

12. How can you defend the statement that trees are crop plants?

13. Why is selective cutting better than older practices?

14. What are the main destroyers of forest resources today?

15. How does a fall of the water table affect springs, wells, streams, and crops?

16. What are things we can do to check run-off and conserve water in the soil?

17. In what way is fall of the water table related to floods?

18. (a) Do reservoirs give us a complete solution of the run-off problem? (b) Give reasons for your answer.

19. What steps must be taken to clean and purify city water taken from a stream?

20. Why don't we use sea water on a larger scale?

GETTING THE FACTS . . .

1. Plan and carry out a field trip to study erosion, and ways that are used or can be used to check erosion. You may also be able to visit an abandoned farm or a farm that has been later restored.

2. Make a study of soil conservation in your community. Try to find out the following things: (a) what types of erosion are common; (b) what measures are used to check erosion; (c) what row crops and what soil-building and cover crops are grown; (d) what kinds of crop rotations are being used; (e) what fertilizers are commonly used.

3. *Out-of-doors Demonstration.* Using a pile of dirt or sand, some cuttings of sod, and a garden hose, plan and carry out an erosion demonstration. Test the idea that sod on a slope tends to check erosion.

4. Arrange a trip to visit a factory (if there's one in your community) where products are made out of wood. Examine different wood samples. Find out what uses are made of each type.

5. Try to visit a forest area that's in an early stage of a succession. Find out what types of young trees are common. Find out what the climax trees of the region are, and why they're climax trees.

6. Study the water supply problem of your community. Try to find out the following things: (a) why the present source of water is used; (b) what measures are taken to clean and purify the water; (c) what plans are made for the future.

Topic 2

HOW WE KEEP A BALANCE AMONG LIVING THINGS

Ever camped out? Maybe so and maybe not. If not, you've probably taken an auto trip and seen the great outdoors. You've seen places like this and you've enjoyed them.

Many people take to the outdoors each year. They like to relax and to enjoy nature and her beauties. They get away from work and worries. This is recreation. If you want to enjoy nature you must know how to keep a balance among living things. You must preserve wildlife.

There are other benefits from a balanced nature. Let's learn something about them.

AMONG THE NEW WORDS FOR THIS TOPIC

- **BALANCE IN NATURE.** The situation in nature in which the different food groups are in balance. No type is too abundant.
- **COVER.** Natural objects which provide shelter for wild animals.
- **WILDLIFE.** Wild plants and animals of communities.

CHAPTER 81

Our Wildlife Must Be Protected

" If everyone stopped hunting and fishing," Jim told Ed, " there would soon be as much game and fish as ever."

" I don't think so," Ed replied. " You need more than that to restore wildlife. What would a lot of the animals eat? Where would they live? "

Why wildlife disappears. Ed had a good point. To be sure, hunting, fishing, and trapping have had a large part in making some wildlife rare. You've read about what happened to the passenger pigeon in Chapter 37. Today there isn't one left. At least three other types of native birds have also disappeared. Several species have nearly reached the vanishing point. *Wildlife* includes those plants and animals which man doesn't raise.

Maybe you know what happened

Fig. 81-1. Bison once roamed much of our country. Today they exist only because of protection.

Fig. 81-2.   Wildlife adds to the pleasures of recreation for many people.

to the *bison* (*by*-sun).   These are the animals which many people call buffaloes.   But they're really bison. Years ago, bison herds roamed as far east as Pennsylvania.   Indian tribes depended on them for meat.   Then the white man and his hunters moved in.   Many bison were killed for no good reason at all.   Fifty years ago bison were just about to disappear entirely.   Since then they've slowly increased.   But only because they've been carefully protected and now live on government (and a few private) lands.

Could you hope to have as many bison today as there were 200 years ago?   Probably not.   The broad prairies where they once roamed are mostly gone.   Millions of acres of grassland have been plowed up to grow crops.

Farmers wouldn't want bison in their fields.

Now let's think about the case of many streams and rivers and the fish in them.   During the last hundred years, a lot of streams have dried up in summer.   A lot of other streams have become polluted.   In either case, these streams aren't places where most fish can survive.   The men who run fish hatcheries can raise fish.   They can stock ponds and streams with the fish.   But they've learned that the fish won't last long where there's no food, or where the water dries up in hot weather.

How about birds and other animals? The story is much the same in a good many cases.   Native plants have been cut down or plowed under.   These plants once furnished food for wildlife. They also furnished cover, which means a place to hide. So there's less food to be eaten, and less chance to escape from natural enemies.

Wildlife values. Now you may ask, "Why worry about it? Isn't a field full of corn or wheat better than a field full of wildlife?"

The answer is that you don't have to choose one or the other. If you know how, you can generally have both.

Wildlife has real value to us. We still get a fairly large amount of food from such sources. You've learned that we get other things such as furs, leather, and pearls.

Then too, wildlife has an important relation to our recreation. Looking after the needs of campers, hunters, and fishermen is big business in some states. People in such states soon realize that wildlife is one of their natural resources. So do the people all over the country who manufacture vacation equipment and supplies.

The greatest value of wildlife is the effect of one kind of living thing on another. You know that some plants and animals are pests. Well, many types of wildlife destroy pests.

Fish keep water insects in check. Birds keep land insects in check. Birds also eat weed seeds. Some reptiles, birds, and mammals eat rodent pests. Some useful insects eat insect pests.

And so it goes. Taken together, the plants and animals tend to have a sort of check and balance system. No type is likely to be abundant. You

Fig. 81-3. A tray of fish eggs in a fish hatchery. When the eggs hatch, the young fish are raised in tanks and pools. Later, they are used to stock streams and lakes.

can see that no pest is likely to be a big pest unless it's common. This is what we mean when we say that *nature keeps living things in balance.*

Wildlife conservation. What, then, must we do to protect our wildlife resources?

The first thing is to know and observe our fish and game laws. Enough fish and game must be saved each year to provide for the next year.

A second step is to stop polluting streams. Then the streams can produce food for fish. When they're stocked with fish from a hatchery, you know that the fish have a real chance.

What about streams and lakes that dry up? Well, here the story goes back to erosion and the water table. By checking erosion you check runoff of surface water. Let the water seep into the soil and you build up the water table. Build up the water table and the springs run. When springs

Fig. 31-4. A small-mouth black bass. Many fishermen eagerly seek this fresh-water fish. It can be raised in many man-made ponds.

run, the streams and lakes don't dry out.

In recent years farmers have learned to make ponds on their farms. These ponds provide water for livestock. They're often useful sources of water for fighting fires. At the same time they tend to keep up the water table. Food fish can be raised in them. Water birds find them useful in flying from their summer homes to their winter homes.

Various bushes and cover crops, planted in gullies to check erosion, provide food and cover on land. Bushes and smaller plants along fence rows do the same thing. Here again, what we do to save the soil helps the needs of wildlife.

Special tracts of land are sometimes set aside as *refuges*. From these refuges wildlife spreads out to other areas.

CHECK YOUR FACTS . . .

Number 1 to 6 on a sheet of paper. Mark each of the following items True *or* False.

1. Cover tends to preserve many types of wildlife because it enables them to escape from their natural enemies and to survive.

2. In a balanced natural community, various types of animals tend to become unusually abundant, and are likely to become serious pests.

3. Various types of wildlife serve as natural controls on the increase of plants and animals that are pests.

4. The problem of controlling erosion is related to the problem of conserving wildlife.

5. You have to choose between raising crops and conserving wildlife, because you can't do both.

6. Putting an end to hunting and fishing would soon restore the wildlife of North America.

Fig. 81-5. Egg masses (left), and "nest" of the tent caterpillars. These common pests are leaf-eaters. Some of our native birds eat these caterpillars.

CHAPTER 82

You Should Practice Conservation Every Day

"Aren't *any* kinds of wildlife common today?" you ask.

Yes, they are. But the list won't make you very happy. If you compare the present with the early days, we have more of some things. We have more ragweeds, more mosquitoes, more houseflies, more mice, and more rats. You could go on and add a number of other things to the list. It would still be about the same kind of list.

Pests from other lands. In fact, many of our weed and insect pests come from the Old World. So do some of our worst plant diseases. They came in by accident for the most part, along with seeds and other plant materials.

You can see that the control of these pests is related to conservation. For pests destroy the products of our natural resources. They reduce the amount of foods and other materials we obtain. They also injure the quality of many materials. Part of the conservation problem is to deal with the pests.

We carry on constant warfare against pests. Some of the battles are fought in the fields and forests. Some of them are fought in warehouses, stores, and homes. It isn't just a problem of producing the things we need.

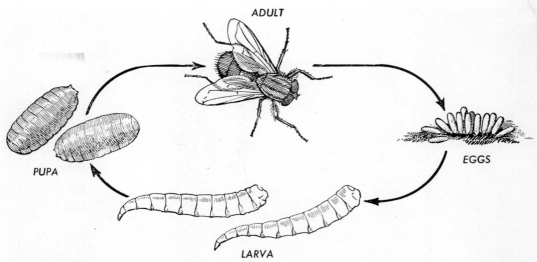

Fig. 82-1. **The life cycle of a housefly. One way to control this pest is to get rid of places where it can breed.**

Often we have to protect the products until we actually use them.

We have upset the balance of nature in many communities. In some cases this couldn't have been avoided. In other cases it was needless and foolish. At any rate, rapid increase of pests has often made the use of special controls necessary.

What are these man-made controls? You've read about some of them in earlier chapters. We'll briefly summarize them here.

Some pests can be held in check

Fig. 82-2. **A pocket gopher. This small burrowing animal is a serious pest in some parts of our country. It eats the roots of crop plants.**

by denying them a place to live. For instance, take the housefly shown in Fig. 82-1. Its eggs and larvae live in moist horse manure. When you get rid of piles of horse manure you get rid of houseflies. And you remember that one way to control mosquitoes is to drain marshes and pools where they breed.

A related method is to keep pests from getting food. This is a method that works well in warehouses, stores, and homes. It's used to protect foods from rats and mice. If foods are in rat-proof and mouse-proof containers, the foods are safe. Also, the rodents are forced to move in order to find a living.

Crop rotation will control some pests. Suppose these pests cause a disease of potatoes. If a change is made to another crop which the pests don't feed on, the pests die out. But not always! Some pests feed on a number of weeds as well as crop plants.

You can do much the same thing when you plant forest trees. Suppose a certain disease of trees is common in the area. This disease attacks tree species A but not tree species B. Or suppose it's a problem of an insect pest that attacks species A but not species B. In either case, one solution is to plant species B. That is, provided it's as good for your purpose as species A.

Man-made controls also include all sorts of mechanical devices. Among them are the plows and cultivators that are used to uproot weeds. Flame-

Fig. 82-3. A praying mantis. This useful insect acts as a natural control of certain insect pests.

throwing devices are also used to burn away weeds. But they can't be used in all cases. For one thing, they're a fire hazard.

Other mechanical devices include various kinds of traps. You no doubt have seen several kinds of traps used to catch mice, rats, or gophers. There are also many kinds of traps which can be used to catch insect pests.

There are a number of chemical weapons. We use them as poison sprays, poison baits, poison dusts, and poison gases. Some are good for certain purposes. In fact, we could hardly get along without them. But there are usually problems in using poisons. Among these problems are the following: (1) they may kill not only pests,

Fig. 82-4. A ladybird beetle. This is another type which eats insect pests.

but other living things also; (2) pests sometimes develop special varieties which resist the poisons; (3) their use may be expensive, especially in the case of large fields and forests; (4) rains may wash away dusts and dried sprays, leaving the plants unprotected.

In recent years we've added a number of weed killers to the chemicals we use. For instance, you can now get weed killers which get rid of poison ivy. They're a good solution for people who get ivy poisoning. It's much safer to spray the ivy than to dig it out.

Natural controls. You may ask, " What about the cost of all these man-made controls? " The yearly cost is great.

Now we come back to conservation to look for a better solution. We know that when we move into a natural community things happen. The balance which exists among plants and animals is upset more or less. Probably the old balance can never be restored. But a new balance which includes ourselves can be established in time.

If we use proper wildlife conservation and make the best use of good land, we can hope for such a balance. With it goes a reduced number of pests. This means less effort and less cost on our own part.

Conservation means the wise use of resources. Our natural resources include minerals, water, soil, and wildlife. Wise use of these resources means that we have more of the things that we need. It also means that these things will be better in quality.

This, then, is conservation. It's a matter of dollars and cents. It gives promise that the products of tomorrow will be better than the products of today.

CHECK YOUR FACTS . . .

Number 1 to 6 on a sheet of paper. Mark each of the following items True *or* False.

1. The only purpose that can be served by crop rotation is to increase the fertility of the soil.

2. The main idea in conservation is to

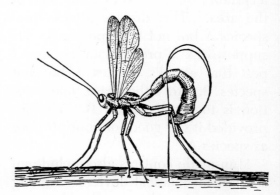

Fig. 82-5. A four-winged fly which destroys various insect pests.

avoid using materials which come from plants and animals.

3. A community which includes man is certain to be badly out of natural balance.

4. One objection to the use of man-made controls is that they're often expensive.

5. Some pests can be controlled by denying them a food supply.

6. Conservation means the wise use of natural resources.

Wildlife consists of those plants and animals we don't raise. Hunting, fishing, and trapping have reduced wildlife, but so has destruction of foods and places to live. We hope to conserve wildlife because it's one of our natural resources. This can be done by observing laws, by ending stream pollution, by building up the water table, and by protecting plants which provide cover and food.

Meanwhile, we have a problem of pest control. To a large extent it's because we have disrupted the natural balance of communities. We're forced to use a lot of man-made controls, and this is expensive. A better solution is to establish a new natural balance in communities. Such a balance greatly lessens the need for special controls. This is a part of conservation, which is the wise use of natural resources.

W H A T   D O   T H E S E   W O R D S   M E A N ?

Balanced nature	**Cover**	**Production**
Conservation	**Pest**	**Wildlife**

ASK YOURSELF . . .

1. (a) Are hunting and fishing the only practices which tend to destroy wildlife? (b) Why?
2. Give four reasons why wildlife is of value.
3. How is stream pollution related to the welfare of wildlife?
4. How is the run-off of rain and melting snow related to the welfare of wildlife?
5. How are cover and food related to the welfare of wildlife?
6. In what ways do pests affect the quantity and quality of our production?
7. How is a balanced nature related to the control of pests?
8. What man-made devices are used to control pests?
9. What is the true meaning of conservation?

GETTING THE FACTS . . .

1. Examine specimens or charts of: (a) insects which are pests of crop plants; and (b) insects which serve to control such pests in fields and gardens.

2. Arrange a field trip to observe: (a) the extent to which cover is provided for wildlife; (b) the native plants which provide food for wildlife.

3. Visit streams in your community. Find out whether they're polluted, and if so, what causes the pollution. Learn what fish are present in the streams, and whether the fish population has changed in recent times.

4. After checking the references on this page, discuss what is meant by the word *predators*. Are predators merely destructive? Do they have possible value?

Books You May Like . . .

Finch, V. C., Trewartha, G. T., and Shearer, M. H. THE EARTH AND ITS RESOURCES. McGraw-Hill Book Co., New York. 1948. An easy reading reference on resources. Emphasis is on climate, weather, types of land, soil, water resources, and minerals.

Gustafson, A. F., and others. CONSERVATION IN THE UNITED STATES. Comstock Publishing Co., Ithaca, New York. 3rd Edition, 1949. This useful book will serve as a reference on such topics as the conservation of water, soil, forests, grazing lands, fisheries, game and fur animals, and wildlife.

Hawley, Ralph C., and Stickel, Paul W. FOR-EST PROTECTION. John Wiley and Sons, New York. 1948. A useful reference on forest conservation, which gives special attention to the problems of forest fires.

Hill, Albert F. ECONOMIC BOTANY. McGraw-Hill Book Co., New York. 1937. A standard source of facts concerning plant production, which will be useful as a reference.

Martin, A. C., Zim, H. S., and Nelson, A. L. AMERICAN WILDLIFE AND PLANTS. McGraw-Hill Book Co., New York. 1951. A good reference on the foods, habits and importance of wildlife, and the relationship of trees, shrubs, weeds, water plants, and crop plants to wildlife.

Smith, Guy-Harold (Editor). CONSERVATION OF NATURAL RESOURCES. John Wiley and Sons, New York. 1950. Articles by experts dealing with such topics as soils, tree crops, irrigation, grasslands, forest resources, water supplies, wildlife, fisheries, recreation, and national planning.

United States Department of Agriculture. TREES. THE YEARBOOK OF AGRICULTURE. U.S. Government Printing Office, Washington, D.C. 1949. A series of articles by experts on the uses and conservation of forest products.

United States Department of Agriculture. CROPS IN PEACE AND WAR. YEARBOOK OF AGRICULTURE. U.S. Government Printing Office, Washington, D.C. 1950–1951. A series of articles by experts on the production of crop plants.

United States Department of Agriculture. IN-SECTS. YEARBOOK OF AGRICULTURE. U.S. Government Printing Office, Washington, D.C. 1952. A series of articles by experts on insects and the problem of insect control.

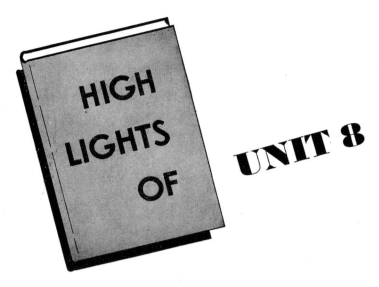

HIGH LIGHTS OF UNIT 8

Conservation is the science of using natural resources wisely.

A fertile topsoil is necessary for good crops. Such a topsoil can be lost through erosion. Its fertility can be destroyed by planting certain crops year after year. But the soil can be kept fertile by checking erosion, by crop rotation, and by using fertilizers.

Forests, like soil, are natural resources. We're learning to keep them constantly in production by selective cutting of trees. We try to protect them against fires, insects, and diseases.

Water is another valuable resource. Rapid run-off is wasteful and results in failure to maintain the water table. It also results in floods, drying up of springs, and drying up of streams.

Wildlife is another important resource. It provides food and other materials. It also provides recreation. It can be conserved by observing laws, and by maintaining suitable places for plants and animals to live.

Conservation of wildlife is necessary if we're to have natural balance in our communities. When such a balance exists, pest control ceases to be so great a problem.

Important Plant Groups . . .

FERNS AND SEED PLANTS. Plants with a special system to conduct liquids. Divided into three other groups as follows:

    THE FLOWERING PLANTS. Seed plants which develop seed covers. Here you find most of our garden flowers and crop plants.

    THE CONE–BEARING PLANTS. Seed plants which bear cones, such as the pines, spruces, firs, hemlocks, and arbor vitaes.

    THE FERNS. Four modern groups of ferns are known today.

HORSETAILS. Sometimes called scouring rushes. Their larger ancestors formed coal deposits in ancient swamps.

CLUB MOSSES. Sometimes called " ground pines." Large ancestors also formed coal deposits in ancient swamps.

MOSS PLANTS. Various types of mosses, and the related liverworts.

TRUE FUNGI. Four groups of simple plants without the ability to make food. They lack the green-colored material, chlorophyll.

RED ALGAE. Many-celled types for the most part. Food-makers which have red pigment.

BROWN ALGAE. Many-celled types. Food-makers which have brown pigment.

DIATOMS. One-celled food-making plants. Their cell walls contain silica.

GREEN ALGAE. A group of simple plants which have the ability to make food. They have the necessary green-colored material, chlorophyll, in their cells.

FISSION PLANTS. Mostly one-celled plants which reproduce by dividing into two new cells. They consist of two other groups as follows:

    BLUE–GREEN ALGAE. A group of simple algae.

    BACTERIA. Simple, non-green types, which are all parasites or saprophytes and which cannot make their own food.

Important Animal Groups . . .

THE **VERTEBRATES.**   Animals with backbones.

  THE **MAMMALS.**   Duckbills, kangaroos, opossums, moles, shrews, bats, carnivores, rodents, rabbits, hoofed animals, monkeys, apes, and other types.

  THE **BIRDS.**   Loons, herons, ducks, geese, shore birds, pigeons, pheasants, chickens, hawks, owls, sparrows, warblers, thrushes, and other types.

  THE **REPTILES.**   Turtles, crocodiles, alligators, lizards, iguanas, and snakes.

  THE **AMPHIBIANS.**   Salamanders, toads, and frogs.

  THE **BONY FISH.**   Herring, salmon, flounders, mackerels, carp, catfishes, and many other types.

  THE **SHARKS AND RAYS.**   Dogfish sharks, great white sharks, hammerhead sharks, sting rays, torpedo rays, and other types.

THE **ARTHROPODS.**   A group of invertebrates with jointed legs.

  THE **ARACHNIDS.**   Spiders, scorpions, centipedes, chiggers, ticks, and mites.

  THE **INSECTS.**   Dragonflies, bugs, beetles, butterflies, moths, flies, mosquitoes, and many other types.

  THE **CRUSTACEANS.**   Crayfish, crabs, lobsters, and shrimps.

THE **MOLLUSKS.**   A group of invertebrates with outer shells or an inner rod-like support.   They include the clams, oysters, snails, squids, and devil fish.

THE **SEGMENTED WORMS.**   A group of invertebrates which include the earthworms and leeches.

THE **ECHINODERMS.**   A group of invertebrates which live only in the sea. They include the starfishes, sea cucumbers, and sea urchins.

THE **ROUNDWORMS.**   A group of invertebrates which are largely parasites on plants and animals.

THE **FLATWORMS.**   Another group of worm-like invertebrates.   Many of them, like the tapeworms and flukes, are parasites.

THE **CORALS.**   A group of invertebrates which include the hydras, corals, and sea anemones.

THE SPONGES.   A group of invertebrates which includes various simple sponges and sponge colonies.

THE PROTOZOA.   A group of simple invertebrates, many of them one-celled.   Here you find Amoeba, Paramecium, and many other types.

GLOSSARY

Glossary of Words . . .

ABDOMEN (ab-*doh*-m'n), the cavity in the trunk of the body below the diaphragm.

ACTIVE IMMUNITY, a condition when one's own blood forms a substance that protects him from a disease.

ADHESIVE (ad-*hee*-siv), a glue-like substance used to bind two objects together.

ADRENALIN (ad-*ren*-uh-lin), a hormone secreted by the adrenal gland.

ADRENAL (ad-*ree*-n'l) GLAND, the gland at the upper end of a kidney that secretes the hormone adrenalin.

ACQUIRED CHARACTER, a character that isn't inherited. It results from effects of the environment on body cells.

AGAR (*ah*-gahr), a food substance made from algae.

ALGAE (*al*-jee), green plants belonging to one of the simpler plant groups.

ALLERGY (*al*-er-jee), a reaction to certain substances which affect one person but not necessarily other people.

AMINO (ah-*mee*-noh) ACIDS, substances from which living things build proteins.

AMPHIBIANS (am-*fib*-ee-uns), cold-blooded animals with backbones but without scales and plates, such as frogs, salamanders, and toads.

ANIMAL KINGDOM, one of the great groups of living things, including all the animals.

ANNUAL (*an*-yoo-ul) PLANT, one which completes its life cycle in one growing season.

ANTIBIOTICS (an-tee-by-*ot*-iks), drugs obtained from bacteria and fungi which limit the growth of certain germs in living things.

ANTISEPTIC (an-tih-*sep*-tik), a substance which destroys germs or checks their activity.

APPENDIX, the structure attached to a small pouch of the large intestine at a point where the small intestine joins the large intestine.

ARTERY (*art*-er-ee), a large blood vessel which carries blood from the heart to the body tissues.

ARTIFICIAL RESPIRATION, a method of reviving people whose breathing movements have been slowed down or stopped temporarily.

AURICLES (*aw*-rih-k'ls), the two upper regions of the heart.

AXON (*aks*-uhn), the process of a nerve cell through which messages travel to muscle cells.

BACKBONE, a row of small bones called vertebrae in the back region.

BACTERIA (bak-*tih*-ree-uh), small one-celled plants without green-colored material and organized nuclei.

BALANCE IN NATURE, the situation in nature in which the different food groups are in balance.

BALANCED DIET, one that provides for all of the food needs of the body.

BASIC FOOD, the simple sugar made by green plant cells.

BEHAVIOR (bee-*hay*-vyer), the sum total of your actions and responses.

BIENNIAL (by-*en*-ih-ul) PLANT, a plant which completes its life cycle in two growing seasons.

BILE, a secretion of the liver which is discharged into the small intestine.

BIOLOGY (by-*ol*-uh-jee), the science of living things — plants, animals, and man.

BLADDER, the organ which receives liquid wastes in the form of urine.

BLOOD, the plasma or basic fluid in the animal body which contains red and white blood cells.

BLOOD PRESSURE, the pressure of blood as it is forced through the arteries and veins.

BODY CAVITY, the cavity in the human body in which the heart, lungs, and organs of digestion are found.

BODY CELLS, those cells in the plant or animal body which perform all life activities except reproduction.

BODY SEGMENT, a body division of a flatworm or similar animal.

BODY WALL, the layers of cells and tissues which surround a body cavity.

BOTANY (*bot*-uh-nee), the study of plant life.

BRAIN, the part of the human body which controls the nervous system.

BREAST BONE, a flat bone or group of bones in the chest region.

BRONCHIAL (*bronk*-ee-ul) **TUBES,** the tubes through which air passes to the lungs from the windpipe.

BUD (ANIMAL), an offshoot growth of certain lower animals which may become a new individual.

BUD (PLANT), the young flower or leaf cluster of a seed plant before it has opened.

BUDDING, a kind of reproduction which takes place without sex cells.

CALORIE (*kal*-or-ee), a unit of energy. Often used to describe the amount of energy in different foods.

CANCER (*kan*-ser), an overgrowth of tissue which may spread from the place of origin to other parts of the body.

CANINE (*kay*-nine) **TEETH,** in the human body two pointed teeth in each jaw found just behind the incisor teeth.

CAPILLARY (*kap*-il-air-ee), a very small blood vessel. Normally connects a branch artery with a branch vein.

CARBOHYDRATES (kahr-boh-*hy*-drayts), sugars and starches used as food.

CARNIVORES (*kahr*-niv-ohrs), flesh-eating animals which include wolves, dogs, cats, leopards, lions, seals, bears, minks, foxes, and skunks.

CARRIER, a person whose body contains germs but who may have no outward signs of disease.

CARTILAGE (*kahr*-ti-lij), an elastic tissue which makes up most of the skeleton of a young child. Becomes largely changed to bone in the adult.

CELL MEMBRANE, the thin membrane which surrounds the protoplasm of a cell.

CELLS, tiny units of which living things are made.

CELL WALL, the non-living covering of a plant cell.

CEREAL (*seer*-ee-ul), certain edible grains including wheat, corn, rice, oats, rye, and barley.

CEREBELLUM (ser-uh-*bel*-um), the part of the human brain lying at the back of the brain and below the cerebrum. It is a control center for the muscles.

CEREBRUM (*seh*-reh-brum), the part of the human brain which is the center for memory and intelligence.

CHECK DAMS, small dams in gullies and creeks used to slow down the flow of water to prevent erosion.

CHEST, the region of the human body trunk above the diaphragm.

CHLOROPHYLL (*klor*-roh-fill), the green-colored substance in all green plants which they use in making food.

CHROMATIN (*kroh*-mah-tin), the material in the nucleus of a cell that forms the chromosomes.

CHROMOSOMES (*kroh*-moh-sohms), masses of material which appear in the nucleus of a cell during cell division. They carry the genes.

CILIA (*sih*-lee-uh), tiny, hair-like processes of a single cell.

CIRCULATION (serk-you-*lay*-shun) **IN MAN,** the normal flow of blood from the heart through the blood vessels.

CITRUS FRUITS, fruits such as oranges, grapefruits, lemons, and limes.

CLASS, a group of related plants or related animals.

CLAY, a fine-grained soil formed when a certain type of rock breaks down.

CLOT, a mass formed by blood substances, which serves to check bleeding.

COCA, a plant whose leaves yield the drug cocaine.

COCOON (kuh-*koon*), a case in which the pupa of an insect is enclosed.

COLD, an ailment of the breathing apparatus caused by a virus or by viruses.

COLD–BLOODED ANIMALS, those whose body temperature changes with the changes in the temperature around them.

COLLAR BONE, the bone attached to the breast bone, which extends out to the point of the shoulder.

COMMUNITY, a part of the environment set off from other parts by natural barriers.

COMPOUND EYES, eyes composed of many units, such as the compound eyes of grasshoppers.

CONNECTIVE TISSUES, certain tissues of the human body such as the tissues which cover muscles and muscle fibers.

CONSERVATION (kon-ser-*vay*-shun), the science of using our natural resources wisely.

CONTOUR PLOWING, plowing around a slope instead of up and down.

COVER, natural objects which provide shelter for wildlife.

COVER CROPS, soil-binding crops which are not planted in rows.

CROP ROTATION, the planting of different crops in succeeding years. Thus a crop of corn may be followed for a year or two by clover or alfalfa before corn is planted again.

CYST (*sist*), a protective covering formed around certain one-celled living things.

CYTOPLASM (*sy*-toh-plazm), the living substance in a cell outside the nucleus.

DENDRITE (*den*-dryt), a small projection from the cell body of a nerve cell that receives messages.

DIABETES (dy-uh-*bee*-tez), a condition resulting from lack of insulin in the blood.

DIAPHRAGM (*dy*-uh-fram), the muscular wall separating the chest cavity from the abdomen.

DIGESTION (duh-*jes*-chun), the process of changing foods so that they become soluble in water.

DIGESTIVE CANAL, the canal in which food is digested.

DISLOCATION (dis-loh-*kay*-shun), a condition that exists when bones at a joint are pulled out of place.

DUCTLESS GLANDS, glands having no ducts. They secrete hormones directly into the blood stream.

EARDRUM, a membrane of the ear which vibrates when sound waves strike it.

EARTH'S CRUST, layers of soil and rock found near the surface of the earth.

EGG CELL, a female sex cell.

EMBRYO (*em*-bree-oh), an early stage in development.

ENVIRONMENT, the things and forces around you.

ENZYME (*en*-zyme), a substance which brings about changes in other substances. Thus, a digestive enzyme serves to change foods.

EPIDEMIC (ep-ih-*dem*-ik), an outbreak of disease which affects many people in a certain area.

ERGOT, a drug extracted from a fungus which grows on rye.

EROSION (ee-*roh*-zhun), the wearing away of rocks and soil.

ESOPHAGUS (uh-*sof*-uh-gus), the tube through which food passes in going from the mouth to the stomach.

EUSTACHIAN (yoo-*stay*-kee-un) **TUBE**, the tube that connects the throat with the middle ear.

EXHALE, the process of forcing air out of the lungs.

EXTERNAL SKELETON, an outer covering of animals, such as the outer covering of a grasshopper.

EYE SPOT, a structure which is sensitive to light.

FATS, food substances containing carbon, hydrogen, and oxygen. They include the plant oils.

FERNS, a group of green plants which develop leaflets above ground.

FERTILIZATION (fer-til-ih-*zay*-shun), the act of a sperm (male sex cell) uniting with an egg cell (female sex cell).

FLATWORM, a worm with a flat body divided into segments, such as a tapeworm.

FLORIST, one who buys and sells flowers.

FOOD CHAIN, series of plants and animals which are dependent, one on the other, for food.

FOODS, carbohydrates, fats, proteins, minerals, and vitamins that build up protoplasm and provide energy for work.

FORAGE CROP, a grass or similar crop which provides food for livestock.

FOREST RANGER, a specially trained man who supervises a state or national forest.

FORESTRY, the science concerned with the growth and use of trees.

FRACTURE, a break in a bone.

FRUIT, a plant structure which is mainly a ripe ovary and its contents.

FUNGI (*fun*-jye), non-green plants belonging to one of the lower plant groups.

GENES (*jeens*), tiny units in the chromosomes of a cell that determine heredity.

GENUS (*jee*-nus), a group of related plants or related animals.

GERM, a tiny plant or animal which causes disease. Not visible to the unaided eye.

GERM LAYER, one of three layers formed in the early development of an animal.

GILLS, special organs in a fish through which oxygen from the water enters the blood.

GLANDS, groups of cells that secrete substances used in various parts of the body.

GRAFTING, a method of joining two plant stems together so the resulting growth will give a better yield of fruit.

GRASSLAND, land which is largely covered with grasses rather than trees.

GRAVEL, a soil made up of coarse rock fragments.

GRAY MATTER, special type of nerve tissue in spinal cord and brain.

GROUND WATER, water from rain or melted snow that has seeped down into the soil.

HABIT, a response you make so often that it is just about automatic.

HEART, the organ which pumps blood through blood vessels to all the tissues of the body.

HEART MUSCLE, muscle tissue found in the walls of the heart.

HEMOGLOBIN (*hee*-moh-globe-in), the red-colored matter in red blood cells.

HEREDITY (hair-*ed*-ih-tee), the process in which characters are passed on from one generation to the next.

HEROIN (*hair*-oh-in), a habit-forming drug.

HOOKWORM, a roundworm parasite which feeds on blood.

HORMONE (*hor*-moan), the secretion of a ductless gland which is carried by the blood stream. It regulates ways in which parts of the body develop and function.

HOST, a plant or animal from which a parasite gets its food.

HUMAN BIOLOGY, the part of biology which deals with the parts and uses of man's body.

HYBRID (*hy*-brid), a plant or animal which has genes of different type for any character.

HYPOTHESIS (hy-*poth*-uh-siss), a "best guess" about a question or problem in the light of known facts.

IMMUNE (im-*yoon*), not subject to a certain disease.

INCISOR (in-*sy*-zer) **TEETH**, chisel-like teeth across the front of the mouth, used in biting.

INFECTION (in-*fek*-shun), a condition due to the presence of germs in a living tissue.

INHALE, the process of taking air into the lungs.

INNER EAR, the innermost part of the ear which contains the end organ of hearing.

INSULIN (*in*-suh-lin), the hormone secreted by the ductless glands in the pancreas.

INTELLIGENCE (in-*tel*-uh-junss), the ability to use past experience to solve a complex problem.

INTESTINES (in-*test*-ins), organs concerned with digestion and absorption of food.

INVERTEBRATE (*in*-ver-tuh-brate), an animal without a backbone.

INVOLUNTARY MUSCLE, one not controlled by will.

IRIS, the colored part of the eye, as seen from the outside.

IRRIGATION (ih-rih-*gay*-shun), bringing water to soil by artificial means.

JOINT, the place where two or more bones come together.

KIDNEYS, two organs in the human body which remove wastes from the blood in the form of urine.

KNEE CAP, a small, flat bone at the knee joint.

KNOWLEDGE, facts or experiences that are remembered.

LARGE INTESTINE, the part of the digestive canal through which solid wastes pass out of the body.

LARVA (*lar*-vuh), the worm-like feeding stage of moths and other insects with similar life cycles.

LATEX (*lay*-tex), the boiled down sap of a rubber tree.

LEECH, an animal parasite that attaches itself to the skin and sucks blood.

LENS, that part of the human eye which focuses light rays.

LIFE CYCLE, stages in the life of a plant or animal.

LOAM, a type of soil which contains many elements and is often quite fertile.

LUNGS, breathing organs in the body cavities of some higher animals.

MAMMAL (*mam*-m'l), warm-blooded, air-breathing animals with backbones, whose bodies are more or less covered with hair.

MANTLE, the membrane around the fleshy body of a clam.

MEDULLA (meh-*duhl*-uh), the part of the human brain joined to the spinal cord. It controls some involuntary acts.

MEMORY, the ability to remember past events.

MIDDLE EAR, the part of the ear which connects with the throat.

MIGRATION (my-*gray*-shun), travel from one place to another place and back again.

MINERAL COMPOUNDS, compounds found in soil which are used by green plants to make proteins.

MITOSIS (my-*toh*-siss), a type of cell division in which the division of chromosomes is equal.

MOLAR TEETH, teeth at the back of the mouth cavity which are used to crush and grind food.

MOLDS, one of the many types of fungi.

MOLLUSKS (*mol*-usks), animals which often have hard shells such as clams, oysters, and snails.

MOSSES, small green plants which usually grow in moist places.

MUSCLE, a tissue which produces motion by contraction (shortening). Made up of muscle cells or fibers.

MUSCLE CELLS, those which make up muscle tissue.

MUTATION (mew-*tay*-shun), a new character which can be inherited.

NARCOTIC (nar-*kot*-ick), a drug which dulls pain and brings on sleep. Some narcotics are habit-forming.

NATURAL RESOURCES, useful things in nature, such as minerals, water, soil, and wildlife.

NERVE, a bundle of axons through which messages pass. Held together by an outer covering of connective tissue.

NICOTINE (*nik*-uh-teen), a poisonous substance found in tobacco.

NITROGEN COMPOUNDS, a group of mineral compounds used by green plants.

NITROGEN CYCLE, stages in the use of nitrogen by green plants and the return of nitrogen to the soil and air.

NOVOCAINE (*no*-vuh-kayne), a man-made drug similar to cocaine.

NUCLEUS (*noo*-klee-us), a special structure of the living cell. It contains the chromosomes.

NURSERYMAN, one who raises and sells trees, shrubs, and vines.

NYMPH (*nimf*), early stage in the life cycles of some animals, such as grasshoppers.

OPIUM (*oh*-pee-um), a drug that comes from the unripe fruits of the poppy plant.

OPTIC NERVE, the large nerve connecting the eye and brain.

ORCHARDIST, one who works with all kinds of fruit trees.

ORGAN, a group of tissues which carry out a special activity.

OUTER EAR, the part of the ear consisting of an ear flap and a tube leading to the eardrum.

OVARY (*oh*-vah-ree), that part of the female body which contains the egg cells.

PANCREAS (*pan*-kree-uss), an organ which secretes digestive enzymes and a hormone.

PARASITE (*par*-uh-syte), a plant or animal which lives at the expense of another living thing.

PASSIVE IMMUNITY, that produced when an immune serum is added to the blood.

PASTEURIZED (*pass*-ter-yzed) MILK, milk heated enough to kill dangerous germs.

PELVIS, the bones of the hip girdle.

PENICILLIN (pen-ih-*sil*-in), an antibiotic that comes from a mold and is used to treat various diseases.

PERENNIAL (per-*en*-ee-al), a plant which lives through several growing seasons.

PEST, any plant or animal that prevents the conservation of our natural resources.

PETALS, certain colored parts of a flower.

PHYLUM (*fy*-lum), a large group of related plants or related animals.

PISTIL (*pist*-il), the female part of a flower.

PLANARIAN (plan-*ar*-ee-an), a flatworm that is not a parasite.

PLANT FIBERS, parts of plants that can be removed and used in various ways.

PLANT KINGDOM, the great group of living things to which all plants belong.

PLASMA (*plaz*-muh), the basic fluid of blood.

PLASTICS, substances made in a laboratory or factory which can be molded into desired shapes.

PLYWOOD, thin sheets of wood and adhesives, pressed together to form a solid mass.

PNEUMONIA (noo-*moh*-nee-uh), a disease of the lungs, caused by over 30 different kinds of germs.

POLLEN (*pah*-len) GRAINS, tiny grains produced by the stamens of a flower, from which the male sex cells come.

POLLINATION (*pahl*-ih-nay-shun), the transfer of pollen grains from the male part of a flower to the female part of a flower.

PREMOLAR TEETH, those on each side of the jaw in front of the molars, and behind the canine teeth.

PROTEINS (*proh*-tee-ins), foods containing carbon, hydrogen, oxygen, nitrogen, and sometimes phosphorus and sulfur.

PROTOPLASM (*pro*-toh-plazm), the living substance of a cell.

PROTOZOA (proh-toh-*zoh*-uh), a group of simple animals, most of which are one-celled.

PUPA (*pew*-puh), a resting stage in the life cycle of certain insects.

PUPIL, the opening in the front of the human eyeball.

PUS, fluid formed in a wound which shows that infection is present.

QUININE (*kwy*-nyne), a drug obtained from the bark of a tree which is used to kill malaria germs.

RED BLOOD CELLS, tiny red cells in human blood whose main function is to carry oxygen from the lungs to the cells of the body.

REGENERATE (ree-*jen*-er-ayte), to develop new parts to replace those which have been destroyed.

REPRODUCTION (ree-pro-*duck*-shun), the process of producing offspring.

REPTILES (*rep*-tils), cold-blooded, air-breathing animals with scales and plates and backbones. Lizards, snakes, and turtles belong to this group.

RESISTANCE, an immunity or partial immunity to a disease.

RESPONSE, the reaction to a stimulus.

RETINA (*ret*-ih-nuh), an inner layer of the human eyeball, where light rays reach the nerve cells.

RILL EROSION, the formation of tiny rills in the soil surface. Usually caused by running water.

RODENTS (*roh*-d'nts), a group of gnawing animals which includes rats, mice, squirrels, and woodchucks.

ROOT CAP, the mass of cells which more or less covers a root tip.

ROOT HAIR, the hair-like growth from a single, outer root cell.

ROUGHAGE, solid matter which the body does not digest. Becomes a part of solid waste.

ROUNDWORM, a worm with a complete digestive canal, but not divided into segments.

RUST, a fungus which is often a parasite on crop plants.

SAND, a soil made up largely of small rock particles.

SAPROPHYTE (*sap*-roh-fyte), any living thing which lives on dead or decaying matter.

SCIENCE (*sy*-enss), that branch of knowledge which uses scientific methods to test hypotheses.

SCIENTIFIC METHODS, the methods used by scientists in solving problems.

SEED, a plant embryo produced by a seed plant.

SEED PLANT, one which produces seeds.

SEGMENTED WORM, a worm with a body divided into segments and having a complete digestive canal.

SELECTION, a process used to develop better types of domestic plants and animals.

SELECTIVE CUTTING, the process of cutting only those trees in a forest which have reached the peak of their growth.

SETTLING BASINS, special tanks or reservoirs through which water passes in being purified for drinking. Sediments settle to the bottom.

SEX CELLS, those cells in the plant or animal body which may produce new individuals.

SHEET EROSION, a type of erosion in which soil particles are carried away from all parts of the surface.

SHOULDER BLADE, a bone attached at the point of the shoulder only. It extends down into the muscles of the back.

SILICA (*sih*-lih-kah), a glass-like material making up the skeletons of some protozoa.

SILT, soil formed from soil particles that have been carried by water.

SIMPLE SUGAR, a basic food which contains carbon, hydrogen, and oxygen.

SKULL, that part of the skeleton which includes the bones of the head region.

SMALL INTESTINE, the part of the human intestine that is attached to the stomach. Most absorption of digested food takes place here.

SOIL, a mixture of rock particles and the decayed remains of plants and animals.

SOLUBLE SUBSTANCES, those that will dissolve in a liquid.

SPECIAL SENSES, the senses of sight, hearing, taste, smell, and touch.

SPECIES (*spee*-sheez), one particular kind of living thing.

SPERM CELL, a male sex cell.

SPINAL CORD, a control center of the nervous system.

SPONGIN (*spun*-jin), a material which makes up the skeletons of some sponges.

SPORE, a tiny plant or animal cell which can produce a new individual without being fertilized.

SPRAIN, a condition resulting when the muscles at a joint are stretched too much.

STAMEN (*stay*-men), a male part of a flower.

STIGMA (*stig*-muh), a female part of a flower.

STIMULUS (*stim*-yew-lus), something which causes you to react.

STINGING CELLS, the cells on the body of Hydra and other animals which are used in defense and to obtain food.

STRIP FARMING, the practice of planting alternate strips of row crops and cover crops. The cover crops tend to check erosion.

STRYCHNINE (*strik*-nin), a drug from an Oriental tree sometimes used as a medicine. It is a poison also.

STYLE, the tube leading from the stigma to the ovary of a flower.

SUBSOIL, a lower level of soil, often lacking in decayed remains of plants and animals.

SUCCESSION (suk-*sesh*-un), the series of changes through which a plant community goes in reaching its final growth stage. Successions also take place in animal groups.

SUCKER, the part by which a leech attaches itself to the skin of a host.

SULFA (*sul*-fuh) **DRUGS,** a group of coal-tar drugs used to control various germ diseases.

SWEAT GLANDS, glands in the human skin whose main work is to get rid of surplus body heat.

SYNTHETIC (sin-*thet*-ick) **RUBBER,** rubber-like material made from materials such as coal and alcohol.

SYSTEM, a group of related organs which carry out a general function.

TADPOLE, an early stage in the life cycle of a frog or toad.

TANNIN, a product obtained from the bark of trees such as hemlocks, chestnuts, and oaks. It is used to tan animal hides.

TAPEWORMS, flatworms which are parasites in the bodies of animals and man.

TENDONS, masses of connective tissue at the ends of muscle.

TENTACLES (*ten*-tuh-k'ls), projections around the mouth opening of a Hydra which are used to capture food.

TESTIS (*tes*-tis), the organ in male animals that develops the male sex cells or sperms.

TETANUS (*tet*-uh-nus), a serious type of wound infection caused by a germ.

THYROID (*thy*-royd) **GLAND**, a ductless gland in the neck region. It regulates the speed at which body cells use energy.

TISSUE, a group of similar cells doing some special work.

TOPSOIL, the upper level of soil, usually rich in decayed remains of plants and animals, and full of tiny, living organisms.

TOXIN (*tocks*-in), a poison produced by certain organisms.

TOXOID, a killed or weakened toxin used to develop immunity to a disease.

TRACHEA (*tray*-kee-uh), the tube through which air passes from the back of the mouth to the lungs. Also called the windpipe.

TREE SURGERY, work which requires a knowledge of pruning and treating diseased trees.

TRICHINA (trih-*ky*-nuh) **WORM**, a roundworm that may be found in pork. A parasite of man, pigs, and rats.

TUBERCULOSIS (too-ber-kyoo-*loh*-siss), a germ disease sometimes centered in lung tissue.

TUMOR (*too*-mer), an overgrowth of cells in any body tissue.

URINE (*yoo*-rin), a liquid waste, removed from the human blood by the kidneys.

VACCINATION (*vak*-sih-nay-shun), the act of putting cowpox material just under the skin so as to make a person immune to smallpox.

VACCINE (*vak*-seen), a substance used to provide immunity to a germ disease.

VACUOLE (*vack*-yoo-ole), a space in the living substance of a cell. Liquid wastes sometimes collect in such spaces.

VALVES (HEART), muscle flaps which regulate the flow of blood in and out of heart chambers.

VARIATION (vair-ee-*ay*-shun), the differences between members of a species.

VEIN, a blood vessel which carries blood from the tissues toward the heart.

VENTRICLES (*ven*-trih-k'ls), the two lower chambers of the human heart.

VERTEBRA (*ver*-tuh-bruh), one of the many bones making up the backbone of a vertebrate.

VERTEBRATE (*ver*-tuh-brate), an animal which has a backbone.

VILLI (*vill*-eye), small projections on the inside of the small intestine in man. They contain blood and lymph vessels which absorb digested food.

VIRUS (*vy*-rus), a simple form of living thing which causes disease. A virus passes through a stone filter which no other living thing can go through.

VITAMINS (*vy*-tuh-mins), substances present in foods in small quantities which are necessary to good health.

VOLUNTARY MUSCLE, one that is controlled by will.

WARM—BLOODED ANIMALS, those with a body temperature that is not affected by surrounding temperature.

WATER TABLE, the upper level at which ground water stands in the soil.

WEED, any plant which grows where you don't want it.

WHITE BLOOD CELLS, those which destroy disease germs and other foreign materials in the human blood stream and tissues.

WHITE MATTER, masses of axons in the cerebrum and spinal cord of man.

WILDLIFE, plants and animals that we do not raise.

WINDPIPE, the tube through which air passes from the back of the mouth to the lungs.

WOOD PULP, wood that has been broken down into separate fibers.

YEASTS, one type of simple, non-green plants.

ZOOLOGY (zoh-*ol*-uh-jee), the study of animal life.

INDEX

Index

Abdomen, 185, 186, 187
Absorption of foods, 206–208
Acquired characters, 335
Active immunity, 284
Adaptations, 45
Adhesive, 104, 108
Adrenal glands, and behavior, 257
Adrenalin, 257
Agar, 68
Air, contents of, 56
Air pressure, 57
Air sacs, of lungs, 233
Alcohol, 110; and the body, 222; from yeast, 76
Algae, 35, 67–69; and water supplies, 371
Allergies, 218–220
Alligators, 158–159, 172, 173
Amino acids, 206
Amoeba, 26–29; cyst reproduction of, 326
Amphibians, 155–157
Animal groups, 389–390
Animal kingdom, 34
Animal spores, 326
Animals, domestic, 167–171; domestic, chart of, 169; fur-bearing, chart of, 174–177; as germ carriers, 285–286; important types of, 36; joint-legged, 137–146; method of reproduction, 326–328; one-celled, 36; warm-blooded and cold-blooded, 58–59
Annuals, 324
Anteater, 37–38, 327
Anthrax, 13–14
Antibiotics, 294–295
Antiseptic, 271
Antitoxin, 284
Ape, 165
Aphids, 142–143; reproduction of, 328
Appendicitis, 208–209
Appendix, 201, 204; and bacteria, 208
Apple rust, 79

Apples, 99–100
Aquarium, 43–44
Arctic tern, 160, 162
Armadillo, 164
Arsenic, 143
Arteries, 230; hardening, 232
Artificial respiration, 234–235
Athletes' foot, 80
Aureomycin, 295
Auricles, of the heart, 229, 296
Automatic reactions, 251–252, 254
Axons, 250–251; in brain structure, 254

Backbone, 188, 190, 191, 192
Bacteria, 13, 31, 35, 69–74; and the appendix, 208; in decay, 74; and food poisoning, 220; and germs, 267, 268; growth of, 70–71; in intestines, 208; and the nitrogen cycle, 73–74; in soil, 48; types of, 69–70; useful, 72–74
Balance, in nature, 377, 380, 382
Balance, organ of, 248–249
Balanced diet, 200, 213–214
Bananas, 100–101
Barriers, to life, 56–59
Basic food, 38
Basic food groups, 200, 214
Basset hound, 334
Bat, 165; wing of, 34, 37
Bathing, 241
Bean seed, sprouting of, 93, 325
Beans, 99
Beavers, 164, 174, 175, 176
Behavior, and hormones, 256–258; and the nervous system, 250
Beriberi, 215, 217
Biennial, 324–325
Big Trees, of California, 32
Bile, 206, 239
Bills, of birds, 161, 162

Biology, 4; and careers, 4–7; and hobbies, 8–10

Birds, 36, 159–162; protection of, 162

Bison, 375–376

Black bass, 378

" Black death," 269–270

Black widow spiders, 139, 140

Blackheads, 241

Bladder, 187, 237

Blister rust, 80

Blood, and the body cells, 234; cells of, 228–229; circulation of, 228–232; defense against germs in, 276

Blood clot, 228

Blood pressure, 231–232

Blood vessels, in earthworm, 132; of man, 230

Bloodhound, 335

Blue whale, 32–33

Boa, 174

Body, regions of the, 185–188

Body cavity, of human, 185, 187; of Hydra, 125

Body wall, of Hydra, 125

Body wastes, disposal of, 236–239

Boll weevil, 143

Bones, in human body, 189–193

Botany, 4

Brain, human, 185, 188; and the nervous system, 251–252

Breast bone, 190, 192

Breathing, in man, 232–234; organs of, 233

Breed, 34

Broken bones, 192–193

Bronchial tubes, 233

Budding, reproduction by, 326

Buds, of Hydra, 125; of moss, 81–82; of sponges, 126; of yeast cells, 75–76

Buffaloes, 375–376

Butterfly, dead-leaf, 30

Calcium, in the diet, 212; amount in protoplasm, 25

Calories, 209, 210, 211; charts of, 210, 211

Camel, 169, 171

Cancer, 297–298; signs of, 298

Canine teeth, 201, 202

Capillaries, 230

Carbohydrates, composition of, 73; digestion of, 205, 206; foods rich in, 207; per cent of, in common foods, 213; and in plants, 54

Carbon, in protoplasm, 25

Carbon dioxide, and the Amoeba, 28; and breathing, 233; in manufacture of plant foods, 53–54; from yeast, 76

Carnivores, 166–167

Cartilage, 191

Cattle, 167, 168, 169, 170–171; Hereford, 335; hybrid, 347

Cedar trees, and apple rust, 79

Cell body, of nerve cell, 250

Cell membrane, 26, 27

Cell wall, 23, 25

Cells, 23–25; division of, 310–313

Celluloid, 108

Cereal grains, 95–97

Cerebellum, 252

Cerebrum, 252, 254

Chalk deposits, 149

" Charley horse," 197

Charts, average daily food needs, 211; chemicals in protoplasm, 25; common diseases, 275; common domestic animals, 169; digestive fluids, 205; dominant and recessive characters, 343; energy value of foods, 210; fur-bearing animals, 175; important animal groups, 389–390; important animal types, 36; important plant groups, 387; important plant types, 35; per cent of fat, carbohydrate, and protein in foods, 213; plant and animal groups, 34; steps in the scientific method, 13; vitamins, 217

Check dams, 360–361

Chemical fertilizers, 361

Chemicals, in fighting disease, 292–295; in protoplasm, 25

Chest cavity, 186, 187

Chicken, embryo of, 316

Chickens, 161, 167, 169; and selective breeding, 347

Chiggers, 140

Chinchilla, 175

Chloromycetin, 294

Chlorophyll, 31, 53

Chromatin, 308–309

Chromosomes, 308–309
Cilia, 121, 122
Cinchona trees, 293
Circulation, in man, 228–232
Citrus fruits, 99
Clam, 36, 133–136
Class, 34
Clay, 48
Clot, blood, 228
Club mosses, 35
Coal, formation of, 83
Cocaine, 112, 223
Coconut oil, 106–107
Coconut palms, 65
Cocoons, 144
Codfish, 153, 332
Cold-blooded animals, 58–59
Colds, 234, 275, 276–277
Collar bone, 190, 192
Collecting, 8
Community, 38–40
Compound eyes, of grasshopper, 141
Compound fracture, 193
Conclusion, forming a, 12
Connective tissue, 195–196
Conservation, 353; of forests, 365–366; through pest control, 379–382; of soil and fertility, 356, 358, 360–361; of water supplies, 369–370; of wildlife, 377–378, 382
Constipation, 212, 215
Contour plowing, 358
Control group, 14
Coral reefs, 68, 127
Corals, 36, 124–127
Corn, 96; hybrid, 344, 345–346; rotation planting of, 361
Cotton, 103, 104, 105; and the boll weevil, 143
Cottonseed oil, 106
Cover, for wildlife, 377, 378
Cover crops, 358–359
Cowpox, and vaccination, 281–282
Crabs, 138, 139
Crayfish, 36, 137–139
Crop plants, 94–97
Crop rotation, 361
Cross-pollination, 320–322
Cultured pearls, 136

Cyst, 51, 52; reproduction by, 326
Cytoplasm, 26, 27

Dates, 100
DDT, 143, 146
Dead-leaf butterfly, 30
Decay, process of, 74
Decompression tank, 57
Deer, 164
Dendrites, 250–251
Devil fish, 136, 137
Diabetes, 258
Diaphragm, 185, 186; in breathing, 234
Diarrhea, 212
Diet, balanced, 200, 213–214; and blood pressure, 231
Digestion, human, 201–208; in the mouth, 201, 203–204; organs of, 186, 201–202; in the small intestine, 205–206; in the stomach, 205
Digestive canal, of crayfish, 138; defenses against germs in, 274, 276; of earthworm, 131–132
Digestive cavity, of planarian, 128
Digestive fluids, chart of, 205
Digestive organs, man's, 186–187, 201–202, 204–206
Dinosaurs, 33, 338
Disease, chemicals against, 292–295; control of, 285; epidemics of, 268–269; fungi as a cause of, 80; and insects, 269, 272–273; of the lungs, 236; mosquitoes and, 145–146, 273; use of penicillin against, 294; rats and, 165–166, 269; resistance to, 277; sulfa drugs and, 293; ticks and, 140
Disease carriers, 285–286
Disease germs, 267–270
Diseases, chart of common, 275
Dislocations, 188–189
Displaced fractures, 193
Division of labor, among the cells, 194, 308
Dogs, 167–168, 334, 335
Domestic animals, 167–171; chart of, 169
Dominant genes, 342–343
Drugs, antibiotics, 294–295; biology and manufacture of, 6; habit-forming, 222–223; from plants, 111–112; sulfa, 293

Duckbill, 165, 327

Ductless glands, 256–258; the adrenals, 257; of the pancreas, 257; the thyroid, 257

Ear, human, 186, 248–249; structure of, 248

Eardrum, 248, 249

Earth's crust, 46

Earthworm, 36, 131–132

Egg cells, in animals, 308; of moss, 82; reproduction by, 327

Elkhound, 335

Embryo, 315–316; seed as container of, 324

Energy, effect of thyroid gland on, 211; from food, 209–214

Environment, 21, 22; of living things, 30–31; and natural selection, 338–339; and survival, 337–338

Enzymes, 204, 205

Epidemics, 268–269

Ergot, 112

Ermine, 175

Erosion, 355–359; causes of, 355–356; and floods, 369; prevention of, 356–361; types of, 360

Esophagus, 201, 203, 204, 205

Eustachian tube, 248, 249

Eye, care of the, 248; defects of the, 247; human, 186, 246–248; structure of, 246

Eye spots, of planarian, 128

Eyestrain, 247

Exhaling, 233–234

Experimental group, 14

Experiments, method of performing, 11–12

External skeletons, 138

Facts, 12

Family, 34

Farm pond, 363, 378

Farming, 6

Farsightedness, 247

Fats, composition of, 73; digestion of, 205, 206; foods rich in, 207; per cent of, in common foods, 213; and plants, 54

Feathers, 160, 162

Ferns, 35, 81–83

Fertility, of soil, 48, 359, 361

Fertilization, 314–315

Fertilized egg, 314–315

Fertilizers, natural and chemical, 361

Fibers, from plants, 102–104

Figs, 100

Fingernails, care of the, 240–241

Fish, 36, 152–155

Fishing, methods of, 153, 154

Flatworms, 36, 128–129; regeneration in, 311

Fleas, and the plague, 269–270

Flesh eaters, 38, 39, 40

Flesh-eating mammals, 166–167

Flies, control of, 380; and garbage, 287; and germs, 272; life cycle of, 291–292, 380

"Floating ribs," 192

Floods, 369–370

Florist, 5

Flower gardening, 10

Flowers, edible, 92; parts of, 92–93; pollination of, 320–322; sex cells of, 320

Food, absorption of, in man, 206–208; allergies to, 219–220; chart of average need for, 211; chart of energy value of, 210; digestion of, in man, 201–208; and energy, 209–214

Food chain, 40

Food groups, 200, 214; in community, 38–39

Food industry, 6

Food poisoning, 220

Food-makers, 38, 39

Foot-candle, 248

Forage crops, 95

Foraminifera, 149

Forest fires, 366–367

Forest rangers, 366

Forestry, and biology, 6

Forests, 363–366; national and state, 365

Fox farming, 175–176

Fractures, simple, compound, and displaced, 193

Frogs, 36, 155–157

Fruits, definition of, 93; kinds of, as food, 99–101; relation to seeds, 322–323

Fungi, 35, 75–80; and disease, 80

Fur farming, 174–176

Fur products, cost of manufacturing, 176–177

Fur-bearing animals, chart of, 175

Furs, 164, 167, 174–177

Gall bladder, 203, 204

Galls, on plants, 301

Garbage, and flies, 287; problem of, 287–288

Gardening, 9–10

Genes, 309; dominant and recessive, 342–343

Genus, 33, 34

Germ layers, 328

Germs, 32, 267–270; and biting insects, 272–273; and body defenses, 273–277; carriers of, 285–286; contact with, 267–273; defenses against, in blood and tissue, 276; defenses against, in digestive canal, 274, 276; in food and liquids, 272; resistance of, to drugs, 293; skin and, 274

Giant, 256

Gills, 138; of fish, 152

Glands, 186; adrenals, 257; ductless, 256–258; of the pancreas, 257; salivary, 204, 205; thyroid, 257

Gnawing mammals, 163–166

Goats, 169, 170, 172

Goiter, 257

Government work, biology in, 7

Grafting, 312–313

Grain alcohol, 110

Grains, cereal, 95–97

Grapes, 100

Grasshopper, 141–143; wing of, 34, 37

Grassland, 356

Gravel, 48

Gray matter, of the brain, 254

Great Barrier Reef, 127

Greyhound, 334

Ground water, 51–52

Growth, of animal tissue, 303, 311–312

Guinea hens, 161, 162, 168, 169

Guppies, 328

Habit-forming drugs, 222–223

Habits, 255

Haddock, 153

Hair, care of, 239–240

Halibut, 153

Hardening of the arteries, 232, 296–297

Harmful drugs, 222–223

Hay fever, 219

Head region, of body, 185–186, 188

Headaches, 247

Health conditions, in cities, 291

Hearing, organ of, 248; sense of, 186, 248–249; and structure of the ear, 248–249

Heart, of crayfish, 138; diagram of human, 296; diseases of, 295–297; flow of blood in human, 229–230; position of the, 186, 187; valves of, 230

Heart muscle, 195, 196

Hemoglobin, 228

Heredity, 308–309; 338–339; and Mendel's law, 340–343

Hereford cattle, 335

Heroin, 223

Herrings, 154

High blood pressure, and hardened arteries, 296–297

Higher plants, 325; seed producing in, 35, 87–93

Hip bones, 190, 191

Hobbies, and biology, 8–10

Homo sapiens, 33

Hookworm, 129–130

Hormones, 211; and behavior, 256–258

Horses, 169, 172

Horsetails, 35

Host, 80, 128

Houseflies, control of, 380; and garbage, 287; and germs, 272; life cycle of, 291–292, 380

Human biology, 4

Human body, regions of, 185–188

Human skeleton, 189–193

Hybrids, 341–342; use of, 345–346

Hydra, 124–125; budding of, 326–327

Hydrogen, in protoplasm, 25

Hypothesis, 12

Immunity, 281–284; active and passive, 284; development of, 276–277; to diseases, 13, 268; to smallpox, 281–282; to tetanus, 283–284; to typhoid fever, 282–283

Incisors, 201, 202

Industry, water used in, 370

Infantile paralysis, 252, 275

Infection, and blood pressure, 231–232; and germs, 270–271; and white blood cells, 276

Inhaling, 233–234

Injuries, muscle, 196–197

Inner ear, 248, 249

Insects, 36, 139–146; control of, 142–143; and germs, 272–273; and public health, 288

Insulin, and behavior, 258

Intelligence, 253–254

Intestines, 186, 187, 201; absorption in, 206–208; bacteria in, 208; digestion in, 205–206

Invertebrates, 152

Involuntary controls, 251–252

Involuntary muscles, 195, 196

Iodine, and the thyroid, 212, 257

Iris, of the eye, 246

Iron, in diet, 212

Irrigation, 46, 368

Jaw bone, 190, 191

Jenner, Dr. Edward, 281–282

Joint-legged animals, 137–146

Joints, 188

Kangaroo, 165, 172, 173

Kidneys, 187; and the adrenal glands, 257–258; diseases of the, 239; and disposal of body wastes, 237–239

Kingdom, plant and animal, 34

Kiwi, 161

Knee cap, 190, 193

Knowledge, 254

Ladybird beetle, 382

Lamb, 175

Landscape gardening, 5–6

Large intestine, 201, 204, 207–208; absorption of water in, 207–208

Larvae, 144

Latex, 105–106

Leather, 171–174

Leaves, edible, 91–92

Leeches, 132

Lens, of eye, 246

Lenses, to correct eye defects, 247

Leopard, 175

Lice, 273

Life, barriers to, 56–59

Light, for reading, 247–248

Light meters, 247–248

Limbs, of human, 188

Lime, in bones, 191

Limestone, and coral reefs, 127

Linen, 103, 104

Linseed oil, 107

Liquid wastes, of human body, 237–238

Lister, Joseph, 270, 271

Liver, 187, 203, 204, 206, 207

Liverworts, 35

Lizards, 158–159; leather from, 172, 173

Llamas, 170

Loam, 48

Lobsters, 138–139

Lockjaw, 283–284

Lumber, 102–104, 363

Lungfish, 45

Lungs, 156, 186, 187; diseases of, 236; and disposal of body wastes, 237; working of, in breathing, 232–234; X-ray of, 295

Lynx, 175

Malaria, cause of, 124, 275; and mosquitoes, 145, 273; and quinine, 111, 293

Mammals, 36, 162–167; leather from, 171–173; structures of, 163

Mantle, of clam, 133, 135

Marijuana, 223

Marten, 175

Medical assistants, and training in biology, 6–7

Medicines, biology and manufacture of, 6

Medulla, 252

Memory, 253, 254

Mendel, Gregor, 340

Mendel's law, 341–342; application of, 344–347

Merthiolate, and wounds, 271, 292

Mice, 164, 166

Microscope, 23; diagram of, 43

Middle ear, 248, 249

Midget, 256

Migration, 160

Milk, and public health, 290

Mineral compounds, green plants and, 89

Minerals, needed by the body, 212, 213

Mink, 175, 176, 177

Mitosis, 310–311

Molars, 202–203

Molds, 39, 75–77; penicillin, 77

Mole, 165

Mollusks, 133

Morphine, 223; and drug laws, 291

Mosquitoes, 145–146; and disease, 273

Mosses, 35, 81–82

Moth, 144

Mother-of-pearl, 135, 136

Mountain lion, 164

Mouth opening, of Paramecium, 121; of planarian, 128

Muscle cells, 195, 196

Muscles, human, 194–197; kinds of, 195

Mushrooms, 78–79

Muskrat, 164, 175, 176, 177

Mutations, 335; and selective breeding, 346–347

Nails, care of the, 240–241

Narcotic drugs, 223

National forests, 365

Natural fertilizers, 361

Natural resources, 354; forests, 363–366; topsoil, 362; water supplies, 367–368; wildlife, 377

Natural selection, theory of, 338–339

Nearsightedness, 247

Neck region, of body, 185–186

Nerve, 251

Nerve cells, 194, 250–251; in the cerebrum, 254

Nerve centers, of human body, 251; injuries to, 252

Nerve chain, in crayfish, 138; in earthworm, 131, 132

Nerves, and behavior, 250–252

Nervous system, of earthworm, 132; of man, 185, 250–251

Nicotine, in insect sprays, 143; and smoking habit, 221

Night blindness, 214, 217

Nitrates, and soil fertility, 361, 362

Nitrogen, in protein, 73; in protoplasm, 25

Nitrogen compounds, 73

Nitrogen cycle, 74

Nose, 186

Novocaine, 112

Nucleus, 24–25

Nurseryman, 5

Nursing profession, 7

Nutria, 175

Nuts, 101

Nymphs, 142

Octopus, 136, 137

Oil, deposits of, 83, 123; from fish, 153, 154; from plants, 106–107

Olives, 100

Opinions, 12

Opium, 112, 223

Opossum, 175

Optic nerve, 246

Orchardist, 5

Order, 34

Organ, 25; of balance, 248–249; of hearing, 248

Ostriches, 161, 162, 167, 169, 170

Otter, 175

Outer ear, 248

Ovary, of animals, 308; of flower, 93, 320, 321

Oxygen, and Amoeba, 28; and breathing, 232–234; and energy, 227; man's need of, 232; from plants, 53–54; in protoplasm, 25

Oyster, 120, 133–136

Pancreas 187, 202, 204; and behavior, 257; and digestion, 205

Paper, 103

Paramecium, 121–123

Parasites, 32, 38, 79; of wild and domestic animals, 168; worm, 128, 130, 132

Passenger pigeon, 163

Passive immunity, 284

Pasteur, Louis, 13–14, 271

Peaches, 99–100, 322, 323

Peanut oil, 107

Pearls, 134–136

Pears, 99–100

Peas, 99; Mendel's experiments with, 340–341

Pellagra, 215, 217

Pelvis, 190, 193

Penguins, 161

Penicillin, 77, 236; and disease, 294

Perch, 152, 153

Perennials, 325

Personal appearance, importance of, 239

Perspiration, 238

Pests, chemicals to control, 381; crop rotation to control, 381; insects, 139–146; natural controls for, 382; relation to conservation, 379–382; rodents, 164–166

Petals, 92, 93

Pets, and biology, 10

Phosphorus, in diet, 212; in protoplasm, 25

Phylum, 34

Pigeon, 169

Pigs, 168–170, 172

Pimples, 241

Pistil, 93, 320, 321

Pit viper group, 158

Plague, 269–270; immunity to, 284

Planarian, 36, 128

Plant eaters, 38, 39, 40

Plant fibers, 102–104

Plant galls, 301

Plant groups, 387

Plant kingdom, 34

Plant lice, 142–143

Plant oils, 106–107

Plant saps, 105–106

Plants, algae, 67–69; dry-land (desert), 50; drugs from, 111–112; higher, 325; important types of, 35; life cycle of, 324–325; regeneration in, 312–313; seed, 35, 87–93; simple, 325; sunlight and, 54–55; uses of simple sugar by, 54

Plasma, blood, 228

Plastics, 108–110; uses of, 109–110

Plywood, 103–104

Pneumonia, 236, 275

Pocket gopher, 380

Poison, in control of rodents, 166

Poison ivy, 218–219; weed killers for, 382

Poison oak, 219

Poison sumac, 219

Poisonous animals, 139, 140

Poisonous snakes, 158

Polio, 252, 275

Pollen, 26, 93, 320, 321; allergies to, 219

Pollination, 320–322

Pond scums, 85

Ponds, drying up of, 50–51; farm, 363, 378

Poppy plant, 112

Population changes, and longer life, 282

Praying mantis, 381

Premolars, 203, 204

Protein, composition of, 73–74; digestion of, 205, 206; foods rich in, 207; per cent of, in common foods, 213; and plants, 54

Protoplasm, 23–25; composition of, 25, 72–73; and energy, 227

Protozoa, 123; and germs, 267, 268

Public health, 285–288; and insects, 288; and milk supply, 290; and water supply, 289–290

Pulse, 230–231

Pupae, 144

Pupil, of eye, 246

Pure food and drug laws, 289–292

Pus, and infection, 271

Pythons, 157–158

Quarantines, 286

Quinine, 111, 293

Rabbit, 175

Racoon, 175–176

Ragweeds, and allergy, 219

Rate of survival, 336–337

Rats, 164–165; and the plague, 269–270

Reaction time, effect of alcohol on, 222

Reactions, automatic, 251–252, 254

Recessive genes, 342–343

Recreation, and wildlife, 376, 377

Red blood cells, 228–229

Refuges, for wildlife, 378

Regeneration, 307, 310–312

Reindeer, 169

Repair, of animal tissue, 307, 311–312; in plants, 312

Reproduction, 307–309; of algae, 67; of Amoeba, 29, 326; of animals, 326–328; of aphids, 328; of bacteria, 70; by budding, 326; of crayfish, 138; by eggs, 327; of frog, 156; of grasshopper, 142; of hookworm, 129; of Hydra, 125, 326–327; of live young, 327–328; by mitosis, 310–312; of molds, 76; of mosquitoes, 145; of mosses and ferns, 82; of moth, 144; of mushrooms, 79; of Paramecium, 122–123; of plants, 320–325; of rusts, 79; by seed, 93, 316; by sex cells, 314–316; of sponges, 126; of tapeworm, 128–129; of yeasts, 76

Reptiles, 36, 155–159; leather from, 173–174

Reservoirs, 369–370

Resistance, to disease, 277

Response, 222, 250, 254

Responses, habits as, 255

Retina, 246, 247

Ribs, 190, 191

Rice, 97

Rickets, 216, 217

Rill erosion, 360

Ringworm, 80

Rockweeds, 68, 69

Rodents, 163–166; control of, 166

Root cap, 89, 90

Root hairs, 89, 90

Root systems, types of, 89

Roots, 88–91

Rose cold, 219

Rosin, 107

Roughage, in diet, 211–212, 213, 216

Roundworms, 36, 128, 129–130, 328

Rubber, 105–106; synthetic, 106, 109, 110

Rusts, 79

Sable, 175

Salamanders, 155–156

Saliva, 204, 205

Salivary glands, 204, 205

Sand, 48

Saprohytes, 38–39

Sardines, 154

Sargasso Sea, 65

Sassafras leaves, 333

Scallops, 134

Science, 4

Scientific method, 12–13

Scorpions, 139, 140

Scurvy, 214–217

Sea anemone, 36

Sea cucumber, 36

Sea horse, 306

Sea urchin, 36

Seal, 175

Seaweeds, 68

Seed plants, 35, 87–93

Seeds, edible, 91–92; formation of, 320–323; means of scattering, 323–324; relation to

fruits, 322, 323; reproduction by, 316; sprouting of, 323–325

Selection in nature, 338–339

Selective breeding, 344–347

Selective cutting, 365

Self-pollination, 320–322

Senses, 186, 246–249

Sepals, 92, 93

Settling basins, 371

Sewage, problem of, 287–288

Sex cells, 307–309; of flowers, 320

Sharks, 172

Sheep, 169–172

Sheet erosion, 360

Shoulder blade, 190, 192

Shrimps, 40, 138, 139

Sight, sense of, 186, 246–248

Silica, 123

Silt, 48

Simple fracture, 193

Simple plants, 325; algae, 67–68; bacteria, 69–74; fungi, 75–80; mosses and ferns, 81–83

Simple sugar, 38; and plants, 53–54

Skeleton, of human, 189–193; purpose of, 191

Skin, care of, 241; as defense against germs, 274; and disposal of waste, 238

Skull, human, 190, 191

Skunk, 175, 176

Small intestine, 201, 202, 204, 205–206; absorption of food in, 206–208

Smallpox, 275; immunity to, 281–282; virus of, 285

Smell, sense of, 186, 249

Smoking, 183, 221

Snails, 36, 136, 137

Snakes, 157–158; leather from, 172, 173–174; reproduction of, 328

Sneezing, 271–272

Soil, 46–49; fertility of, 48, 359, 361; formation of, 46–47; types of, 48

Solid wastes, of human body, 238–239

Solubility, of foods, 204

Soybeans, 362

Special senses, 186, 246–249

Species, 33, 34; increase of, 336; variation in, 333–336

Sperms, in animals, 308; of moss, 82

Spiders, 26, 36, 139–140

Spinal cord, 185–186, 188, 192; as control center, 251–252, 254

Sponges, 36, 124–127

Spongin, 125

Spore cases, of ferns, 81, 82

Spores, 76, 79; of animals, 326

Sports, and biology, 10

Sprains, 188

Springs, and the water table, 368–369

Sprouting, of a seed, 324–325

Squid, 36, 136, 137

Squirrel, 164, 175

Stamens, 92–93, 320, 321

Starch, digestion of, 205; test for, 225

Starfish, 36, 120, 133; regeneration in, 311–312

State forests, 365

Stems, 90–91

Stigma, 320, 321

Stimulus, 222, 250, 254

Stinging cells, of Hydra, 125

Stomach, 186, 187, 202, 204, 205; digestion in, 205

Streptomycin, 294

Strip farming, 358–359

Struggle for existence, 337

Strychnine, 112

Style, 320, 321

Subsoil, 47, 49

Succession, 364

Suckers, of leeches, 132

Sugar, 110; test for, 225

Sulfa drugs, and disease, 293

Sunlight, and growth of green plants, 53–55

Surinam toad, 327

Survival, and environment, 337–338; rate of, 336–337

Sweat gland, 238

Synthetic rubber, 106, 109, 110

System, 25

Tadpoles, 156–157

Tail bone, 190, 192

Tannin, 172

Tapeworm, 36, 128–129

Tarantulas, 139, 140

Taste, sense of, 186, 249; and the tongue, 204

Teeth, care of the, 240, 241–242; human, 189, 201, 203, 204

Temperature, of warm-blooded animals, 58

Tendons, 196

Tent caterpillars, 379

Tentacles, of Hydra, 124, 125

Terraces, against erosion, 358

Terrarium, 61

Testes, 308

Tetanus, 275; development of immunity to, 283–284

"The bends," 56–57

Thyroid gland, 211; and behavior, 257; and iodine, 212

Ticks, 140

Tissue, 25; defense against germs in, 276

Tissue cells, reproduction of, 307, 310–312

Toads, 155–157, 327

Tobacco, and blood pressure, 231–232; and the smoking habit, 221

Tomatoes, 98–99, 322, 323

Tongue, 186, 188, 201, 204

Topsoil, 47, 49; effect of forest fires on, 366; erosion of, 355–356; restoring, 361–362

Touch, sense of, 186, 249

Trachea, 233

Tree surgery, 6

Trichina worms, 129; reproduction of, 328

Trunk region, of body, 185, 186–187

Tuberculosis, 236, 275; from milk, 272, 290

Tumor, 297–298

Tung oil, 107

Turkeys, 161, 169; and selective breeding, 346–347

Turpentine, 107

Turtles, 158–159

Typhoid fever, 272, 275; development of immunity to, 282–283

Typhus fever, 273, 275

Ultraviolet rays, and Vitamin D, 215

Undulent fever, from milk, 272, 290

United States Public Health Service, and quarantines, 286–287

Urine, 237

Vaccination, 281–282

Vaccine, 283

Vacuole, 27, 28

Valves, of the heart, 230, 296; of mollusks, 133

Variation, 333–336; inherited and acquired, 334–335; mutations, 334–335

Vegetable gardening, 9–10

Vegetables, 98–99

Veins, 230

Ventricles, of the heart, 229–230, 296

Vertebrae, 190, 191, 192

Vertebrates, 152; amphibians, 155–157; birds, 159–162; fish, 152–155; mammals, 163–167; reptiles, 155–159

Villi, 206, 208

Virus, of smallpox, 285

Viruses, 31–32; of common cold, 234, 236; and disease, 267

Vision, defects in, 247

Vitamins, 213, 214–218; chart of, 217; from fish, 153–154

Voluntary muscles, 195–196

Waksman, Dr. Selman A., 294

Walrus, 164, 166, 167

Warm-blooded animals, 58–59

Wastes, disposal of body, 236–239

Water, in the diet, 211–212, 213; and erosion, 355, 356, 557; and industry, 370; in manufacture of plant foods, 53; necessity of, 49–52

Water cycle, 368

Water supplies, 367–371; conservation of, 369–370; importance of, 289–290; pollution of, 370; purification of, 371

Water table, 51–52, 368–369

Water vapor, and breathing, 234

Weed, 98

Whale oil, 167

Whalebone, 167

Whales, 163, 164, 167; blue, 32–33

Wheat, 95–96

White blood cells, 229; during infection, 276

White matter, of the brain, 254

Wildlife study, 9; conservation of, 377–378, 382; disappearance of, 376–377; refuges for, 378; value of, 377

Wind, and erosion, 355, 356, 357

Windpipe, 202, 212, 233

Wings, types of, 37

Wisdom teeth, 204

Wood alcohol, 110

Wood pulp, 103

Worm cysts, 36

Worm parasite, 36

Worms, 127–130

Yeasts, 75–76; carbon dioxide and alcohol from, 76

Yellow fever, immunity to, 284; and mosquitoes, 145, 273, 275

Zoology, 4